SAMPLED-DATA CONTROL SYSTEMS

McGraw-Hill Series in Control Systems Engineering

JOHN R. RAGAZZINI AND WILLIAM E. VANNAH, *Consulting Editors*

CALDWELL, COON, AND ZOSS · Frequency Response for Process Control

CHANG · Synthesis of Optimum Control Systems

COSGRIFF · Nonlinear Control Systems

DEL TORO AND PARKER · Principles of Control Systems Engineering

GIBSON AND TUTEUR · Control System Components

GILLE, PÉLEGRIN, AND DECAULNE · Feedback Control Systems

GOODE AND MACHOL · System Engineering

LANING AND BATTIN · Random Processes in Automatic Control

LEWIS AND STERN · Design of Hydraulic Control Systems

RAGAZZINI AND FRANKLIN · Sampled-data Control Systems

SAVANT · Basic Feedback Control System Design

SMITH, O. J. M. · Feedback Control Systems

TRUXAL · Control Engineers' Handbook

SAMPLED-DATA
CONTROL SYSTEMS

John R. Ragazzini

Dean, College of Engineering
New York University

Gene F. Franklin

Assistant Professor of Electrical Engineering
Stanford University

McGRAW-HILL BOOK COMPANY, INC.

New York   Toronto   London

1958

SAMPLED-DATA CONTROL SYSTEMS

Library of Congress Catalog Card Number 58-8856

5 6 7 8 9 – M P – 9 8 7 6

51145

THE MAPLE PRESS COMPANY, YORK, PA.

PREFACE

This book deals with the theory of sampled-data systems, a subject which has been of increasing interest and importance to engineers and scientists for the past decade. The science and art of communications have profited from the realization and application of the fact that intelligence can be transmitted and stored in discrete pieces or as a sequence of numbers spaced in real time. As we hope to have shown in this book, the control systems field can similarly benefit by the utilization of this concept. Even though we treat sampled-data systems primarily from the viewpoint of the control function, it is not surprising that many concepts have been borrowed from the communications field. Control systems are essentially power devices which respond to intelligence that has been processed in subsystems similar to those in the communications field. Furthermore, the same body of theory can be used to describe the over-all performance of the control system, even though its primary function is the controlled actuation of power elements and processes.

Sampled-data systems are characterized by the fact that the signal data appear at one or more points in the system as a sequence of pulses or numbers. A central problem in the theory of such systems is that of describing the response of linear continuous elements, or pulsed filters, as they are sometimes called, to pulse sequences applied to their input. The use of the z transformation and the all-important pulse transfer function of the pulsed filter makes this problem relatively straightforward. A unique component found in sampled-data control systems is the digital controller, which is a computer that accepts a sequence of numbers at its input, processes it in accordance with some logical program, and applies the resultant sequence to the controlled element. In view of the operation of this type of controller, it is possible to implement it by means of a conventional digital computer or its equivalent in the form of a mixed or wholly analogue computer. If the numerical process programmed in the computer is linear, it can be expressed mathematically in terms of a recursion formula which is transformed into a generating function having similarity to the pulse transfer function of a pulsed linear filter. It is not unexpected to find the same general theory applying equally well to pulsed linear filters and to the description of linear numerical processes. Sampled-data theory which is developed in this book serves as a common base for the analysis and synthesis of linear digital systems, pulsed continuous systems, and their combinations often found in practice.

Contributions to the theory of sampled-data systems have been made by scientists, mathematicians, and engineers throughout the world. An examination of the list of references and bibliography in this book will reveal papers from many countries, including England, France, the U.S.S.R., and the United States. As in the case of all new fields, the research papers listed are not equally significant. The philosophy we have used in writing this book is that a major responsibility of the author is to sift, evaluate, and interpret the significant contributions. This is particularly important when a book is among the first, if not the first, in its field, for all too often its coverage tends to set the pattern for subsequent books. It would have been far easier for us to write a book which is merely an organized compendium of the papers in the field. It has been much more difficult to be selective, and we fully expect that others who are well-versed in this field may not agree with our choice of material.

As a result of the application of this philosophy, this is a rather short book. We have tried to avoid overwhelming our readers with verbiage or confusing them with a large number of disconnected items which might have been included for the sake of completeness. We have directed this book to readers who are mature technically and who are capable of referring to the literature when necessary. To make this easier, the book is documented as fully as possible.

This is not a book for beginners in the field of control systems. It is assumed that the reader is a graduate student, practicing engineer, or scientist who has had a thorough training in differential equations, the Laplace transformation and its applications, linear feedback control theory, and the elements of probability and statistics. On the other hand, it is an introductory text, and the reader need have had no prior contact with the theory of sampled-data systems or numerical processes. While specifically directed to control systems, there is much material in this book which has general application. This includes the z transformation, data-reconstruction theory, applications of transform methods to numerical processes, and the theory of sampled random time functions.

The level of presentation is such that the book can be used as a text for a graduate course on the subject. Depending on the preparation of the students, this could be a one-semester course of three hours per week or a two-semester course of two hours per week. In exceptional cases, where the students have had a thorough grounding in linear systems, feedback control, and the Laplace transformation, it is possible to use this book in a senior course. The material has also been used as the basis of a seminar in which literature study was the main element of the course.

The authors have been engaged in the study of sampled-data systems for a number of years and have supervised doctoral research in this field at Columbia University and presently at Stanford University as well. A strong impetus to the advancement of this activity was and is now provided by the United States Air Force Office of Scientific Research, under whose auspices much of the research in sampled-data systems was done at Columbia University. This support is gratefully acknowledged by us, our colleagues, and graduate students.

An attempt to list all those individuals who have been of assistance to us in one way or another would surely lead to the embarrassment of having omitted some. Risking this, however, we shall mention a few and recognize their many suggestions with thanks. Included are Professors Lotfi A. Zadeh, John E. Bertram, George M. Kranc, and Bernard Friedland, Dr. Rudolph E. Kalman, and the many graduate students and research assistants with whom we have been associated.

JOHN R. RAGAZZINI
GENE F. FRANKLIN

CONTENTS

Preface   v

1. Introduction   1

2. The Sampling Process   12

3. Data Reconstruction   29

4. The Z-transform Analysis of Linear
   Sampled-data Systems   52

5. Sampled-data Systems   86

6. Application of Conventional Techniques to
   the Design of Sampled-data Control Systems   117

7. Digital Compensation of Sampled-data Systems   145

8. Behavior of Systems between Sampling Instants   199

9. Multirate Sampled Systems   220

10. Sampled-data Systems with Random Inputs   250

11. Miscellaneous Applications of Sampled-data Theory   282

Appendix I.   Table of Z Transforms   314

Appendix II.   Table of Advanced Z Transforms   318

Appendix III.   Output Transforms for Basic Sampled-data
                Systems   320

References   321

Additional References   324

Index   327

CHAPTER 1

INTRODUCTION

The trend of the past few decades has been toward dynamical systems that operate with variables which are in the form of a sequence of numbers. These variables are generally quantized in amplitude and are available only at specified instants of time, which are usually equally spaced. By contrast, a continuous, or analogue, system has variables which are continuous functions of time, that is, their values are known at all instants of time. Both types of system can have imperfections in the amplitude of the signal variables. For instance, the discrete system, in which the variables are sequences of numbers, may operate with these variables quantized so that even if there is no other source of amplitude error, there is the uncertainty in the magnitude equal to one quantum. In continuous systems, imperfections in the data-transmission and transducing devices, as well as unwanted noise, produce uncertainties in the amplitude of the system variables which are similar to those of the discrete systems. The major point of difference between analogue and discrete systems lies in the fact that analogue, or continuous, systems have variables which are known at *all* instants of time, whereas discrete systems have variables which are known only at *sampling instants*.

A system in which the data appear at one or more points as a sequence of numbers or as pulses is known as a *sampled-data system*. A system in which the data are everywhere known or specified at all instants of time is known as a *continuous*, or *analogue*, system. This book deals with sampled-data systems, the theory underlying their operation, and the synthesis of systems of this type which fulfill certain practical objectives.

1.1 The Sampling Operation

In any dynamical system found in nature, there exist dependent and independent variables which are related to each other by linear or non-linear differential equations. In the systems approach, independent variables are referred to as *inputs* and dependent variables as *outputs*. In complex systems there are also intermediate variables, which are considered as being internal in the system, although they can be brought out as outputs should the necessity arise. Assuming for purposes of discussion that $f(t)$ is a variable of interest, it is plotted in Fig. 1.1 as a continuous function of time. The plot or some analytic expression for $f(t)$ will describe the function completely as a function of time.

If, now, the value of $f(t)$ is read or sampled at equal intervals of time T so that the function is described by the sequence of numbers

$$f(0), f(T), f(2T), f(3T), \ldots, f(nT), \ldots \qquad (1.1)$$

it is seen that a limited description of the function $f(t)$ has been given. For instance, the value of $f(t)$ at $f(1.5T)$ is not available, so that a certain

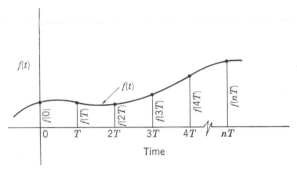

F$_\mathrm{IG}$. 1.1. The sampling operation.

amount of information has been lost in the process of expressing $f(t)$ as a number sequence given by (1.1). On the other hand, if the function is well-behaved, the intermediate values of $f(t)$ can be interpolated between samples with acceptable accuracy. If the function is not well-behaved, it means that large and unpredictable variations in $f(t)$ have occurred between sampling instants. The number sequence such as that of (1.1) then gives only a poor approximation of the variable.

It is seen from this simple qualitative discussion that the sampling frequency must be related to the characteristics of the function being sampled, lest important information be lost in the sampling process. At the same time, if the sampling frequency is well chosen relative to the characteristics of the time function being sampled, only negligible information is lost in the sampling process. In the latter circumstance, the use of more samples would merely burden the system by carrying unessential information that could have been obtained by the simplest of interpolative processes.

Considerations such as these suggest that continuous systems are capable of carrying and transmitting far more information than is required or justified by the dynamical-system characteristics. In the frequency domain, this is equivalent to stating that a capability of some components of the system to carry and transmit excessively large bandwidths is not justifiable if some of the cascaded components transmit restricted bandwidths. If there are practical advantages to be gained by transmitting and processing only a sequence of numbers as opposed to a continuous variable, then a proper selection of sampling frequency and the use of a sampled-data system seems desirable.

There are situations when the data-gathering devices themselves are capable of producing only discrete sets of numbers rather than a continuous variable. For instance, a scanning search radar will generate a fix on a target only once every scan. In some large-scale radars, this might occur only once every 10 or 15 sec. Between these scans, or "looks," no information exists as to the variations in target position. Another possibility is the use of time-shared data links in which information can be transmitted only once every cycle time. In such situations, a system which incorporates one of these devices as an element is, of necessity, a sampled-data system. On the other hand, it will be shown later that there are certain advantages to be gained by deliberately converting a continuous feedback control system into a sampled-data system. The use of sampled-data controllers results in systems having dynamical performance which cannot be matched by the continuous system from which they are derived.

1.2 Data Reconstruction

It was stated in the previous section that the continuous function from which the number sequence is obtained can be reconstructed by processes of interpolation or extrapolation. In numerical computation, this is done by using many samples obtained before or after the region of interest. On the other hand, real-time dynamical systems can use only past samples since the future samples are not known. Thus, data reconstruction must be a process of extrapolation using only the preceding set of samples. This process is sketched in Fig. 1.2, where a continuous function is being extrapolated from the latest sampling instant at nT. The extrapolation in real-time systems is carried out for only one sampling interval, extending from nT to $(n + 1)T$. Since the value of the function is known exactly at the next sampling instant $(n + 1)T$, this most recent value can be used as the base for an extrapolation into the next sampling interval. Thus, the extrapolation process is reiterated as each new sample becomes available. There are a number of techniques and extrapolation formulas which can be used to implement this process. In all cases, the objective is to reproduce as well as possible a reasonable facsimile of the actual time function from which the sample or number sequence was derived.

The reason why data reconstruction is important in the field of dynamical sampled-data systems is that physical plants and dynamical devices are basically analogue, or continuous, in form. For instance, in a control system, the actuator may be an electric motor which responds to a continuous signal input and delivers a continuous output. If such a motor is incorporated into a sampled-data feedback control system, continuous signal at its input must somehow be reconstructed to obtain satisfactory

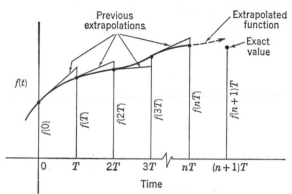

FIG. 1.2. Data reconstruction process.

operation. The devices which reconstruct continuous data from a sequence of samples or numbers are generally called *data holds, extrapolators, desampling filters,* or some similar descriptive name. They all have the same function and, from the practical viewpoint, they are made as simple as possible. In obtaining this physical simplicity, accuracy of extrapolation is often sacrificed.

1.3 Open-loop Sampled-data Systems

A sampled-data system is an interconnected group of dynamical elements in which the signal data appear at one or more points in the system as a sequence of numbers. Figure 1.3 shows the simplest form of

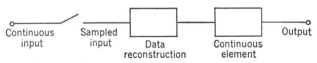

FIG. 1.3. Typical open-cycle sampled-data system.

open-cycle sampled-data system. As a result of a sampling operation, the continuous input signal is converted into a sequence of numbers equally spaced in time by a sampling interval T. The operation of sampling is shown schematically by a switch which is presumed to close momentarily at each sampling instant. The sequence of samples emerging from the switch is reconstructed into an approximation of the input function before being applied to the continuous element. The output of this element is the useful output of the system.

The schematic representation of Fig. 1.3 is intended to show only a possible sequence of operations, not necessarily the physical elements themselves. For instance, this system could represent a pulse-code communications system in which the sampling and coding operation is symbolized by the switch. The quantizing aspect of the operation is ignored here, since it is assumed that the input is quantized infinitely fine. Thus, the input amplitude is presumed to be perfect in this representation. The data-reconstruction element reconstructs a continuous signal from the sequence of samples as well as is practical. Usually, this can be relatively crude, and the physical device takes the form of a simple clamp or boxcar circuit. The continuous element is the device which is being driven by the reconstructed signal, and its output is the useful signal.

The theory which underlies the performance of this system should take into account two deteriorating aspects: the quantizing effect and the sampling effect. Both of these tend to distort or deteriorate the signal in some way. It is much easier to take into account the effect of sampling since it will be shown that this can be described by means of linear difference equations. On the other hand, the quantizing effect is much more difficult to account for, since it is described by nonlinear equations. All the theory in subsequent sections will deal with the linear problem, on the assumption that the quantization of the variables is made fine enough to produce negligible effect. Generally, the theoretical objectives which apply to systems of the type shown in Fig. 1.3 are to obtain the output sequence or continuous output in terms of the input sequence and the system parameters.

1.4 The Sampled-data Feedback System

If the system configuration includes elements which feed the output variable back to the input and if a sampling operation is included, the system is referred to as a *sampled-data feedback system*. If the objective of the system is to control one or more variables in the system so that they have a desired functional relationship with the inputs and disturbances, the qualifying term *control* is included in the name.

A simple sampled-data feedback control system is shown in Fig. 1.4. In this system the error signal is sampled and is reconstructed before being applied to the continuous element. The latter may be the plant or process which is being controlled, including amplifiers, instruments, and actuators. This error-sampled system can be compensated by the addition of networks in the continuous element, just as in the case of ordinary continuous feedback systems. The problem of designing such networks is considerably more complex, however, because of the presence of the sampling operation.

A configuration which is unique to sampled-data systems is one in which a digital controller is used, as shown in Fig. 1.5. In this system, the controller accepts a sequence of numbers and processes them, usually linearly, to produce an output number sequence. The latter sequence is

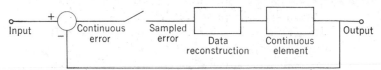

FIG. 1.4. Typical error-sampled feedback control system.

reconstructed into a continuous command signal and is applied to the plant. If the linear program of the digital controller is properly designed, the over-all system can be stabilized and its dynamical performance made to conform to fairly rigid specifications. The digital controller

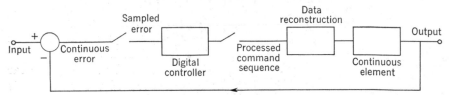

FIG. 1.5. Sampled-data feedback control system using digital controller.

may be implemented by digital-computer techniques or it may employ a mixture of analogue and digital components. Its main requirement is that it be capable of receiving a sequence of numbers equally spaced in time and of processing them in real time into a command signal. It will be shown later that controllers of this type can produce systems whose performance cannot be duplicated by all-continuous systems.

The problems which must be studied in sampled-data feedback control systems include all those encountered in continuous systems. First, a criterion for stability must be derived and adapted for application to physical problems. Second, a means for relating the input and output which is as direct and simple as the Laplace transform in continuous systems must be developed, along with a means for shaping and compensating the system. A unique property of sampled-data systems is that the output will contain a small periodic output component which is the result of intermittency in the signal within the system caused by the sampling operation. This periodic variation is known as *ripple*, and methods for analyzing this component and reducing or controlling its magnitude are required.

There are many possible configurations possible in addition to those shown in Figs. 1.4 and 1.5. Sampled signals may exist at several points in the system as well as in the error line. There may be dynamical elements in the feedback line, and there may be multiple loops. The transform methods for sampled-data systems must be applicable to all possible configurations.

1.5 The Z Transformation

Continuous linear dynamical systems are described mathematically by a set of linear differential equations. While their solution can be carried out by classical methods, the use of the Laplace transformation organizes and simplifies the process. What is even more important, inversion of the transform of the variable of interest is rarely necessary in order to deduce the important characteristics of the system and their relation to the system constants. Mapping techniques on the complex plane in the form of transfer loci or root loci further clarify the properties of the system. Certainly, the value of the Laplace transform as a tool for the analysis and synthesis of linear continuous systems is indisputable.

Linear sampled-data dynamical systems are shown to be described by a set of linear difference equations, provided that all the samplers in the system are synchronous, that is, their sampling periods are equal or related by integers. Some of this earlier work, as reported by Oldenbourg and Sartorius,[46] was motivated by the use of intermittent error-sensing devices such as the chopper-bar galvanometer, shown schematically in Fig. 1.6. In this type of device, a small error voltage or current is applied to the galvanometer coil. While the chopper bar is raised, the sensitive galvanometer movement is free and the coil responds with a large displacement in response to the weak signal. Periodically, the chopper bar is lowered and the projecting galvanometer needle causes a bell crank to be rotated more or less proportionately to the deflection angle θ. The bell crank causes the output shaft to rotate with a torque capacity determined by the chopper-bar drive rather than the galvanometer-coil drive.

The main point of interest here is that a datum is stored in the output shaft just once per cycle of the chopper-bar drive. In a sense, the intermittency of the output signal has been accepted in return for a high sensitivity of the system. The early work by Oldenbourg and Sartorius generalized systems of this type into the form of the sampled-data block diagrams of Figs. 1.4 and 1.5. It was shown that these systems could be described by a set of linear difference equations whose solution could be obtained by classical methods. The linear sampled-data system was therefore placed in the same status as the continuous system, using classical methods to solve the differential equations.

In the field of mathematics, Demoivre and Laplace[9,33] developed a form of transform calculus which could be applied to the solution of linear difference equations. This approach was adapted to the solution of pulsed filters and sampled-data systems by Hurewicz,[17] who laid much

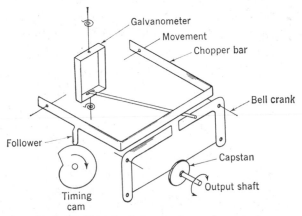

Fɪɢ. 1.6. Sketch of chopper-bar galvanometer.

of the basic groundwork for the transform method of analysis of sampled-data systems. Subsequent investigations[1,2,34,47] further extended this initial work. The result of these efforts was the development and refinement of the so-called *z transformation* and its application to the analysis and synthesis of sampled-data systems.

The z transformation is entirely analogous to the Laplace transformation and its application to continuous systems. It turns out that, for systems having lumped constants, that is, those which are described by linear difference equations with constant coefficients, the z transformation gives expressions which are rational polynomial ratios in the variable z. This variable is complex and is related to the complex frequency s used in the Laplace transform by the relation $z = e^{Ts}$. In z-transform theory, such concepts as the transfer function, mapping theorems, combinatorial theorems, and inversion bear the same powerful relation to sampled-data systems as does the Laplace transformation to continuous systems.

Without going into detail at this point, the general concept of the z transformation as applied to systems is shown in Fig. 1.7. Here the output number sequence of the system is related to the input number sequence by a linear difference equation. If the sampled output is $c^*(t)$ and the input is $r^*(t)$, and if the z transforms of these sequences are $C(z)$ and $R(z)$, respectively, a pulse transfer function $G(z)$ can be found which relates them in the following manner:

$$C(z) = G(z)R(z) \tag{1.2}$$

The form and constants of the pulse transfer function $G(z)$ are a property of the system and can be found in terms of the system constants. These relations will be rigorously derived in later chapters.

The relation expressed in (1.2) is dependent on the fact that the input and output samples are taken with the same sampling instants.

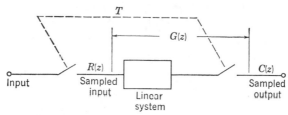

FIG. 1.7. The pulse transfer function $G(z)$.

It is possible to extend the concepts of the z transformation to include the case where the output and input samples are taken at some integral multiple of a basic sampling rate. For instance, if the basic rate is taken as unity, the input and output sampling operations can take place at two and three times the basic rate, respectively. Such systems are referred to as *multirate* sampled-data systems, and suitable modifications in z-transform theory can be made to cover these cases. A typical system is shown in Fig. 1.8, where the input sampler operates with a sampling

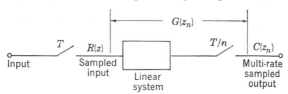

FIG. 1.8. Multirate sampled-data system.

interval T, while the output sampler has a sampling interval T/n. The pulse transfer function relating these sequences at input and output is the multirate pulse transfer function $G(z_n)$. If $R(z)$ is the z transform of the input sequence and $C(z_n)$ is the multirate z transform of the output, then they are related as follows:

$$C(z_n) = G(z_n)R(z) \tag{1.3}$$

Inversion of (1.3) will yield the multirate output sequence.

Sampled-data systems are often subjected to inputs or disturbances which are random. To handle this situation analytically, a number of concepts and definitions analogous to those for continuous systems must be devised. Such terms as auto- and cross-correlation function of sample sequences, sampled power spectra, and cross spectra are used. Relations which give the shaping effects of a linear sampled-data system can be found, just as in the case of continuous systems. Techniques are available to optimize the performance of sampled-data systems based on mean-square criteria used in the design of sampled-data feedback control systems and filters.

1.6 Miscellaneous Uses of Sampled-data Theory

If a linear system contains variables which are actually sampled, analysis by use of the z transformation is exact. Interestingly enough, the same theory can be applied approximately to models of continuous systems in which sampling of the variable is introduced artificially as an aid to analysis. For instance, with the continuous feedback control system shown in Fig. 1.9a, it is often desired to obtain the response of the

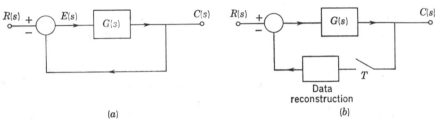

(a)   (b)

FIG. 1.9. (a) Continuous feedback system.   (b) Sampled model of feedback system for computation.

system to an input in the time domain using ordinary inversion of the Laplace transform of the output variable. In principle, this is very simple and straightforward, but if an accurate solution is desired, the process can be quite laborious, requiring the use of calculating machines.

It so happens that one of the techniques for inversion of the z transform is directly accomplished by routine numerical processes. This advantage can be applied to continuous systems by constructing a sampled model which gives solutions with tolerable error. Such a model for feedback systems often takes the form shown in Fig. 1.9b. By selecting the sampling rate high enough and using a sufficiently sophisticated data-reconstruction element, acceptable accuracy can be achieved. As a matter of comparison, the sampling interval is exactly analogous to the quadrature interval which would be selected in the numerical integration of a differential equation. The sampled-data approach has the advantage, however, that a physical interpretation of the process is readily seen. Having selected the sampled model of the continuous system, its analysis becomes one of numerical methods simply carried out by a desk calculator or digital-computer program.

The use of a sampled model in this as well as other applications has the advantage of making clear just where the sampler should be placed to improve accuracy. For instance, in a low-pass system, the output contains only a few high-frequency terms, so that the use of output sampling as shown in Fig. 1.9*b* results in less error than with the sampler at the error line. In this manner, the numerical method is related to the physical system more closely, and the theory applicable to sampled-data systems can be used directly.

1.7 Summary

The theory of sampled-data systems deals with linear systems in which the data appear at one or more points as a pulse sequence or a sequence of numbers. The analysis of such systems requires a mathematical description of the sampling process, of the data-reconstruction process, and of the relation between input and output variables, using a form of transform calculus known as the z transformation. The latter is completely analogous to the Laplace transform as applied to continuous systems, and the various theorems, rules, and restrictions are very similar. An important advantage of the z transform is that its inversion can be carried out directly by means of desk calculators.

An important feature of sampled-data systems is that they can be compensated by means of digital controllers which process number sequences rather than continuous time functions. It is possible to obtain transient performance whose quality cannot be matched by fully continuous systems. The subsequent chapters will be devoted to a development of the underlying theory and application to sampled-data systems, particularly feedback systems. The synthesis of sampled-data systems which fulfill some specified performance will be an important aspect of this development.

CHAPTER 2

THE SAMPLING PROCESS

The characterizing feature of a sampled-data system is the fact that data appear at one or more places in the system as a sequence of pulses or numbers. The process which converts continuous data into such a sequence is called the sampling process. In view of its importance, the process must be thoroughly understood and represented mathematically. Fortunately, there exists a considerable body of literature in the field of communications theory where this problem has been considered. Before introducing some of this theory, a few concepts of sampling will be considered qualitatively, with particular emphasis on their application to control systems.

A schematic representation of the sampling process is given in Fig. 2.1, where it is seen that a continuous time function $f(t)$ is observed by

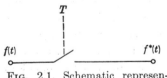

FIG. 2.1. Schematic representation of sampling operation.

means of a switch which closes briefly every T sec. The mechanical device implied by this representation is not binding and is used only for pictorial simplicity. The sampling of the time function $f(t)$ may be carried out by electronic devices or may be only implicit in that the data exist only as a sequence of samples to begin with. The closure of the switch is of very short duration compared with the time between closures. This means that the value of the function at the output of the switch is the instantaneous value of the function $f(t)$ at the particular instant of time when the switch closes. The output of the switch is a sequence of pulses or numbers whose values are $f(T_1)$, $f(T_2)$, . . . , $f(T_n)$, where T_1, T_2, . . . , T_n are the instants of time when the switch has closed. It is clear that some information has been lost in the process, since the output sequence contains no data in the interval between sampling instants.

While theory has been developed to handle the case where the intervals between sampling instants are not equal, the majority of practical situations in control systems have equal or quasi-equal sampling intervals. In this case, the output of the sampling switch produces a sequence of numbers $f(T)$, $f(2T)$, . . . , $f(nT)$, where T is the *sampling interval* and

$T, 2T, \ldots, nT$ are the *sampling instants*. The sampled time function
$f(t)$ appearing at the output of the sampling switch, or *sampler*, as it is
usually called, is referred to as $f^*(t)$, where the asterisk implies the
sampled version of a function of time $f(t)$. A graphical representation
of $f^*(t)$ is shown in Fig. 2.2. In order to develop analytical approaches

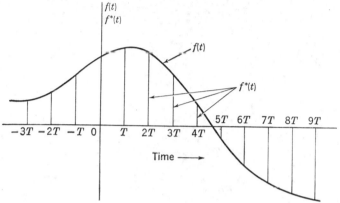

FIG. 2.2. Sampled time function.

to the sampled-data control-system problem, a mathematical description
of this process must be obtained.

2.1 Mathematical Description of Sampling Process

A practical sampling operation cannot ignore the fact that the sampler
remains closed for a finite, though short, length of time. For this
condition, the "samples" are elements of finite duration γ whose amplitudes during the closure interval follow the amplitude variations of the
time function $f(t)$ and are zero at all other times. This type of sampling
operation is shown graphically in Fig. 2.3.

The sampled function $f^*(t)$ appears here as a sequence of samples of
finite duration γ. The process may be thought of as being the result
of multiplying a sampling function $p(t)$ and a data-carrying function $f(t)$,
as shown in Fig. 2.3. This is a process of modulation, where a "carrier"
$p(t)$ is being modulated by a signal function $f(t)$. Mathematically, the
process may be represented by the expression

$$f^*(t) = f(t)p(t) \tag{2.1}$$

In view of the fact that the sampling interval T is constant, thus making
$p(t)$ a periodic function, it is possible to expand $p(t)$ into a Fourier series

$$p(t) = \sum_{k=-\infty}^{+\infty} C_k e^{j2\pi kt/T} \tag{2.2}$$

where the various C_k's are the Fourier coefficients of the exponential series.   Substituting (2.2) back in (2.1), there results a representation of the sampling process which is useful in giving an insight into its characteristics and implications.   The expression so obtained is

$$f^*(t) = \sum_{k=-\infty}^{+\infty} C_k f(t) e^{j2\pi kt/T} \tag{2.3}$$

It is of interest to observe the Fourier transform of the sampled function $f^*(t)$ and to contrast it with the Fourier transform of the con-

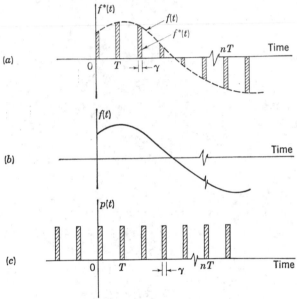

Fig. 2.3. Finite pulse sampling operation.

tinuous function $f(t)$ from which the sequence was obtained.   Recalling the shifting theorem which states that

$$\mathfrak{F}[e^{\lambda t} f(t)] = F(j\omega - \lambda) \tag{2.4}$$

where $F(j\omega)$ is the Fourier transform of $f(t)$, and applying this relationship to the expression (2.3), there results the infinite summation

$$F^*(j\omega) = \sum_{k=-\infty}^{+\infty} C_k F\left[j\left(\omega - \frac{2\pi k}{T}\right)\right] \tag{2.5}$$

where $F^*(j\omega)$ is the Fourier transform of the sampled sequence $f^*(t)$. This expression is very important in determining the effects of sampling on the information content of the original signal $f(t)$. $F^*(j\omega)$ is seen to consist of a summation of weighted spectra, each of which is the same as the central term except for the weighting constant C_k and the shifted argument $j(\omega - 2\pi k/T)$.

The sampled spectrum $F^*(j\omega)$ is sketched in Fig. 2.4. The original spectrum $F(j\omega)$, from which the sampled signal spectrum $F^*(j\omega)$ is derived, is shown in this figure. The effect of the sampling process is to introduce a succession of spurious spectra which are proportional to the signal spectrum and which are shifted periodically by a frequency separa-

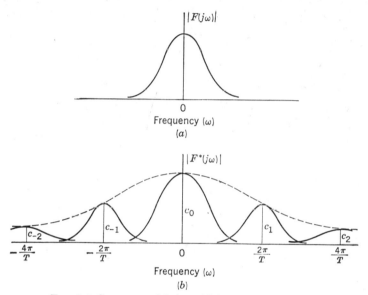

FIG. 2.4. Spectrum of finite-width sampled function.

tion $2\pi k/T$. It is evident that this spectrum bears little resemblance to that of the original signal and that means must be found to recover the original information in any useful application.

The central signal spectrum can be extracted by rejecting the spurious higher-frequency spectra by means of a low-pass wave filter. It is evident that even if this filter were "perfect," in the sense of passing perfectly a given spectrum and rejecting perfectly an unwanted spectrum, the signal spectrum could never be fully extracted unless it were band-limited, that is, unless it contained no components above a given frequency. The "spillover" effect produced by an infinite spectrum such as that shown in Fig. 2.4 always produces distortion in any recovered signal. Sampled-data systems are subject to a signal-recovery problem of this type, and imperfect signal recovery always produces ripple effects on the output of such a system. Basic limitations on the information capacity of sampled-data systems result from the information loss brought about by the sampling process. For this reason, a good under-standing of the phenomenon is required by a study of the sampling theorem.

2.2 The Sampling Theorem

Insight into the limitations imposed by the sampling operation in sampled-data systems can be obtained by consideration of the sampling theorem developed by Shannon.[47] Essentially, this theorem states that, for signals having a *finite bandwidth*, including frequency components

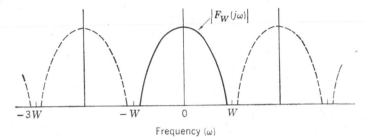

FIG. 2.5. Finite bandwidth signal spectrum.

up to but not beyond a frequency of W radians/sec, a complete descrip-tion of that signal is obtained by specification of the values of the signal at instants of time separated by $\frac{1}{2}(2\pi/W)$ sec. The converse of this theorem is particularly useful in sampled-data systems, where a signal must be reconstructed from samples separated by a particular sampling interval. The converse can be stated that, for a band-limited signal which contains no frequency components beyond W radians/sec, it is theoretically possible to recover completely the signal from a sequence of samples which are separated by time intervals of $\frac{1}{2}(2\pi/W)$ sec. In view of the basic importance of the theorem, a proof will be given.

The Fourier spectrum $F_W(\omega)$ of the signal $f(t)$ is plotted as a solid line in Fig. 2.5. It is noted that the spectrum contains no frequencies higher than W radians/sec. A convenient representation of this spectrum is by means of a Fourier series whose fundamental period is $2W$. This repre-sentation produces additional spectra shown by dashed lines in Fig. 2.5, but these are of no consequence if it is recalled that the representation is valid only over a frequency range of from $-W$ to W radians/sec. The periodic spectrum can be represented by means of a Fourier series in ω with a fundamental frequency of $2W$ as follows:

$$F_W(\omega) = \sum_{n=-\infty}^{+\infty} C_n e^{-j\frac{n\pi}{W}\omega} \tag{2.6}$$

where the C_n's are the various Fourier coefficients of the exponential series are defined by

$$C_n = \frac{1}{2W} \int_{-W}^{+W} F_W(\omega) e^{j\frac{n\pi}{W}\omega} \, d\omega \tag{2.7}$$

The significance of this representation is that, if all the values of C_n can be obtained, the Fourier spectrum $F_W(\omega)$ is fully defined and the signal is thereby fully specified. Thus, if information is available which permits the evaluation of the coefficients as expressed in (2.7), the Fourier transform of the signal—and, consequently, the signal itself—is fully specified. Turning one's attention to the time function $f(t)$ and its Fourier transform $F_W(\omega)$, the following inverse transform relationship exists:

$$f(t) = \frac{1}{2\pi} \int_{-W}^{+W} F_W(\omega) e^{j\omega t} \, d\omega \tag{2.8}$$

where the finite limits are justified by the fact that the Fourier spectrum $F_W(\omega)$ is band-limited at $-W$ and $-W$ radians/sec. Now, if the time in (2.8) is set to a specific value $n\pi/W$, then the integral (2.8) becomes

$$f(n\pi/W) = \frac{1}{2\pi} \int_{-W}^{+W} F_W(\omega) e^{j\frac{n\pi}{W}\omega} \, d\omega \tag{2.9}$$

It is seen that, except for a constant, the integral (2.9) is identical to that in (2.7), which is required to specify the Fourier coefficients in (2.6). The significance of this result is that a specification of the time function only at instants of time $n\pi/W$ is required to specify the Fourier transform of that signal and, therefore, the signal itself.

The implications of this result are that for the class of signals whose Fourier spectra are finite, that is, are zero for frequencies above a specified value W, the function is completely described by a set of samples whose interval is π/W sec. This corresponds to one-half the highest frequency content of the signal. Thus, for band-limited signals whose highest frequency component is W radians/sec (or F cps), no loss of information is experienced if that signal is sampled at a frequency of W/π (or $2F$) samples/sec. In sampling such signals, the sampling frequency must be *two* or more times the highest frequency contained in the signal to ensure no loss of information. For reasons that will become more evident later, practical considerations dictate a sampling frequency considerably higher than this theoretical minimum.

The converse of this theorem can be readily understood by referring to (2.5), which gives the Fourier spectrum of a signal $f(t)$ which has been sampled by a periodic sampling function $p(t)$. Figure 2.6 shows a finite spectrum $F_W(\omega)$ and the repeated spectra $F_W^*(\omega)$ which result from the sampling process.   While the amplitude of the various repeated spectra depends on the switching function $p(t)$, their respective bandwidths are unaffected by this function.   The figure shows the condition for a sampling frequency which is twice the maximum frequency content W of the signal.   It is seen that there is no spectrum overlap, as had been the case for infinite spectra illustrated in Fig. 2.4.

If it is desired to recover the original signal from the sampled sequence, it is necessary to separate the signal frequency spectrum from the infinite

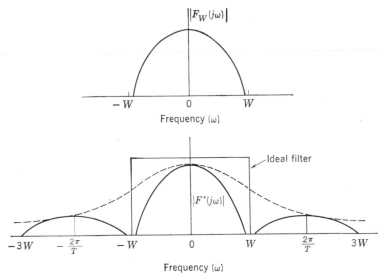

Fig. 2.6. Sampled signal spectrum.

repeated spectra by means of a low-pass wave filter.   If this filter were ideal, that is, if its passband produced zero attenuation while perfect cutoff was produced outside this band, it would be possible to extract perfectly the original signal spectrum $F_W(\omega)$.   This shows that, for signals having finite spectra, it is possible to extract without distortion the original signal from a pulse sequence provided that the sampling frequency is twice the maximum frequency contained in that signal.   It should be recognized that this result is based on an idealization of both the signal spectrum and the filter response.

Practical considerations will show that signals generally do not have finite spectra nor do filters have perfect response characteristics.   For that reason, the signal which is recovered from a sample sequence always has a certain amount of distortion, even though the sampling frequency is high relative to the signal frequencies.   This distortion is roughly at sampling frequencies and their harmonics and is referred to as "ripple" in the recovered signal.   In sampled-data feedback control systems, ripple is a form of noise which is superimposed on the desired output and must be considered in the over-all design problem.

2.3 The Impulse Sampling Approximation

Except for the fact that it was periodic, the sampling or switching function $p(t)$ used in the previous section was completely general. In practice, it is generally true that the elements comprising $p(t)$ have a very small duration time γ relative to the sampling interval T. In fact, in digital systems where the sample is in the form of a number whose magnitude represents the value of the function $f(t)$ at a particular sampling instant, the switching-function elements have, in effect, an infinitely small duration time γ. Because an extremely narrow pulse represents the physical situation accurately and also because of the resultant mathematical simplifications, a common form of switching-function element is an impulse, or Dirac, delta function, $\delta(t)$. This treatment of the sampling process [17,38,49] has been successfully applied to the analysis and synthesis of sampled-data systems.

The assumption of impulse sampling causes the expression for $p(t)$ to become

$$p(t) = \sum_{n=-\infty}^{+\infty} \delta(t - nT) \tag{2.10}$$

where $\delta(t - nT)$ represents an impulse of unit area at a time nT. In view of its extensive use in subsequent chapters, the impulse switching function is abbreviated to

$$\sum_{n=-\infty}^{+\infty} \delta(t - nT) \triangleq \delta_T(t) \tag{2.11}$$

When the switching function is assumed to be an impulse train, the sampling operation may be thought of as impulse modulation and has been so referred to in the literature.[38]

If the signal function is $f(t)$, then the output of the impulse modulator may be expressed as

$$f^*(t) = f(t)\delta_T(t) \tag{2.12}$$

It is noted that since the impulse is infinitely narrow in the limit, the only significant value of $f(t)$ is $f(nT)$, the value of the function at the instant of time when the impulse function appears. Thus, (2.12) may be rewritten

$$f^*(t) = f(nT)\delta_T(t) \tag{2.13}$$

The impulse sequence may now be interpreted as being a sequence of delta functions whose respective *areas* are equal to the magnitude of the function $f(t)$ at that instant. In other words, the analogue of the signal datum is the area of the impulse, and if properly used and interpreted, this should cause no difficulties. In some applications where the area of the actual sampling pulse is finite, say γ, the only modification made in the impulse approximation is to replace the unit-area impulse sequence with one whose areas are γ. These cases will be taken up when the particular situation applies.

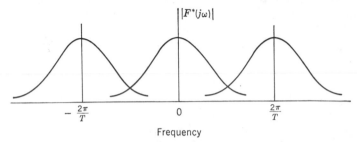

FIG. 2.7. Spectrum of impulse-sampled function.

The implications of the impulse approximation in the frequency domain will now be considered. This can be studied by using the form given in (2.3) by computing the various Fourier coefficients C_k by evaluating these coefficients in the integral

$$C_k = \frac{1}{T} \int_{-T/2}^{+T/2} \delta_T(t) \, e^{j\frac{2\pi k}{T}t} \, dt \tag{2.14}$$

Since the area of the impulse at the origin is unity, the integral has a value of unity, so that the Fourier coefficients are all equal regardless of the value of k and are given by

$$C_k = \frac{1}{T} \tag{2.15}$$

Thus, from (2.5), the Fourier transform of the impulse-modulated function $f^*(t)$ is given by

$$F^*(j\omega) = \frac{1}{T} \sum_{k=-\infty}^{+\infty} F[j(\omega - k\omega_0)] \tag{2.16}$$

where ω_0 is $2\pi/T$.

Thus, when impulse sampling is used, the repeated spectra which result from the sampling process are all equal in relative magnitude and are separated by a frequency ω_0. The main difference between this spectrum and that obtained with a finite-width sampling function is that the repeated spectra are all equal, instead of diminishing, as is the case with finite sampling function. These repeated spectra are plotted in Fig. 2.7.

Without attempting an exhaustive discussion of the problem, the applicability of the impulse approximation to the special case of feedback control systems will be discussed. The transfer functions of the elements of such systems are generally low-pass in frequency response. The essential requirement in determining the validity of the impulse approximation is that the impulse response of the feedforward (or any other transfer functions to which the pulses are applied) be acceptably equivalent to the pulse response. For low-pass systems this condition is usually satisfied if the pulse duration is small compared with the time constants of the

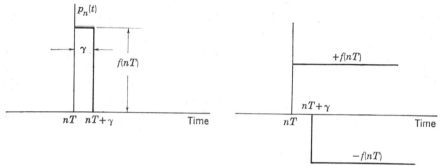

FIG. 2.8. Finite-width pulse.

system. Although a pulse sequence would rarely be applied directly to the plant or continuous element of the control system without some form of data reconstruction, the impulse approximation can be assumed as being adequate if the condition mentioned above is met. On the other hand, in most practical systems the plant is preceded by a data-reconstruction component which is even less sensitive to pulse width than the plant, as will be seen later.

In order to obtain a quantitative estimate of the error introduced by the impulse approximation, one can assume that the actual pulse is a flat-topped pulse whose amplitude is that of the sampled function $f(t)$ at the sampling instant nT and whose duration is γ, as illustrated in Fig. 2.8. As seen in the figure, the pulse may be thought of as being the sum of a step function at the time nT and a delayed negative step function at a time $(nT + \gamma)$. Thus,

$$p(nT) = f(nT)[u(t - nT) - u(t - nT - \gamma)] \qquad (2.17)$$

where $p(nT)$ is the pulse initiated at the sampling instant nT and $f(nT)$ is the value of $f(t)$ at the same instant. The Laplace transform of this pulse, $P_n(s)$, is given by

$$P_n(s) = f(nT)\left(e^{-nTs}\frac{1 - e^{-\gamma s}}{s}\right) \qquad (2.18)$$

By expanding the exponential $e^{-\gamma s}$ into a power series in s, $P_n(s)$ becomes

$$P_n(s) = f(nT)\gamma e^{-nTs}\left(1 - \frac{\gamma s}{2!} + \frac{\gamma^2 s^2}{3!} - \cdots\right) \qquad (2.19)$$

This result shows that the response of a linear system to a finite-width pulse is the sum of the impulsive response of the system and its various derivatives. Thus, if the pulse is applied to a relaxed system whose transfer function is $G(s)$ and whose impulsive response is $g(t)$, the output of this system, $c(t)$, to a pulse given by (2.17) becomes

$$c(t) = f(nT)\gamma\left[g(t) - \frac{\gamma}{2!}g'(t) + \frac{\gamma^2}{3!}g''(t) - \cdots\right] \qquad (2.20)$$

It is important to note that if the various derivatives of the impulsive response are small, as is usually the case in low-pass systems, all but the first term of (2.20) may be negligible. In applying the impulse approximation, this assumption is made. An estimate of the error so introduced may be obtained by evaluating some of the terms in (2.20) which are neglected.

EXAMPLE

The system transfer function $G(s)$ is $1/(s + a)$, and the impulsive response is e^{-at}. The various terms in (2.20) are

$$g(t) = e^{-at}$$
$$g'(t) = -ae^{-at}$$
$$g''(t) = a^2 e^{-at}$$
$$\text{etc.}$$

From (2.20), the output of the system in response to a finite-width pulse is

$$c(t) = f(nT)\gamma\left(e^{-at} + \frac{\gamma a e^{-at}}{2!} + \frac{\gamma^2 a^2 e^{-at}}{3!} + \cdots\right)$$

The summation is factored and rearranged to the following:

$$c(t) = \gamma f(nT)e^{-at}\left(1 + \frac{a\gamma}{2!} + \frac{a^2\gamma^2}{3!} + \cdots\right)$$

The first term of the series is the impulsive response of the system to an impulse whose area is equal to that of the actual pulse. The remaining terms are corrections to this first estimate. For instance, it is readily seen that if $a\gamma$ is 0.1, that is, if the duration of the pulse is 10 per cent of the time constant of the system, $1/a$, the response differs from the impulsive response by about 5 per cent.

The approach used in the preceding discussion and example assume that the pulse resulting from a finite sampling time is flat-topped. It is recognized that this characterization is not precise since the actual pulse would have a top which follows the actual function being sampled. The effects produced by non-flat-topped pulses are of second order in so far as low-pass system are concerned and are of little consequence in practical problems.

While the details of data reconstruction are discussed in the next chapter, certain preliminary considerations should be reviewed as to their effect on the assumption of impulse sampling. In practice the more common situation is that the pulse sequence is applied to some type of "data hold." The function of such an element is to reconstruct, in so far as possible, the original continuous function from which the pulse sequence was derived. Typical of such a device is the simple clamp circuit which accepts a short pulse and "stretches" it to a duration equal to the sampling interval. The effect of such a clamp can be reproduced mathematically using the impulse approximation by assuming that the clamp circuit responds to the *area* of the impulse rather than the *magnitude* of the pulse. This simple mathematical strategem introduces no error and makes possible the simplifications of the impulse approximation with little or no loss of accuracy. For this reason, the impulse approximation is almost always used in the analysis and synthesis of sampled-data feedback control systems.

2.4 Laplace Transform of the Impulse Sequence

As in the case of the continuous system, the Laplace transform finds considerable utility in sampled-data systems. As a result it is desirable to consider the Laplace transform of an impulse-modulated function $f^*(t)$. If it is assumed that the function $f(t)$ from which $f^*(t)$ is derived is Laplace transformable, and it is zero for negative time then $f^*(t)$ is

$$f^*(t) = \sum_{n=0}^{\infty} f(nT)\delta(t - nT) \tag{2.21}$$

where $f(nT)$ is the value of $f(t)$ at the sampling instant nT. Thus a typical term of the sequence is an impulse at time nT whose area is $f(nT)$. The Laplace transform of this typical term is

$$\mathcal{L}[f(nT)\delta(t - nT)] = f(nT)e^{-nTs} \tag{2.22}$$

The Laplace transform of the impulse sequence $F^*(s)$ is thus

$$F^*(s) = \sum_{n=0}^{+\infty} f(nT)e^{-nTs} \tag{2.23}$$

For practical problems, it would be awkward if the Laplace transform were an infinite summation which could not be expressed in closed form. Fortunately, this is not the case for those time functions $f(t)$ whose Laplace transform can be expressed as a ratio of polynomials in s. This will be proved in later chapters but will be demonstrated with a simple example here.

EXAMPLE

The function $f(t)$ is the unit step function $u(t)$. This means that all values of $f(nT)$ are equal to unity for positive n and the Laplace transform $F^*(s)$ given in (2.23) is simply

$$F^*(s) = \sum_{n=0}^{+\infty} e^{-nTs}$$

The infinite summation is recognized as a geometric progression in e^{-Ts} whose sum is

$$F^*(s) = \frac{1}{1 - e^{-Ts}}$$

It is seen in this example that $F^*(s)$ could be readily expressed in closed form in terms of e^{-Ts}. This simplification was in consequence of the assumption of impulse sampling, with the result that the Laplace transform of each term of the sequence was simply the value $f(nT)$ and a delay factor e^{-nTs}. Had the switching function $p(t)$ been of different form, the Laplace transform of the typical term of the sequence would have contained contributions of the switching pulses themselves and the resultant expressions would have been much more complex. Another point which is brought out in this simple example is the mathematical desirability of having all equal sampling intervals. Had they been unequal, the infinite series would not have been a simple geometric progression with a constant ratio and its summation could not have been expressed in closed form. Fortunately, the assumptions which had to be made are also representative of the practical situation.

An alternate form of Laplace-transform representation of the impulse sequence can be obtained by using the form for $f^*(t)$ given in (2.12):

$$f^*(t) = f(t)\,\delta_T(t) \tag{2.24}$$

Since $\delta_T(t)$ is a periodic function, it is expressed in terms of a Fourier series, all of whose coefficients are equal to $1/T$, as shown in (2.14) and (2.15). Thus (2.20) can be written as

$$f^*(t) = \frac{1}{T} \sum_{n=-\infty}^{+\infty} f(t)e^{jn\omega_0 t} \tag{2.25}$$

where ω_0 is the sampling frequency and is equal to $2\pi/T$. Taking the Laplace transform of each term in the series and making use of the shifting theorem, the Laplace transform of $f^*(t)$ becomes

$$F^*(s) = \frac{1}{T} \sum_{n=-\infty}^{+\infty} F(s + nj\omega_0) \qquad (2.26)$$

where $F(s)$ is the Laplace transform of the continuous function $f(t)$ from which the sequence was obtained.

It is of interest to note the equivalence between the expressions for $F^*(s)$ as given in (2.26) and (2.23):

$$\frac{1}{T} \sum_{n=-\infty}^{+\infty} F(s + nj\omega_0) = \sum_{n=0}^{+\infty} f(nT)e^{-nTs} \qquad (2.27)$$

This equivalence was discovered more than a century ago by Poisson and is essentially equivalent to the Poisson summation rule.[49] To illustrate the form in which Laplace transforms of impulse-sampled sequences appear using this form of transform, an example will be used.

EXAMPLE

The function $f(t)$ will be taken as the unit step $u(t)$ as in the preceding example. The Laplace transform of the unit step is $1/s$, so that the Laplace transform of the impulse sequence obtained from sampling a unit step is

$$F^*(s) = \frac{1}{T} \sum_{n=-\infty}^{+\infty} \frac{1}{s + nj\omega_0}$$

Unlike the previous example, this infinite summation cannot be readily expressed in closed form in terms of rational polynomials in s.

The fact that the infinite summation in this example cannot be expressed in closed form limits the usefulness of the form of $F^*(s)$ as given in (2.26). On the other hand, it shows much more clearly some of the periodic properties of the Laplace transform of a pulse sequence. $F^*(s)$ is seen to be periodic in $j\omega_0$, a fact which is useful in establishing many of the theorems governing the manipulation of pulse transforms. In many cases, only a few of the terms of (2.26) produce significant effects in a linear system, and by taking into account only the first few terms of the series, applications to the synthesis of sampled-data systems can readily be made. It is true, nevertheless, that in most sampled-data-system problems, the form of $F^*(s)$ given in (2.23) finds more application.

Much more will be said on the subject in later chapters dealing with the z transformation.

2.5 Comparison with Carrier-modulation System

In previous sections the process of sampling has been treated as a form of modulation in which the switching or sampling function $p(t)$ is a periodic pulse train. The unusual feature of sampled signals of the type described is that the signal spectrum can be recovered by a linear filter. For instance, in the case of signals having finite spectra, a perfect low-

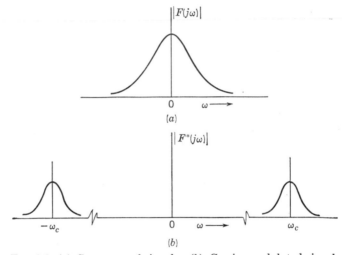

FIG. 2.9. (a) Spectrum of signal.   (b) Carrier-modulated signal.

pass filter whose bandwidth extends from zero to half the sampling frequency can recover the signal perfectly, provided that the sampling rate is sufficiently high. It is of interest to compare this type of sampling with the more usual form employed in a-c feedback control systems.

In the usual carrier system, the signal modulates a sinusoidal carrier whose expression is

$$p(t) = E_c \cos \omega_c t \tag{2.28}$$

The expression for this carrier-modulated signal is thus

$$f^*(t) = E_c f(t) \cos \omega_c t \tag{2.29}$$

Expressing the cosine in its exponential form, $f^*(t)$ becomes

$$f^*(t) = [\tfrac{1}{2} f(t) e^{j\omega_c t} + \tfrac{1}{2} f(t) e^{-j\omega_c t}] E_c \tag{2.30}$$

Obtaining the Fourier transform of $f^*(t)$ by application of the shifting theorem, $F^*(j\omega)$ is

$$F^*(j\omega) = [\tfrac{1}{2} F(j\omega + j\omega_c) + \tfrac{1}{2} F(j\omega - j\omega_c)] E_c \tag{2.31}$$

This spectrum is plotted in Fig. 2.9, where the familiar sideband spectra in the signal at the output of the modulator are seen. This form of modulation is the one found in most carrier-suppressed data systems used in feedback control devices.

The important characteristic to note is that the total spectrum does not contain the signal spectrum, so that no linear filter can possibly extract the signal by frequency discrimination or rejection. Demodulation schemes employing nonlinear devices such as the standard phase detector are used to translate the modulated signal spectra. The spectrum of a carrier-suppressed modulated signal should be contrasted to that obtained with pulse or impulse modulation, as illustrated in Figs. 2.6 and 2.7, respectively. The distinctive feature here is that these spectra contain the signal spectrum as one of their components, and if conditions are correct, a linear wave filter can extract the signal with little or no distortion.

The important difference between the modulated functions $p(t)$ in pulse and carrier modulation is that the former function is periodic and contains among its various Fourier components a zero-frequency, or d-c, term, whereas the carrier function does not. In this manner, the pulse-modulation system contains a spectral component which is the unshifted signal component resulting in the recoverable signal spectrum. Despite these differences, carrier-modulated systems using phase detectors can be treated as sampled systems from the point at which demodulation takes place and beyond. The phase detector operates on the basis that once (or twice) each cycle of the carrier a linear detector charges a load condenser to a peak voltage proportional to the amplitude of the latest carrier cycle. In this manner, a signal datum is produced once (or twice) per cycle of carrier and, in effect, a sampling process of the usual form results. The sampling frequency can be considered equal to the carrier frequency or twice the carrier frequency, depending on whether a half- or full-wave detector is used.

2.6 Summary

The sampling operation consists of examining a continuous signal at intervals equal to a time T. The resultant information is a sequence of pulses or numbers, each of which gives the value of the signal at a particular sampling instant. This sampling process can be considered as a modulation process in which the switching function $p(t)$ is a sequence of very narrow pulses. For mathematical convenience these pulses can be approximated by impulses of the same area for the class of problems encountered in feedback control. Properly used, this approximation results in mathematical simplifications which are extremely useful in the analysis and synthesis of sampled-data systems.

The sampling frequencies which must be used are based on an application of the sampling theorem. While, ideally, signals having limited spectra may be sampled at a frequency equal to twice the highest frequency contained in the signal with no loss of information, practical systems always employ much higher sampling frequencies. This is necessitated because practical signal spectra are not finite and signal recovery filters are not perfect. The practical problem is to select sampling frequencies which produce acceptable amounts of distortion or ripple.

The Laplace transform of sampled signals $F^*(s)$ can be expressed in two general forms. One of these forms can generally be reduced to the ratio of finite polynomials in e^{Ts}. The other form is an infinite series of terms in $(s + j\omega_0)$ and cannot be reduced to a closed expression. Both forms find application in the study of sampled-data feedback control systems. One of the characteristics of the pulse sequences used in sampled-data systems is that signal can be recovered by means of a linear filter. This contrasts with carrier systems employed in the field of servomechanisms, where nonlinear devices must be used to recover the signal. Such systems can be treated as sampled-data systems only after the detection process.

CHAPTER 3

DATA RECONSTRUCTION

A sampled time function bears little resemblance to the original function from which it is derived. While the envelope of the sampled function corresponds to the values of the continuous function at sampling instants and may appear to be similar on cursory examination, the wide divergence between the two functions becomes more evident on the basis of frequency spectra. The sampled function contains spurious side spectra introduced by the sampling process. A linear low-pass wave filter can be used to extract the signal spectrum to a certain degree of accuracy. The errors are caused by the overlapping frequency spectra and by the nonideal filtering characteristics of practical filter networks, which do not completely attenuate the side spectra.

In this application, a filter which extracts the signal spectrum may be thought of as a data-reconstruction device or data extrapolator. In effect, the filter does extrapolate a continuous time function into a sampling interval based on the weighted average effects of previous samples. The deviations of this extrapolated time function from the actual function from which the samples were derived is called the "ripple" in the output. From a practical viewpoint, there are good reasons why

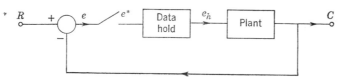

FIG. 3.1. Typical error-sampled feedback control system.

the ripple must be maintained below a certain level. The plant in a system is subjected to command signals which contain ripple components. If they are excessive, the plant components are subject to wear, noise, and unnecessary wastage of control effort. For this reason, the study of data holds used for signal reconstruction must consider this effect as an important engineering design factor.

In typical feedback control systems, the data-reconstruction element is generally referred to as the "data hold," "desampling filter," or "data extrapolator." Figure 3.1 shows a sampled-data feedback control system in which the data-hold element is located immediately after the sampler. The signal is reconstructed from the sampled data into a continuous signal before being applied to the plant. In this context, the effectiveness of the data hold is measured by the difference between the reconstructed time function $e_h(t)$ and the actual error function $e(t)$. In a later chapter, where digital compensation of sampled-data systems is considered, it will be shown that $e_h(t)$ is not necessarily an approximation of $e(t)$ but rather of a modified error function so computed that it produces a desired compensating effect. In this chapter, only those aspects of the problem dealing with the reconstruction of the function without modification are considered.

3.1 The Cardinal Data Hold

In the previous chapter, it was shown that the signal is completely recoverable, provided that the Fourier transform spectrum terminates at a frequency equal to one-half the sampling frequency. An ideal filter which has unity transmission from zero frequency to one-half the sampling frequency and zero transmission everywhere else is known as the *cardinal data hold*. Figure 3.2 shows the frequency response of such a filter which can be expressed by

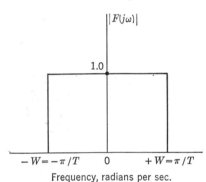

FIG. 3.2. Frequency response of cardinal hold filter.

$$\begin{aligned} F(j\omega) &= 1.0 \qquad -W \leq \omega \leq W \\ F(j\omega) &= 0 \qquad -W \geq \omega \geq W \end{aligned} \qquad (3.1)$$

That such a filter is not physically realizable can be shown by inverting the Fourier transform of (3.1), giving the impulsive response as follows:

$$f(t) = \int_{-W}^{+W} e^{j\omega t} \, df \qquad (3.2)$$

Integrating this expression and simplifying, the impulsive response becomes

$$f(t) = \frac{W}{\pi} \frac{\sin Wt}{Wt} \qquad (3.3)$$

This impulsive response is plotted in Fig. 3.3, where it is seen that the filter is physically unrealizable because there is a finite response prior to the application of the exciting impulse at $t = 0$.

The significance of this result is that, even for those time functions which have a finite spectrum, it is **not** practical to expect a perfect recovery of the original signal from a sample pulse sequence. There will always be a ripple component, as well as a certain amount of distortion. In addition, the types of signal spectra found in practice are rarely limited in frequency content, so that the assumption of a finite spectrum is not usually met. Under these circumstances, even a cardinal

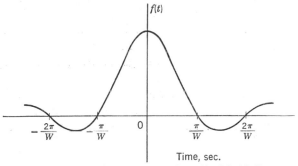

FIG. 3.3. Impulsive response of cardinal hold filter.

data hold will not reproduce the original signal perfectly. For these reasons, the cardinal data hold is only of academic interest and will not be considered further in the study of practical systems.

3.2 Polynomial Extrapolation Systems

As mentioned previously, the process of data reconstruction may be viewed as one of extrapolating a signal during a sampling interval, based on information given only at past sampling instants. The latter restriction is necessitated because the input data are samples or values at sampling instants only and only past data samples may be used, as required by considerations of physical realizability. In carrying out the extrapolation of the time function into a sampling interval, it is necessary to make an a priori assumption of the form of the function itself. For instance, if it is assumed that the function is composed of exponentials, then it follows that the extrapolation should be in the form of exponentials and that the data-hold system must determine the relative magnitudes and exponents which must be used in the particular sampling interval under consideration.

A particular form of extrapolation commonly used in feedback control systems is the one which assumes that the original function can be approximated by a polynomial in time. The decision which must be made a priori is the highest order which is required for an adequate extrapolation. Having set this order, the data hold must compute the best fit to the past data by adjustment of the coefficients of the various terms of the polynomial. If the actual function being reconstructed is a polynomial in time whose order is equal to or lower than the assumed order, the reconstruction will be perfect.   On the other hand, if the actual function is some other form, the polynomial extrapolation will be an approximation whose accuracy must be reviewed from the standpoint of engineering considerations.

A theoretical basis for the polynomial extrapolation based only on samples taken at equally spaced prior sampling instants is the Gregory-Newton extrapolation formula[54] used in the numerical integration of differential equations.   In view of the practical importance of the Gregory-Newton formula in the design of sampled-data systems, its derivation will be given.

A convenient technique for the derivation of the formula is to employ the expression for prediction in the frequency domain.   The transfer function of a system whose output is the value of the input τ sec in the future is

$$F_h(s) = e^{\tau s} \tag{3.4}$$

This expression may be rearranged in the following manner:

$$F_h(s) = [1 - (1 - e^{-Ts})]^{-\frac{\tau}{T}} \tag{3.5}$$

Expanding the expression enclosed in the brackets by means of the binomial expansion, there results

$$F_h(s) = 1 + \frac{1 - e^{-Ts}}{T}\tau + \frac{(1 - e^{-Ts})^2}{T^2}\frac{(T + \tau)\tau}{2} + \cdots \tag{3.6}$$

As will be shown later, the number of terms which are used depends on the order of polynomial which is to be extrapolated.

The transfer function $F_h(s)$ expresses the transfer function of a device whose output is the future value of the input, provided that an infinite number of terms are taken.   The Laplace transform of this output $C(s)$ is given by

$$C(s) = F_h(s)R(s) \tag{3.7}$$

where $R(s)$ is the Laplace transform of the input.   Substituting for $F_h(s)$ the series form of (3.6), $C(s)$ becomes

$$C(s) = R(s) + R(s)\frac{1 - e^{-Ts}}{T}\tau + R(s)\frac{(1 - e^{-Ts})^2}{T^2}\frac{(T + \tau)\tau}{2} + \cdots \tag{3.8}$$

Inverting (3.8), the output of the extrapolator becomes

$$r(t + \tau) = r(t) + \frac{r(t) - r(t - T)}{T}\tau$$
$$+ \frac{r(t) - 2r(t - T) + r(t - 2T)}{T^2}\frac{(T + \tau)\tau}{2} + \cdots \tag{3.9}$$

To be exact, an infinite number of terms of (3.9) must be taken.

Adapting (3.9) to the case of the data hold used in sampled-data reconstruction, it is seen that the time t is taken at a particular sampling instant nT and the prediction time τ is the time measured from this instant. Thus, taking

$$t = nT \qquad (3.10)$$

substitution in (3.9) results in the expression

$$r(nT + \tau) = r(nT) + \frac{1}{T} \{r(nT) - r[(n-1)T]\}\tau$$

$$+ \frac{1}{T^2} \{r(nT) - 2r[(n-1)T] + r[(n-2)T]\} \frac{(T+\tau)\tau}{2} + \cdots \qquad (3.11)$$

where it is understood that the extrapolation is taken from the time nT onward. It is seen that the data which are needed to implement the extrapolation are the values of the function $r(t)$ at sampling instants nT, $(n-1)T$, $(n-2)T$, etc., only. These are the values of the function which are available in a sampled-data system, and for this reason the Gregory-Newton extrapolation formula is very useful.

The polynomial in τ which is generated by (3.11) is seen to contain elements that are recognized as the various back differences of the sampled function. For instance, the second term contained in the (3.11) is the first back difference; the third term, the second back difference; etc. The expression may be written in the form

$$r(nT + \tau) = r(nT) + \frac{\nabla r(nT)}{T}\tau + \frac{\nabla^2 r(nT)}{T^2} \frac{(T+\tau)\tau}{2} + \cdots \qquad (3.12)$$

where the various $\nabla^n r(nT)$ are the back differences of nth order. Several practical conclusions can be drawn from the extrapolation formula in the form given in (3.12). First, to generate an extrapolated function which is derived from a completely general $r(t)$ containing finite back differences of all orders, an infinite number of back samples must be taken into account. On the other hand, if the original $r(t)$ had been an nth order polynomial in time containing only a finite number of terms, the extrapolation would be perfect with only $n + 1$ prior samples taken into account. This is in consequence of the fact that a finite polynomial contains only n finite back differences, where n is the order of the polynomial, all others being zero. If an extrapolator is used which contains an insufficient number of back differences, the extrapolated function will be in error, and the problem of the designer is to keep the magnitude of this error within acceptable bounds.

Equation (3.12) suggests a method of classification for data-hold systems of this type depending on the number of terms contained therein.

For instance, if a very simple form of data extrapolation in which only the first term, $r(nT)$, is taken, the extrapolator is referred to as a *zero-order* hold since the polynomial generated by this system is of zero order. Similarly, if the first two terms are implemented, the classification is *first-order* since the polynomial which will be extrapolated is of first order. It is recognized that the zero-order data hold is also known as a data clamp and that it operates on the assumption that the value of the function in a given sampling interval is equal to the function at the beginning of that interval. This extrapolation is perfect only for functions which are constants. Practical systems rarely employ data extrapolators which are beyond first order, both for reasons of economy and because if too many back differences are taken, an excessive settling time results and noise effects are increased. These points will be discussed later in more detail.

3.3 The Zero-order Data Hold

As indicated in the previous section, the zero-order data hold includes only the first term of the series as expressed in (3.12). This form of data hold is important from a practical point of view because of its simplicity and the fact that it is readily implemented. A standard electronic clamp circuit will set its output at a level equal to or proportional to the magnitude of an input pulse and then reset itself when a new pulse is applied. Such circuits maintain a constant output between pulses and thus implement the zero-order-hold relationship. Similarly, a digital register will hold a number until a reset pulse is applied and a new number set up. In all cases, the output of the device essentially assumes that the continuous function within a sampling interval is constant and equal to the value of the function at the preceding sampling instant.

The form of the reconstructed function at the output of a zero-order hold is shown in Fig. 3.4. The extrapolation in each case is a constant and is refreshed at each sampling instant. Because of the appearance of the reconstructed function, the data hold is sometimes referred to as a "staircase" or "boxcar" data system.

In order to include the effects of a zero-order data hold in a dynamical system, it is necessary that a mathematical description of its effect be obtained and, if possible, a transfer function derived. It is recalled that the transfer function of a linear system is the Laplace transform of the impulsive response of the system. In the case of a zero-order data hold, it is assumed that the short pulse which is applied to its input is approximated by an impulse of an area equal to the magnitude of the pulse. If an impulse of unit area is applied to the data hold, its response should be a unit-magnitude continuous function which is maintained until refreshed by the next impulse. In view of the assumption that the sampling intervals are all equal to T, the extrapolated value of the function should fall to zero T sec after the application of the unit impulse in order that the next impulse may restore the data hold to its new value.

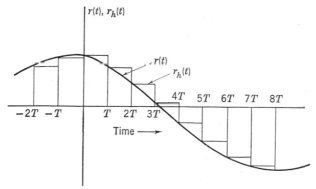

FIG. 3.4. Reconstruction of $r(t)$ by a zero-order data hold.

The impulsive response of the zero-order data hold should therefore appear as shown in Fig. 3.5.

To obtain the transfer function of this system, the impulsive response

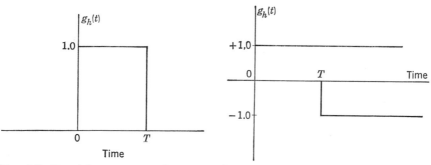

FIG. 3.5. Impulsive response of a zero-order data hold.

FIG. 3.6. Step-function components of impulsive response of zero-order data hold.

can be decomposed into two unit step functions, as shown in Fig. 3.6. The impulsive response is given by

$$g_h(t) = u(t) - u(t - T) \tag{3.13}$$

where $u(t)$ is the unit step function. The Laplace transform of $g_h(t)$ is

$$G_h(s) = \frac{1}{s} - \frac{1}{s} e^{-Ts} \tag{3.14}$$

This transfer function is useful in the analysis of systems which include the zero-order data hold.   As will be seen later, it can be approximated by rational polynomials in s, but this procedure is not necessary in the theory of sampled-data systems, and the exact form will be used.

It is of interest to compare the frequency response of a zero-order data hold with that of the cardinal hold as shown in Fig. 3.2.   The frequency response is obtained by substituting $j\omega$ for s in (3.14), resulting in $G_h(j\omega)$ as follows:

$$G_h(j\omega) = \frac{1 - e^{-j\omega T}}{j\omega} \tag{3.15}$$

By rearranging the terms of (3.15), $G_h(j\omega)$ can be expressed as

$$G_h(j\omega) = T \frac{\sin \omega T/2}{\omega T/2} \underline{/-\omega T/2} \tag{3.16}$$

The amplitude and phase of $G_h(j\omega)$ are plotted in Fig. 3.7.

The frequency response of the zero-order data hold is low pass with full cutoff occurring at frequencies of n/T cps, where n is an integer.

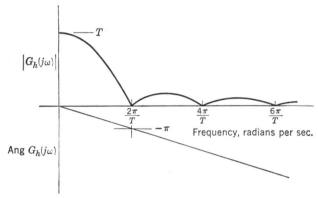

FIG. 3.7. Amplitude and phase frequency response of zero-order data hold.

By contrast, the cardinal data hold has a frequency response which is unity in the passband with perfect cutoff at all frequencies beyond $1/2T$ cps.   In the frequency domain, the imperfections of the zero-order hold are seen to be the result of gradual cutoff up to $1/2T$ cps, as well as response, though at attenuated levels, beyond this frequency.   The transmission of the higher-frequency components of the sampled signal accounts for the ripple in the time domain, as seen in Fig. 3.4.

The phase shift introduced by $G_h(j\omega)$ is of interest to the designer of a control system incorporating a zero-order data hold.   Since most control systems are low-pass in frequency response and lagging phase angles contribute to the instability of the system, the phase lag of $G_h(j\omega)$ complicates the problem of stabilization of feedback control systems. As will be shown later, systems which are stable in the continuous organic form can be unstable when a sampled-data link is introduced in the closed loop.

3.4 The First-order Data Hold

The first-order data hold is a device which implements the first two terms of (3.11) or (3.12). Using the form of (3.11), the output of a first-order data-hold device is

$$r(nT + \tau) = r(nT) + \frac{r(nT) - r[(n - 1)T]}{T}\,\tau \qquad (3.17)$$

This expression shows that the extrapolated function in a particular sampling interval is linear and that the slope of the extrapolated function

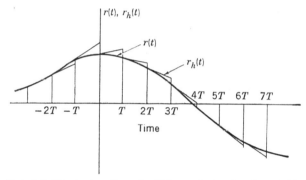

Fig. 3.8. Reconstruction of $r(t)$ by a first-order data hold.

is equal to the first back difference. Figure 3.8 illustrates the reconstructed time function $r_h(t)$ produced by such an extrapolation. The imperfections result from the fact that (3.17) omits the higher-order back differences, which, if nonzero in the original function, can produce considerable error.

As in the case of the zero-order hold, it is desirable to obtain the transfer function of such a device by taking the Laplace transform of the impulsive response. It should be noted that the slope of the straight-line extrapolation is equal to the difference between the most recent sample and the previous sample divided by the sampling time interval. Thus, to obtain correctly the slope within an interval, the impulsive response of the hold in any given interval must contain the effect from the previous interval. Figure 3.9 shows the impulsive response of the first-order hold.

In determining the correctness of this response, it is seen that at the onset of a pulse, the output rises immediately to the value of the pulse. A straight line is then generated whose slope is equal to the value of the sample at that instant divided by the sampling interval T. It should be recalled that in its application, the first-order hold is actually subjected to a pulse train, so that preceding the pulse applied at zero time there had been another pulse applied T sec earlier. This prior pulse generated an impulsive response which contributed a negative slope in the interval under consideration equal to the previous sample divided by the sampling interval T.   In this manner, the slope of the extrapolated signal has the correct slope as required by (3.17).

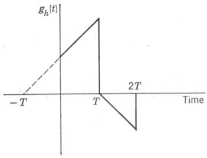

FIG. 3.9. Impulsive response of a first-order data hold.

The impulsive response shown in Fig. 3.9 can be decomposed into a set of component step and ramp functions, as shown in Fig. 3.10.   It is readily verified that the sum of these components produces the correct form for $g_h(t)$.   The Laplace transform of the impulsive response is the sum of the Laplace transforms of the components as follows:

$$G_h(s) = \frac{1}{s} + \frac{1}{Ts^2} - \frac{2}{s} e^{-Ts} - \frac{2}{Ts^2} e^{-Ts} + \frac{1}{s} e^{-2Ts} + \frac{1}{Ts^2} e^{-2Ts} \quad (3.18)$$

Combining terms,

$$G_h(s) = T(1 + Ts)\left(\frac{1 - e^{-Ts}}{Ts}\right)^2 \quad (3.19)$$

This transfer function may be used in the analysis of systems incorporating this type of hold system.

It is of interest to obtain the frequency response of the first-order hold by replacing s by $j\omega$.   Doing so and simplifying the resulting expression, this response is given by

$$G_h(j\omega) = T \sqrt{1 + \omega^2 T^2} \left(\frac{\sin \omega T/2}{\omega T/2}\right)^2 \underline{/-\omega T + \tan^{-1} \omega T} \quad (3.20)$$

This response is sketched in Fig. 3.11, where it is seen that the frequency passband from zero to the first zero-transmission frequency is $2\pi/T$, which is the same as that of the zero-order hold.   The major difference between the two frequency-response characteristics is that the first-order hold accentuates some of the frequencies in the passband excessively. In addition, the transmission of the higher-frequency components is greater and is reflected in the time domain by higher-ripple components under certain circumstances.   On the other hand, the first-order hold is capable of reproducing a ramp function perfectly, as contrasted to the zero-order hold, which can reproduce only a step function or constant signal perfectly after a transient period.

An important factor which affects the performance of systems which include a first-order data hold is the phase shift. As stated before, feedback control systems generally are low-pass, and instability is the result of excessive lagging phase shifts in the control loop. It is noted that the average phase shift of the zero-order hold is approximately half

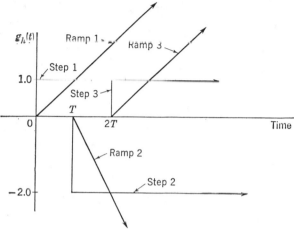

Fig. 3.10. Component functions of first-order data hold.

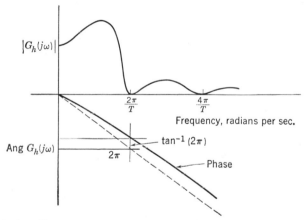

Fig. 3.11. Amplitude and phase frequency response of first-order data hold.

the average phase shift of the first-order hold. For instance, at a frequency of $2\pi/T$ radians/sec, the phase shift of the former is $-\pi$ radians, while that of the latter is $(-2\pi + \tan^{-1} 2\pi)$ radians, or about $-280°$. For this reason, the inclusion of such a data hold in a feedback control system generally complicates the problem of stabilization, so first-order holds are not commonly employed in practical feedback control systems.

3.5 Partial-velocity-correction First-order Hold

A cursory examination of the function which is reconstructed by a first-order data hold as illustrated in Fig. 3.8 will show that under some circumstances, the amount of ripple content may be excessive. For instance, if the function from which the pulse train is derived contains sizable higher-order derivatives, the underlying assumption implied in a first-order data hold that all differences other than the first are zero can

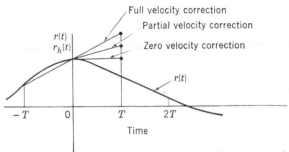

FIG. 3.12. Partial-velocity-correction data hold.

be seriously misleading. Heuristically, a means for reducing this error is that of extrapolating the function in any given sampling interval with only a fraction of, rather than the full, first difference. The process is illustrated in Fig. 3.12 in the first sampling interval from 0 to T sec. Here the extrapolated function is a straight line whose slope is only k times the first difference, where k is a number less than unity.

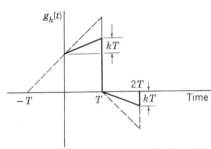

FIG. 3.13. Impulsive response of partial-velocity-correction data hold.

It is difficult to arrive at a particular value of k except for specific cases. The frequency response can be used to estimate the value of k which will, on the average, result in extrapolations having least error. It is recalled that the frequency response of a full-velocity-correction zero-order hold showed an excessive transmission of components in the higher range of the passband from 0 to $2\pi/T$ radians/sec. A criterion which can be applied to the choice of the velocity extrapolation constant k is that the frequency response in the passband be maximally flat.

In order to set the value of k, it is necessary to obtain the transfer function of the partial-velocity data hold in a manner similar to that employed in the previous section. Figure 3.13 shows the impulsive response which will produce an extrapolation like that of Fig. 3.12. The dashed lines show the full-velocity-correction impulsive response from Fig. 3.9. The impulsive response can be decomposed into a number of elementary step and ramp functions, as shown in Fig. 3.14. The Laplace transform of the partial-velocity hold is the sum of the Laplace transforms of the components as follows:

$$G_h(s) = \frac{1}{s} - \frac{1+k}{s} e^{-Ts} + \frac{k}{s} e^{-2Ts} + \frac{k}{Ts^2} - \frac{2k}{Ts^2} e^{-Ts} + \frac{k}{Ts^2} e^{-2Ts} \qquad (3.21)$$

which, after combination and simplification, becomes

$$G_h(s) = \frac{1}{s} (1 - e^{-Ts}) \left[1 - ke^{-Ts} + \frac{k}{Ts} (1 - e^{-Ts}) \right] \qquad (3.22)$$

It is noted that when k is unity, (3.22) becomes identical with (3.19).

Replacing s by $j\omega$ in (3.22) the frequency response of the partial-velocity hold is obtained. This becomes, after some simplification,

$$G_h(j\omega) = (1 - k)T \left(\frac{\sin \omega T/2}{\omega T/2} e^{-j\omega T/2} \right) \left[1 + \frac{k}{1-k} (1 + j\omega T) \right.$$
$$\left. \frac{\sin \omega T/2}{\omega T/2} e^{-j\omega T/2} \right] \qquad (3.23)$$

The frequency response $G_h(j\omega)$ is plotted for three values of k in Fig. 3.15. It is seen that for full velocity correction ($k = 1$), the frequency response

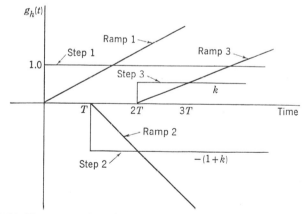

FIG. 3.14. Component functions of partial-velocity-correction data hold.

in the passband is characterized by an overshoot of about 50 per cent. On the other hand, with partial-velocity correction of 0.5 and 0.3, the frequency response has an overshoot of 20 per cent and 0, respectively. It is seen, therefore, that in order to pass frequency components in the passband without overemphasis, a partial velocity correction of about

30 per cent is required. When the velocity correction is zero, the extrapolator becomes the zero-order hold and the frequency response in the passband is monotonic, as seen in Fig. 3.7.

While frequency-response characteristics of the data-hold systems provide only an indirect indication of performance in the time domain, it is generally true that a flat frequency response in the region containing the significant components produces a better reproduction of the signal than does a frequency response which is either peaked or excessively drooping. Time-domain analyses will confirm the results indicated by the frequency-response characteristics. Full velocity correction produces accurate reproduction of signal only when the input signal is a constant or a ramp function. If the function being reproduced contains significant higher-order back differences the errors introduced by using a first-order data hold can be reduced by partial velocity correction. A suggested value for this partial correction is about 30 to 50 per cent of the velocity as measured by the first back difference.

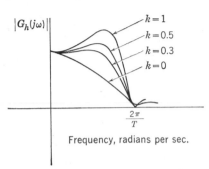

FIG. 3.15. Frequency response of partial-velocity-correction data hold.

3.6 Higher-order Data Holds

Higher-order data holds implement more terms of the Gregory-Newton extrapolation formula than the first one or two as described in the previous sections. Such systems are potentially capable of reproducing higher-order polynomials perfectly after a settling time which depends on the number of past samples included in the approximation formula. Feedback control systems do not generally utilize these higher-order systems, mostly because their excessive phase lags introduce difficulties in stabilization of the loop. Even with more effective digital controllers the requirement that a number of past samples be received before the hold system settles affects the settling time of the entire system adversely.

Another pertinent factor is that of random noise which may be superimposed on the input data samples to the data hold. Practical systems are always subject to random noise, whether it be introduced by external influences or by quantization effects in the digital data. If the random uncertainties in the value of the data samples are linearly independent, then the noise at the output of the data extrapolator is increased as a larger number of samples are used in the computation of its output. For this reason, higher-order data-hold systems have considerably more noise in their outputs than do the lower-order systems. This effect militates against the use of higher-order data-hold systems in situations where the magnitude of the random noise is significant.

The fact that the plant in control systems is usually low-pass in frequency response makes the use of overly complex data-hold systems unnecessary. The inaccuracies in data extrapolation have been referred to as ripple whose frequency components are at sampling frequency and higher. For instance, in a zero-order data hold, the staircase approximation is seen to differ from the actual continuous function from which the pulse sequence is derived by an amplitude-modulated periodic ripple component whose fundamental frequency is the sampling frequency. While the ripple may cause an undesirable amount of shock at the input of the plant, it is nevertheless true that if the plant is low-pass in frequency response, little of this component appears in the output. For this reason, the choice of data hold is largely dictated by the form of the function which is to be reconstructed and the capability of the plant to accept ripple components at the input without adverse effects. Generally speaking, the zero-order data hold is found to be adequate for most systems found in practice. In feedback instrumentation devices whose major purpose is the reproduction of a signal at low power levels, first-order data holds with partial or full velocity correction find application. For process-control systems, however, the usual form of data hold used is of the zero-order variety.

3.7 Implementation of Polynomial Extrapolators

The implementation of polynomial extrapolators generally requires the use of devices which are capable of integrating in the time domain. The simplest form, the zero-order data hold, can consist of a digital register with analogue-to-digital and digital-to-analogue circuits included. Other forms include the use of diodes included in circuits known as clamp circuits. It is only when first- and higher-order data holds are employed that integrators are included as recognizable system elements. As will be shown later, higher-order data holds are best implemented with feedback configurations, although it is possible to design open-cycle systems also. Because of their simplicity, these will be considered first.

A block diagram which will implement a first-order hold is shown in Fig. 3.16. Here the data samples $r(nT)$ are derived from a function $r(t)$ and are applied to a data clamp, which is, in fact, a zero-order data hold. In order to generate the second term of the extrapolation as given in (3.17), a ramp function whose slope is the difference between the present value, $r(nT)$, and the previous value, $r(n-1)T$, must be generated. The constant k is unity for full velocity correction and less than unity for

partial velocity correction.   The integrator implements this part of the
process, and its output, when added to the held value $r_h(nT)$, produces the
reconstructed function $g(t)$.   It is seen that a control function is necessary
in the system because as each sampling instant passes, the stored datum
in the memory $r(nT)$ must be transferred to the status of a past sample
$r(n-1)T$.   In addition, the integrator must be cleared to zero initial
condition to be capable of generating a new ramp function for the next
sampling interval.

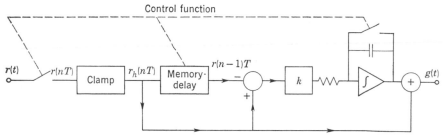

FIG. 3.16. Open-cycle first-order data-hold system diagram.

Data extrapolators of higher complexity than first order can be
devised, based on this open-cycle system, by the addition of more
integrators and a memory of more capacity to hold the past samples
required for the computation.   An important point to be noted is that
the output of the extrapolator depends on the stability of the various
elements.   For instance, if there is a drift component in the integrator,
it will appear directly in the output.   Another complication is the relative complexity of the control function which must clear integrators
and transfer data samples from one position to another in order to maintain the correct "age" for each sample.   The use of feedback methods
reduces the complexity of this function and results in considerable
economies, especially for higher-order systems.

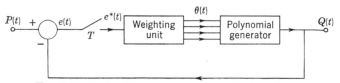

FIG. 3.17. Porter-Stoneman polynomial extrapolator.

The feedback technique was first studied by Porter and Stoneman[48] in
connection with problems of tracking radar targets.   The essential
principle of the feedback data extrapolator is shown in Fig. 3.17.   A
polynomial generator is incorporated in the system, and its output is
compared at sampling instants to the input.   A prediction error sequence
$e^*(t)$ is generated and applied to a weighting unit.   The latter generates

a number of outputs so computed that the output of the polynomial generator is corrected for the next interval. The nature of this correction is such that the polynomial for the interval in question passes through the previous number of samples equal to the order of the polynomial being generated. For lower-order holds, such as the first-order hold, this process is fairly evident. The full-velocity-correction system extrapolates a line which passes through the most recent data sample and the previous data sample. In the case of higher-order systems, the process is not as evident but will be clarified in subsequent discussions.

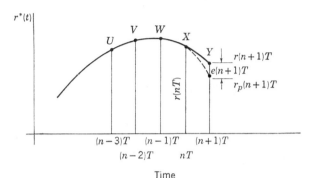

FIG. 3.18. Porter-Stoneman polynomial extrapolation.

Referring to Fig. 3.18, the objective of the extrapolator is to accept a sequence of pulses, $r(nT)$, and to fit a polynomial of appropriate order to these samples. This polynomial is called $Q(t)$, will be assumed to pass through the point U, V, W, and X, and can be expressed as follows:

$$Q(t) = a_0 + a_1(t - nT) + a_2(t - nT)^2 + a_3(t - nT)^3 + \cdots \quad (3.24)$$

where the various a's are constants and the extrapolation holds for the interval from nT to $(n + 1)T$. The dashed line in this interval is the extrapolated polynomial, which reaches a value $r_p(n + 1)T$ at the end of the pertinent sampling interval. The actual value of the sample at this instant is $r(n + 1)T$, and the difference between the actual and predicted samples at this instant is an error $e(n + 1)T$. If the predicted polynomial were exactly the same as the actual polynomial, this error would be zero and no alteration of the coefficients of (3.24) would be necessary. On the other hand, if there is an error $e(n + 1)T$, it shows that a correction must be made on the various coefficients of (3.24) to cause the polynomial to fit the previous sample points during the next interval.

Assuming that there is an error $e(n + 1)T$, a new polynomial $P(t)$ must be generated to fit the function at the previous points now listed as V, W, X, Y, etc. This new polynomial is given by

$$P(t) = b_0 + b_1[t - (n + 1)T] + b_2[t - (n + 1)T]^2$$
$$+ b_3[t - (n + 1)T]^3 + \cdots \quad (3.25)$$

where the various b's are constants which differ from the various a's of (3.24). In the feedback implementation indicated by Fig. 3.17, a correction or difference polynomial $\theta(t)$ must be generated and added to $Q(t)$ to obtain $P(t)$. This difference polynomial $\theta(t)$ may be written as follows:

$$\theta(t) = \Delta a_0 + \Delta a_1[t - (n + 1)T] + \Delta a_2[t - (n + 1)T]^2$$
$$+ \Delta a_3[t - (n + 1)T]^3 + \cdots \quad (3.26)$$

The various Δa's are coefficients which are so chosen that when $Q(t)$ and $\theta(t)$ are added they result in $P(t)$. It is recalled that the requirement on $P(t)$ is that it pass through the latest number of data samples equal to the order of $P(t)$. This requirement is satisfied if the added polynomial $\theta(t)$ is such that at a time $[t - (n + 1)T]$ equal to zero, $\theta(t)$ has a value equal to $e(n + 1)T$ and has zero value for all previous instants since $Q(t)$ already passes through these points. Summarizing, the requirements on $\theta(t)$ are that

$$\begin{array}{ll} \text{at} \quad t - (n + 1)T = 0 & \theta(t) = e(n + 1)T \\ t - (n + 1)T = -T & \theta(t) = 0 \\ t - (n + 1)T = -2T & \theta(t) = 0 \\ \quad \text{etc.} & \end{array} \quad (3.27)$$

It is evident by inspection that a polynomial having zeros at $-T$, $-2T$, etc., will satisfy the zero conditions of (3.27) and that the form of this polynomial is

$$\theta(t) = e(n + 1)T \left\{ \left[1 + \frac{t - (n + 1)T}{T} \right] \left[1 + \frac{t - (n + 1)T}{2T} \right] \right.$$
$$\left. \left[1 + \frac{t - (n + 1)T}{3T} \right] \cdots \right\} \quad (3.28)$$

It is seen that when $[t - (n + 1)T]$ is zero, the value of $\theta(t)$ is $e(n + 1)T$.

To illustrate the evaluation of the various coefficients of (3.26), a third-order polynomial will be considered. In this case, $P(t)$, $Q(t)$, and $\theta(t)$ are third-order polynomials, and (3.28) will contain all three of the factors explicitly stated. Including these factors and multiplying the polynomial out, there results the following:

$$\theta(t) = e(n + 1)T \left\{ 1 + \frac{11[t - (n + 1)T]}{6T} + \frac{[t - (n + 1)T]^2}{T^2} \right.$$
$$\left. + \frac{[t - (n + 1)T]^3}{6T^3} \right\} \quad (3.29)$$

Now, if $\theta(t)$, as given by (3.29), is added to the polynomial $Q(t)$ at the sampling instant $(n + 1)T$, the new polynomial so generated, $P(t)$, will pass through four sample points, ranging from the most recent at

$(n + 1)T$ back to the point at $(n - 2)T$. Generalizing the result to an nth order polynomial, this form of correction will cause the newly generated polynomial to fit the $n + 1$ most recent samples.

The implementation of a scheme employing this principle is essentially that shown in Fig. 3.17, and the detailed technique for accomplishing

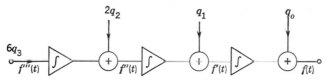

FIG. 3.19. Generation of third-order polynomial.

the result will now be considered. First, the polynomial generator is a cascaded number of integrators, as shown in Fig. 3.19 for the third-order case. To understand its operation, let it be assumed that the output of the last integrator, $f(t)$, is a third-order polynomial given by

$$f(t) = q_0 + q_1 t + q_2 t^2 + q_3 t^3 \qquad (3.30)$$

where the various q's are constants. The function $f'(t)$ appearing at the input of the last integrator is the derivative of (3.30) and is

$$f'(t) = q_1 + 2q_2 t + 3q_3 t^2 \qquad (3.31)$$

and similarly, the inputs to the two preceding integrators, $f''(t)$ and $f'''(t)$, are

$$f''(t) = 2q_2 + 6q_3 t$$
$$f'''(t) = 6q_3 \qquad (3.32)$$

Thus, to generate a polynomial whose coefficients are the various q's given in (3.30), it is necessary to apply steady signals whose values are

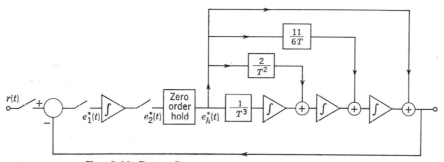

FIG. 3.20. Porter-Stoneman–type polynomial data hold.

$6q_3$, $2q_2$, q_1, and q_0 at the points in the integrator chain shown in Fig. 3.19.

This simple concept can be used to generate the correction polynomials which are added to $Q(t)$ to generate a sequence of corrected polynomials which fit the requisite number of past input samples. The block diagram of such a system is shown in Fig. 3.20, which contains the required number of integrators to generate a third-order polynomial. The additional element which requires explanation is the first integrator which precedes the zero-order hold. It is noted that this integrator has samplers preceding and following it. In effect, this causes the element to act as a summing device which adds all the past error samples in $e_1^*(t)$. This element is necessary when it is considered that the error at any particular sampling instant nT is actually the result of the summation of effects of all previously generated correction polynomials and not just the difference between the most recent error polynomial contribution and the input. The zero-order hold is required to convert the pulse at any instant nT into a constant signal for the following interval as required in the generation of the error polynomial. Thus, the signals applied to the various integrators of the chain are the summation of effects of the previous error polynomials in addition to the changes required for the most recent error polynomial.

The system shown in Fig. 3.20 fulfills the objectives of the extrapolation by inserting weighted components of the error as required by (3.29) in the manner shown in Fig. 3.19. If the input were actually a third-order polynomial and if there were no noise or drift in the system, the output $Q(t)$ would be an exact replica of the input polynomial after a fixed settling time has elapsed. This would mean that the error sequence $e_1^*(t)$ is zero at all times and that the signals which would be applied to the various summing points in the integrator chain would be the constants required to generate the polynomial. On the other hand, if the input were not a polynomial, the system would generate an approximation to the input signal and at each sample time an error pulse $e_1(nT)$ would appear and alter the output polynomial accordingly.

In some applications considered by Porter and Stoneman[48] it was considered undesirable for the output to experience sudden changes or steps. The system illustrated in Fig. 3.20 would act in this manner. This can be seen when it is considered that the presence of an error pulse $e_1(nT)$ causes a sudden change in the output of the zero-order hold and that this change is applied directly to the output at the last summing point in the chain. One way of avoiding this effect is to apply this component of the signal to the next-to-last summing point, that is, preceding the final integrator. In this manner, the output of the system gradually changes to the required value and the complete correction takes place at the end of the sampling interval under consideration rather than at the beginning. The polynomial so generated does not close out the error instantly, but the output is considerably smoother and is often more desirable as a result.

The feedback implementation of higher-order holds is only slightly more complex than the open-cycle implementation illustrated in Fig. 3.16.

It is characterized, however, by one important advantage. It is seen that the feedback system does not require a memory or storage device which holds past samples required to generate the higher-order differences required for extrapolation. The storage is implicit in the integrators, which also serve the purpose of generating the elements of the extrapolated polynomial.

3.8 Exponential Extrapolation

It was stated previously that in an extrapolation or data-reconstruction process, it was necessary to make an a priori assumption as to the form of the original function. In previous sections, it was assumed that the function either was actually a polynomial or could be adequately approximated by one. Another viewpoint is that in which it is assumed that the original function is composed of exponentials in time or that it can be reconstructed by a set of exponentials. In view of the fact that a passive network has an impulsive response which is the sum of exponentials if its structure includes only lumped elements, it follows that the use of passive networks of this type in data reconstruction implies exponential extrapolation.

There exists a large body of theory relating to the approximation and design of passive networks and filters. In their applications to sampled-data systems as data holds, however, only relative simple forms are used. This arises from the fact that the frequency range at which the networks are operated is so low that only a small number of components is usually tolerated and, further, that the ripple requirements are generally not too rigid. An approach to the selection of passive data-hold networks is that of approximating one of the polynomial extrapolators described previously by passive elements. Take as an example the zero-order hold whose transfer function is, from (3.14), given by

$$G_h(s) = \frac{1}{s} - \frac{1}{s} e^{-Ts} \tag{3.33}$$

This expression may be rearranged as follows:

$$G_h(s) = \frac{1}{s}\left(1 - \frac{1}{e^{Ts}}\right) \tag{3.34}$$

The procedure is to expand the exponential term into an infinite series in s and simplifying the expression to the following:

$$G_h(s) = T\,\frac{1 + Ts/2 + T^2s^2/6 + \cdots}{1 + Ts + T^2s^2/2 + T^3s^3/6 + \cdots} \tag{3.35}$$

For an exact reproduction of the impulsive response of a zero-order hold, an infinite number of terms of (3.35) would be required. However, an approximation to the result may be obtained by taking only a finite number of terms in the expansion of e^{Ts}. For instance, if only the first two terms of the expansion are taken, $G_h(s)$ becomes

$$G_h(s) = T \frac{1}{1 + Ts} \qquad (3.36)$$

A simple resistance-capacitance network can be used to obtain this impulsive response. As matter of fact, in many applications, particularly those where the sampling frequency is high, simple RC networks of this type are used as data holds. From the frequency-response point of view, the network is low pass, with a half-power frequency of $2\pi/T$ radians/sec. This should be compared with the response of a zero-order data hold, as shown in Fig. 3.7.

By taking additional terms in the expansion of e^{Ts}, a better approximation to the zero-order data hold may be obtained. Taking an additional term, there results the approximation

$$G_h(s) = T \frac{1 + Ts/2}{1 + Ts + T^2s^2/2} \qquad (3.37)$$

This transfer function can be realized by passive elements, but it can be readily verified that the poles of the transfer function are complex and that the physical implementation of the network requires inductive, capacitive, and resistive elements. While this is no serious theoretical obstacle, the need for passive elements of impractical dimensions often results in feedback control systems having sampling periods measured in seconds and minutes. For this reason, the use of passive networks of any but the simplest form, such as that given in (3.36), are not common.

3.9 Summary

The data hold may be regarded as an element which reconstructs the continuous function from which a sequence of data samples is obtained. Except for certain cases, this reconstruction is approximate at best, and the difference between the output of the data hold and the actual function from which the sequence of samples was derived is known as ripple. Since data samples are available at each sampling instant, the output of the data hold for a particular sampling interval is readjusted as each data sample is received. In view of the requirement of physical realizability, only past data samples can be used in estimating the output of the data hold. From the viewpoint of the frequency domain, data holds are low-pass filters which pass the signal spectrum and reject the spurious side spectra which result from the sampling process.

As in all extrapolation processes, an a priori assumption is made as to the class of function which best fits the input function. For instance, one of the most common forms of extrapolation used in sampled-data systems is one which assumes that the input function is or can be approximated by a polynomial in time. For practical reasons, this polynomial contains a finite number of terms whose coefficients are computed within the data-hold element. The zero-order data hold uses only the zeroth-order term of the polynomial, thereby deriving its name. In practice, it is rare to find data holds which implement anything higher than the first-order term. Aside from the question of complexity, the reason for this is that feedback systems are usually low pass, and their stability is adversely affected by the increased phase lags found in the frequency response of higher-order data holds.

The use of a feedback implementation for polynomial data holds has a number of advantages, the most important of which is that it does not require the storage of data samples in elements such as tapes or drums, as would be the case with open-cycle implementations. The feedback extrapolator can be implemented using only continuous integrators of the electronic or mechanical variety. In the case of the zero-order data hold, implementation by simple elements such as diodes and capacitors is possible. It is only in higher-order systems that the more complex form of implementation must be used.

Low-pass passive networks can be used as data holds. A simple resistance-capacitance network is shown to approximate the zero-order data hold. Even better approximations can be obtained by the use of more passive elements, including inductances as well as resistances and capacitances. The criteria which govern the degree of complexity which is used in feedback control applications are generally the amount of ripple which the plant can accept without damage to itself and the amount of jitter at ripple frequencies which can be tolerated in the controlled variable. It is true, however, that relatively unsophisticated methods of data reconstruction are adequate in most practical control-systems applications.

CHAPTER 4

THE Z-TRANSFORM ANALYSIS OF LINEAR
SAMPLED-DATA SYSTEMS

It has been stated that linear difference equations relate the variables in linear sampled-data dynamical systems as do differential equations in linear continuous systems.[46] While classical methods can be employed to obtain the solution of difference equations, the use of transform methods results in considerable simplification and understanding of the problems associated with the analysis and synthesis of sampled-data systems. A form of transform calculus now known as the "z transformation" has been available in one form or other for many years.[9,35] Recent work has been directed toward the organization and unification of the theory.[17,1,52,36,49,19,etc.] It is now possible to apply z-transform techniques directly to the problem of sampled-data systems and, more particularly, feedback systems. The z transformation can be studied as a modification of the Laplace transformation or approached directly as the operational calculus of number sequences. In some cases one approach is better than the other, but the resulting theory is the same and various theorems and rules can be derived readily.

4.1 Introduction to the Z Transform

It has been shown in Chap. 2 that the Laplace transform of an impulse sequence $f^*(t)$ has a Laplace transform $F^*(s)$ which is given by the infinite summation

$$F^*(s) = \sum_{n=0}^{\infty} f(nT)e^{-nTs} \qquad (4.1)$$

where $f(nT)$ is the value of the function $f(t)$ at sampling instants and for the condition that the impulse approximation is acceptable. It was also stated and demonstrated by example that infinite sequences like that of (4.1) could be expressed in closed form provided that the Laplace transform $F(s)$ of the original function $f(t)$ from which the sample sequence $f^*(t)$ was obtained is the ratio of polynomials in s. This will be proved rigorously in the next section. The important point here is that whether it is in closed or open form, the Laplace transform contains the complex frequency s as an exponent in e^{Ts}. This suggests the use of an auxiliary variable to replace e^{Ts}, the one chosen being z.[17] Thus, if the change of variable is made such that

$$z = e^{Ts} \qquad (4.2)$$

the transform of a sampled sequence can be expressed in terms of the auxiliary variable z.

The transform given in (4.1) is expressed as a power series in z as follows:

$$F^*(s) = F(z) = \sum_{n=0}^{\infty} f(nT)z^{-n} \qquad (4.3)$$

where $F(z)$ is known as the "z transform" of $f^*(t)$. The variable z may be thought of either as e^{Ts}, as defined in (4.2), or as an ordering variable whose exponent represents the position of the particular pulse in the sequence $f^*(t)$. When viewed in the latter light, $F(z)$ is a "generating function" and may be treated without identification with a Laplace transform.

In studying the z transform, use is made of the complex z plane, just as in the case of Laplace transforms the complex s plane is used. In view of the relationship between the z transform and the Laplace transform, a brief review of common characteristics of the two planes will be given. Referring to Fig. 4.1, the standard s plane and the z plane are illustrated side by side. All the points comprising the imaginary axis of the s plane lie on the unit circle of the z plane because, for $s = j\omega$,

$$z = e^{j\omega T} \qquad (4.4)$$

which is a complex number whose magnitude is unity and whose phase angle is ωT. Thus, the z plane reflects the periodicity of e^{Ts} by repeating the same values every time the angle ωT advances 2π radians. The z plane may be thought of as an infinite series of planes overlaid on each other, or, more formally, as a Riemann surface.

When applied to the sampled-data systems, this apparently ambiguous medium for representation of the properties of $F(z)$ presents no difficulties. It is recalled that

$$\frac{1}{T} \sum_{n=-\infty}^{+\infty} F(s + nj\omega_0) = \sum_{n=0}^{\infty} f(nT)e^{-nTs} \qquad (4.5)$$

and that $F^*(s)$ is periodic in $j\omega_0$. The poles and zeros of $F^*(s)$ are those of $F(s)$, with infinite repetitions displaced by $j\omega_0$. The poles and zeros of $F^*(s)$ repeat themselves in each of the strips of the s plane, as sketched in Fig. 4.1. Because points similarly located in each of the strips plot as the same point in the z plane, each pole of $F(s)$ produces one pole in $F(z)$, and the singularities of $F(s)$ and $F^*(s)$ are represented as a finite number of poles (and zeros) in the z plane. This makes the use of the z plane very desirable and is only one of many reasons why the use of the auxiliary variable z is desirable.

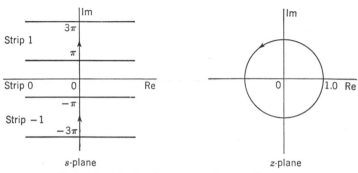

FIG. 4.1. Relation between s plane and z plane.

It is noted that all points in the right half of the s plane map in the region of the z plane outside the unit circle, while those points in the left half of the s plane map into the region inside the unit circle. This simple observation indicates that, if a system is being examined for stability as evidenced by the presence of poles in the right half of the s plane, this condition could be studied by testing for the presence of poles of $F(z)$ outside the unit circle of the z plane.

4.2 Mathematical Derivation of the Z Transform

The characteristics of the z transformation can be obtained on a more rigorous basis by the use of contour integration. Using the impulse approximation, the sampled function $f^*(t)$ has been expressed as

$$f^*(t) = f(t)\delta_T(t) \qquad (4.6)$$

where it is recalled that $\delta_T(t)$ is an infinite impulse sequence with a sampling period of T. As expressed in (4.6), the sampled time function is represented as the product of two time functions whose Laplace transform is obtained by a process of complex convolution. The complex-convolution integral is given by

$$\mathcal{L}[h(t)] = \frac{1}{2\pi j} \int_{c-j\infty}^{c+j\infty} F(p)G(s-p)\, dp \qquad (4.7)$$

where $h(t)$ is a time function which is the product of $f(t)$ and $g(t)$, $F(p)$ is the Laplace transform of $f(t)$, and $G(p)$ is the Laplace transform of

$g(t)$.   The constant c is so chosen that all the poles of $F(p)$ lie to the left of the imaginary axis displaced by c.

The complex-convolution integral can be applied to the case where the two time functions involved are those given in (4.6).   In this case, $F(p)$ is the Laplace transform of the function $f(t)$ being sampled.   The Laplace transform of the impulse sequence $\delta_T(t)$ is given by the following:

$$G(s - p) = \sum_{n=0}^{+\infty} e^{-nT(s-p)} \tag{4.8}$$

This infinite summation can be expressed in closed form by using the formula for the sum of a geometric series.   The expression (4.8) is seen to be an infinite geometric progression with a ratio of $e^{-T(s-p)}$.   Thus, $G(s - p)$ can be written

$$G(s - p) = \frac{1}{1 - e^{-T(s-p)}} \tag{4.9}$$

The integral giving the Laplace transform of $f^*(t)$ can thus be expressed in the following form

$$\mathcal{L}[f^*(t)] = \frac{1}{2\pi j} \int_{c-j\infty}^{c+j\infty} F(p) \frac{1}{1 - e^{-T(s-p)}} \, dp \tag{4.10}$$

Evaluation of (4.10) is accomplished through contour integration by closing the path of integration along the imaginary axis to encompass either the left or right half planes and evaluating the residues at the various poles enclosed.   It is noted that, for stable systems, all the poles of $F(p)$ lie in the left half of the s plane, as shown in Fig. 4.2.   On the other hand, the poles of the second term in the integrand of (4.10) are infinite in number, occurring at the complex frequency p_m, for which the angle of the exponential term is $m2\pi$, where m is an integer.   The condition for the angle of the exponential term to be a multiple of 2π is that

$$p_m = s - j\frac{2\pi m}{T} \tag{4.11}$$

for all integral values of m.   Thus the second function in (4.10) has an infinite number of poles separated by $j2\pi/T$ along the displaced imaginary axis, as shown in Fig. 4.2.   The path of integration is along the imaginary axis displaced by the constant c and is shown in the figure with c so chosen that all the poles of $F(p)$ lie to the left of this line.

To apply the method of residues, a closed contour of integration is formed by closure either to the right or to the left of c, resulting in the contours marked Γ_1 or Γ_2.   It is seen that if closure is effected to the right, there will be an infinite number of poles enclosed, whereas if closure is effected to the left, only the finite number of poles contained in $F(p)$ will be enclosed. This condition results in an infinite number or a finite number of residues, depending on the choice. Using the right-hand enclosure, it is readily seen that the residues which result at the various poles described by (4.11) will be

$$F^*(s) = \frac{1}{T} \sum_{n = -\infty}^{+\infty} F\left(s - j\frac{2\pi n}{T}\right) \tag{4.12}$$

This expression cannot be reduced to closed form and is seen to be identical with (2.26), which was arrived at by a different procedure.

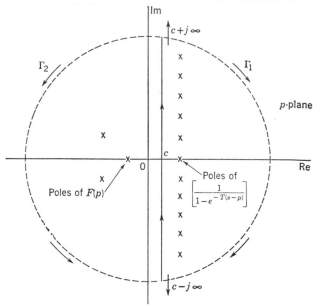

FIG. 4.2. Contours used in evaluation of complex-convolution integral.

If, now, the path of integration is closed to the left, it is seen from Fig. 4.2 that only the finite number of poles of $F(p)$ will be enclosed and that there will be a finite number of residues to evaluate. If the various poles of $F(p)$ are designated as p_k, then the value of the integral is given by $2\pi j$ times the residues at these poles:

$$F^*(s) = \sum_{\substack{\text{poles of} \\ F(p)}} \text{res.}\left[F(p)\,\frac{1}{1 - e^{-T(s-p)}}\right] \tag{4.13}$$

Now, if e^{Ts} is replaced by the auxiliary variable z, (4.13) can be rewritten as follows:

$$F(z) = \sum_{\substack{\text{poles of} \\ F(p)}} \text{res.} \left[F(p) \frac{1}{1 - e^{pT}z^{-1}} \right] \qquad (4.14)$$

This expression shows clearly that for all systems whose Laplace transform $F(p)$ has a finite number of poles, the z transform is a finite polynomial in z or z^{-1}. Also noted is that the order of the polynomial in z is no higher than the order of the polynomial in p.

The result obtained in (4.14) is the same as that which is obtained by expanding $F(p)$ into partial fractions and then applying the simple procedure outlined in the example in Sec. 2.4, term by term. As a matter of fact, as a working method, expansion into partial fractions is often a more direct technique than the formal application of the residue formulas indicated by (4.14). Tables of z transforms are available,[1,49,13] and one is reproduced in Appendix I containing most of the common forms. Tables like this one list the Laplace transform $F(s)$ of the continuous function from which the pulse sequence is obtained, the time function $f(nT)$ giving the value of the function at a sampling instant nT, and the z transform $F(z)$ which corresponds.

EXAMPLE

It is desired to determine the z transform $F(z)$ corresponding to a Laplace transform $F(s)$ given by

$$F(s) = \frac{1}{(s + a)(s + b)}$$

It should be noted that a more formal statement of the problem would be to determine the z transform of the sampled sequence $f^*(t)$ obtained by sampling a continuous function $f(t)$ whose Laplace transform is $F(s)$. The shortened terminology given previously, however, is more convenient and more commonly used. Using the result of (4.14), $F(z)$ becomes

$$F(z) = \frac{1}{b - a} \frac{1}{1 - e^{-aT}z^{-1}} + \frac{1}{a - b} \frac{1}{1 - e^{-bT}z^{-1}}$$

The two terms may be combined over a common denominator,

$$F(z) = \frac{1}{a - b} \frac{e^{-bT}z^{-1} - e^{-aT}z^{-1}}{(1 - e^{-bT}z^{-1})(1 - e^{-aT}z^{-1})}$$

4.3 Inversion of Z Transforms

As in the case of continuous systems, the inversion of the z transform is an important operation which is often carried out in practical problems. The inversion theorem has been formalized[36] and may be derived by applying one of the Cauchy theorems of contour integration in the complex plane. It has been shown in (4.3) that the z transform of a sampled sequence $f^*(t)$ is given by

$$F(z) = \sum_{n=0}^{\infty} f(nT)z^{-n} \tag{4.15}$$

Expressed in open form, this summation is

$$F(z) = f(0)z^0 + f(T)z^{-1} + \cdots f(n-1)Tz^{-(n-1)}$$
$$+ f(nT)z^{-n} + \cdots \tag{4.16}$$

This expansion of $F(z)$ about $z = \infty$ is valid for positive time, that is, for positive n. The process of inversion requires that a relation be found which will give $f(nT)$ explicitly, just as the inversion of $F(s)$ requires a relation which gives $f(t)$.

A step in arriving at the inversion theorem is to multiply the infinite sequence of (4.16) by z^{n-1}, resulting in

$$F(z)z^{n-1} = f(0)z^{n-1} + f(T)z^{n-2} + \cdots + f(n-1)Tz^{-0}$$
$$+ f(nT)z^{-1} + \cdots \tag{4.17}$$

The relation given in (4.17) is now in a form to which the Cauchy theorem in question may be applied.

This particular Cauchy theorem states that if the integral I is defined by

$$I = \frac{1}{2\pi j} \int_{\Gamma} z^k \, dz \tag{4.18}$$

and if Γ is a closed contour which encloses the origin of the z plane, then I will have values given by

$$\begin{aligned} I &= 0 & k &> -1 \\ I &= 1 & k &= -1 \\ I &= 0 & k &< -1 \end{aligned} \tag{4.19}$$

This theorem may be readily proved by taking Γ as a circle, as shown in Fig. 4.3, and then generalizing the result for any other contour which encloses the origin. If the function is regular in the region enclosed between the circle and the irregular contour, which z^k is, of course, then there is no contribution to the integral I beyond that made by the circular path.

This theorem can now be applied to the expression for $z^{n-1}F(z)$, as given in (4.17), by applying the results of (4.19) term by term. Thus,

$$\frac{1}{2\pi j} \int_{\Gamma} z^{n-1}F(z) \, dz = f(nT) \tag{4.20}$$

where the only contribution to the value of the integral is made by $f(nT)$, the coefficient of the z^{-1} term of the series in (4.17). A word is to be included concerning the contour Γ which must be employed in the integration of (4.20). As in all contour integrals, the value of the integral is determined by the singularities in the form of poles of the integrand. Thus, if (4.20) is to have the correct value, it is necessary that Γ include all the poles of $z^{n-1}F(z)$ for all integrals n. The integral (4.20) is thus the inversion theorem when the contour Γ satisfies the stated condition. It will be further discussed in detail, but it should be noted now that the poles of $F(z)$ are all contained inside or on the unit circle for stable systems, so that Γ is usually taken as the unit circle. The integral can be evaluated by the usual residue methods.

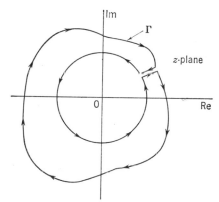

FIG. 4.3. Map showing equivalence between integration along unit circle and general contour.

It is illuminating sometimes to evaluate the inversion integral by first expanding the z transform $F(z)$ into partial fractions and then evaluating term by term using residue methods. In this manner, the contributions from each of the poles of the function $F(z)$ are stated more explicitly. For example, a typical term found on expansion into partial fractions is $F_1(z)$,

$$F_1(z) = \frac{A}{1 - e^{-aT}z^{-1}} \tag{4.21}$$

This function contains a pole in the z plane at e^{-aT}. Rewriting (4.21) in another form, and substituting into (4.20),

$$\frac{1}{2\pi j}\int_\Gamma z^{n-1}F_1(z)\,dz = \frac{1}{2\pi j}\int_\Gamma \frac{Az^n}{z - e^{-aT}}\,dz \tag{4.22}$$

this integral has a residue at e^{-aT}, which, upon multiplication by $2\pi j$ gives the result

$$f_1(nT) = A\,(e^{-aT})^n \tag{4.23}$$

It is seen that if e^{-aT} has a magnitude less than unity, $f_1(nT)$ will tend toward zero as n approaches infinity. While not complete, this is a condition for stability. Thus, stable functions $F(z)$ will have all their poles inside or, in the limiting case, on the unit circle in the z plane. It is for this reason that the contour Γ which is used in the inversion theorem is generally the unit circle.

There are many practical situations where the interest of the designer is only in the first few terms of the pulse sequence resulting from inversion. This is the case where transient response and overshoot are being studied in feedback control systems. For this purpose, an alternate approach to inversion can be employed. The z transforms encountered in practice are generally the ratio of polynomials in z or z^{-1} as expressed by

$$F(z) = \frac{a_0 + a_1 z^{-1} + a_2 z^{-2} + \cdots a_n z^{-n}}{b_0 + b_1 z^{-1} + b_2 z^{-2} + \cdots b_m z^{-m}} \qquad (4.24)$$

This transform can be expanded into a power series in z^{-1} by the simple process of long division of the denominator into the numerator. Carrying out this numerical procedure, there will result

$$F(z) = q_0 + q_1 z^{-1} + q_2 z^{-2} + \cdots \qquad (4.25)$$

This power series in z^{-1} is now identified with the z transform of an impulse sequence, where the power of z is the order or time at which the impulse exists and the various q's are the areas of each impulse. The inversion process is now seen to be merely an arithmetic routine which can be carried out by means of a desk-calculator or similar methods.

EXAMPLE

It is desired to invert the z transform $F(z)$ given by

$$F(z) = \frac{1}{1 - 1.2z^{-1} + 0.2z^{-2}}$$

Expanding into a power series in z^{-1} by long division,

$$
\begin{array}{l}
\phantom{1 - 1.2z^{-1} + 0.2z^{-2} \Big/ 1\,} 1 + 1.2z^{-1} + 1.24z^{-2} + 1.248z^{-3} + \cdots \\
\hline
1 - 1.2z^{-1} + 0.2z^{-2} \,\Big/\, 1 \\
\phantom{1 - 1.2z^{-1} + 0.2z^{-2} \Big/\,} \underline{1 - 1.2z^{-1} + 0.2z^{-2}} \\
\phantom{1 - 1.2z^{-1} + 0.2z^{-2} \Big/\,} 1.2z^{-1} - 0.2z^{-2} \\
\phantom{1 - 1.2z^{-1} + 0.2z^{-2} \Big/\,} \underline{1.2z^{-1} - 1.44z^{-2} + 0.24z^{-3}} \\
\phantom{1 - 1.2z^{-1} + 0.2z^{-2} \Big/\, 1.2z^{-1} - } 1.24z^{-2} - 0.24z^{-3} \\
\phantom{1 - 1.2z^{-1} + 0.2z^{-2} \Big/\, 1.2z^{-1} - } \underline{1.24z^{-2} - 1.488z^{-3} + 0.248z^{-4}} \\
\phantom{1 - 1.2z^{-1} + 0.2z^{-2} \Big/\, 1.2z^{-1} - 1.24z^{-2} - } 1.248z^{-3} \cdots
\end{array}
$$

etc.

The resultant power series shows that the first term of the sequence has a magnitude of 1, the second of 1.2, the third of 1.24, the fourth of 1.248, etc. Thus, $f^*(t)$ is

$$f^*(t) = 1.0\delta(t) + 1.2\delta(t - T) + 1.24\delta(t - 2T)$$
$$+ 1.248\delta(t - 3T) + \cdots$$

This method of inversion is useful in determining the first set of terms.

The process of long division can be organized into a numerical routine which is implemented either by manual desk-calculator methods or programmed on a digital computer.

4.4 Initial and Final-value Theorems

It is often desirable to ascertain the initial and final values of the pulse sequence which result from the inversion of a z transform. These properties have been studied[36,1,19] and can be summarized readily. The initial value of the pulse sequence can be obtained by noting that for physically realizable functions, $F(z)$ can be expanded into a power series in z^{-1} as has been done in previous sections. Thus,

$$F(z) = f(0)z^0 + f(T)z^{-1} + \cdots + f(nT)z^{-n} + \cdots \quad (4.26)$$

It is seen that by assigning a value of infinity to z, the only term having a value in (4.26) other than zero is the first term. Thus, the initial-value theorem is simply stated as

$$f(0) = \lim_{z \to \infty} F(z) \quad (4.27)$$

EXAMPLE

The example used in Sec. 4.1 will be taken for an illustration of the initial-value theorem. It was found there that $F(z)$ was given by

$$F(z) = \frac{1}{a - b} \frac{e^{-bT}z^{-1} - e^{-aT}z^{-1}}{(1 - e^{-bT}z^{-1})(1 - e^{-aT}z^{-1})}$$

The initial value $f(0)$ obtained by substituting infinity for z becomes zero. Thus, the initial value of the pulse sequence $f^*(t)$ resulting from the inversion of $F(z)$ is zero.

It has been pointed out[33] that for the class of z transforms for which the initial value is other than zero, a formal evaluation of the initial value of $f^*(t)$ is only one-half that obtained from (4.27). This arises from the strict application of the complex-convolution integral of (4.10) used to obtain $F(z)$. In this integral, it was implicit that the contribution to the integral resulting from integration along the infinite path used to close the contour was zero, in consequence of the fact that $F(p)$ vanished for infinite arguments. For those functions whose impulsive response has an initial value, the order of p in the numerator and denominator polynomials is the same; hence for infinite values of p, $F(p)$ does not vanish.

It can be readily ascertained that the contribution to the value of $F(z)$ of this infinite path leads to a result which produces only one-half the initial value of $f^*(t)$ as computed from (4.27). The formal application of the inversion process would require that only one-half the value of (4.27) be used, though in fact, in a practical system, the full value would be obtained at a time of 0^+ after application of the impulse. If the z transform is viewed in the light of a generating function, as was suggested previously, rather than as an outgrowth of a strict application of Laplace-transform theory, this difficulty would not be experienced. For

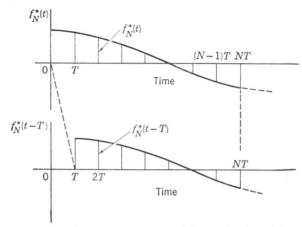

FIG. 4.4. Truncated pulse sequences used for evaluation of final value.

purposes of practical feedback control systems, the convention is adopted that the initial value of the pulse sequence is the *full* value of $f(0)$ as given by (4.27) and that the factor of $\frac{1}{2}$ indicated by the formal mathematics is not representative of the physical system and therefore should be ignored.

The final value of the pulse sequence $f^*(t)$ can also be obtained directly from its z transform, $F(z)$. To derive the result, the pulse sequence $f_N^*(t)$ is formed by truncating the sequence $f^*(t)$ at the Nth sample, where N is some large number. The truncated sequence is shown in Fig. 4.4a, and it is evident that its z transform is

$$F_N(z) = \sum_{n=0}^{N} f(nT)z^{-n} \tag{4.28}$$

If the truncated function is now delayed by one sample time T, then a function $f_N^*(t - T)$ is formed, and the sequence is plotted in Fig. 4.4b. It is evident that the z transform of this delayed function is the same as that of the truncated function, except that an additional delay z^{-1} is included as a factor. Thus,

$$F_N'(z) = z^{-1}F_N(z) = \sum_{n=0}^{N-1} f(nT)z^{-n}z^{-1} \tag{4.29}$$

It is noted that the sequence terminates at $N - 1$ since the absolute time t of truncation remains fixed at NT. Now, if a difference between $F'_N(z)$ and $F_N(z)$ is formed and, further, if the value of z is set equal to unity, it is seen that the only term remaining will be $f(NT)$. Thus,

$$f(NT) = \left[\sum_{n=0}^{N} f(nT)z^{-n} - z^{-1} \sum_{n=0}^{N-1} f(nT)z^{-n} \right]_{z=1} \qquad (4.30)$$

Now, as N is allowed to increase without limit and approaches infinity, it is seen that the two summations in (4.30) each converge to $F(z)$ because, in the limit, N and $N - 1$ converge toward the same value.

The final-value theorem can be stated as follows in consequence of the limit of (4.30) being as described. It is

$$f(\infty) = \lim_{z=1} (1 - z^{-1})F(z) \qquad (4.31)$$

where $f(\infty)$ is the final value of the sample of the sequence $f^*(t)$ whose z transform is $F(z)$. This theorem is of major value to the designer of sampled-data control systems since the specification of such systems generally contains a requirement of steady-state performance.

EXAMPLE

To illustrate the application of the final-value theorem, it will be applied to the example in Sec. 4.3. The z transform of the pulse sequence is

$$F(z) = \frac{1}{1 - 1.2z^{-1} + 0.2z^{-2}}$$

It is noted that this transform can be factored into the following form:

$$F(z) = \frac{1}{(1 - z^{-1})(1 - 0.2z^{-1})}$$

Applying (4.31),

$$f(\infty) = \lim_{z=1} \frac{1 - z^{-1}}{(1 - z^{-1})(1 - 0.2z^{-1})}$$

Canceling the common factor in numerator and denominator, the limit is seen to be

$$f(\infty) = 1.25$$

It is interesting to note that the inversion carried out in the example in Sec. 4.3 resulted in the value of the fourth sample at 1.248, as contrasted to the final value of 1.25. The indication is that the system almost completely settles in four or five samples.

4.5 Delayed Z Transforms

A very useful modification to the ordinary z transform was introduced by Barker[1] and was discussed in later papers on the subject.[3,20] The modification treats the z transform of pulse sequences which are derived from time functions delayed by nonintegral multiples of the sampling frequency. In the case of sampled-data feedback control systems, these transforms find application in the analysis of systems having plants with transportation lags. Delayed z transforms are also useful in studying the behavior of a sampled function between sampling instants. The

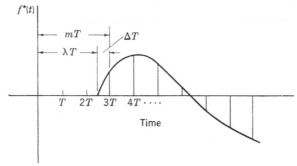

Fig. 4.5. Delayed pulse sequence used to derive $G(z,\Delta)$.

delayed or modified z transform can be studied by referring to Fig. 4.5. Here is seen a continuous function $f(t)$ which has been delayed by a time λT, where λ is generally nonintegral. If λ is integral, the result is trivial since the z transform of the resulting function is simply $z^{-\lambda}F(z)$.

An integer m is chosen such that it is the next highest integer after λ. Thus, a number Δ can be defined so that

$$m = \lambda + \Delta \qquad (4.32)$$

where Δ is a positive number always less than unity. If $F(s)$ is the Laplace transform of the function $f(t)$, then the Laplace transform $F(s,\lambda)$ of the delayed function is

$$\mathcal{L}[f(t - \lambda T)] = F(s,\lambda) = F(s)e^{-\lambda Ts} \qquad (4.33)$$

which, from (4.32), can be written

$$F(s,\lambda) = e^{-mTs}F(s)e^{\Delta Ts} \qquad (4.34)$$

Since m is integral, it presents no problem in obtaining the z transform. The result is simply

$$F(z,\Delta) = z^{-m}F(z,\Delta) \qquad (4.35)$$

where $F(z,\Delta)$ is defined as

$$F(z,\Delta) = \mathcal{Z}[F(s)e^{\Delta Ts}] \qquad (4.36)$$

The symbol z, used here for the first time, indicates the z transform corresponding to the Laplace transform following it.

By treating the delayed transform in this manner, a table of advanced transforms $F(z,\Delta)$ can be used for all situations. By the definition of the z transform, the expression for $F(z,\Delta)$ can be stated as

$$F(z,\Delta) = \sum_{n=0}^{\infty} f(n + \Delta)Tz^{-n} \qquad (4.37)$$

Many of the advanced z transforms can be evaluated directly from (4.37), as seen in the example.

EXAMPLE

It is desired to derive the expression for the advanced z transform for a time function e^{-at} which has been advanced ΔT. In this case, $f(t)$ is

$$f(t) = e^{-a(t+\Delta T)} \qquad (t + \Delta T) \geq 0$$

The z transform corresponding to this function is

$$F'(z,\Delta) = \sum_{n=0}^{\infty} e^{-a(n+\Delta)T}z^{-n}$$

which can, by factoring out $e^{-a\Delta T}$, be written

$$F(z,\Delta) = e^{-a\Delta T} \sum_{n=0}^{\infty} e^{-anT}z^{-n}$$

The summation is an infinite geometric progression, as in the case of ordinary z transforms, and can be expressed in closed form, resulting in

$$F(z,\Delta) = \frac{e^{-a\Delta T}}{1 - e^{-aT}z^{-1}}$$

This simple illustration shows how advanced z transforms can be obtained by going back to the time domain and expressing the sequences in closed form.

Another approach to evaluating the advanced transform is to use the method of complex convolution as expressed in (4.14). Since the path of integration used to obtain the z transform encompasses the left half of the s plane, the added term $e^{\Delta Ts}$ vanishes at infinity and causes no difficulty in the evaluation of the integral by the method of residues. Thus, by direct application of (4.14), the advanced z transform $F(z,\Delta)$

becomes

$$F(z,\Delta) = \sum_{\substack{\text{poles of}\\F(s)}} \text{res.}\ \left\{F(s)e^{\Delta Ts}\ \frac{1}{1 - e^{+sT}z^{-1}}\right\} \qquad (4.38)$$

For practical convenience, various transforms of this type are listed in Appendix II, where they can be readily associated with the corresponding Laplace transforms.

EXAMPLE

The same transform evaluated in the preceding example will be used to illustrate the application of (4.38). In this case, the Laplace transform $F(s)$ of the time function $f(t)$ is

$$F(s,\Delta) = \frac{1}{s + a}\ e^{\Delta Ts}$$

The transform has a pole at $-a$, and the residue at this pole results in

$$F(z,\Delta) = \frac{e^{-a\Delta T}}{1 - e^{-aT}z^{-1}}$$

This result is the same as that obtained in the previous example.

4.6 The Convolution Summation and Pulse Transfer Function

One of the concepts of great value in the analysis of linear systems is that of the transfer function which relates the output and input of the system. For continuous systems whose performance is described

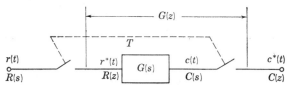

FIG. 4.6. Pulsed linear system showing definition of pulse transfer function.

by a set of linear differential equations with constant coefficients, the transfer function is the Laplace transform of the impulsive response. In linear sampled-data systems, there exists an analogous transfer function known as the *pulse transfer function*,[1] or *pulsed transfer function*.[3] In subsequent discussions, the former nomenclature will be used. The pulse transfer function relates the output and input pulse sequences of a linear sampled system.

Just as in the derivation of the continuous transfer function in which a convolution integral is employed, the derivation of the pulse transfer function uses a convolution summation. As an aid in deriving the required relationships, a system diagram shown in Fig. 4.6 is used. In this approach, a continuous element having a transfer function $G(s)$ receives a pulse sequence $r^*(t)$ at its input. The output is sampled synchronously to produce the output sequence $c^*(t)$. If $R(z)$ and $C(z)$ are the z transforms of the input and output sequences, respectively, then $G(z)$ is the pulse transfer function which relates them.

In deriving $G(z)$ for this pulsed continuous system, or pulsed filter, as it is sometimes called, the impulse approximation will be used. Thus, a train of impulses is applied to the input of the pulsed filter, and the

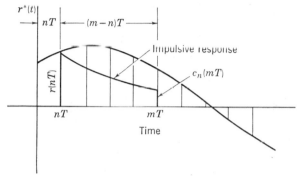

FIG. 4.7. Contribution of $r(nT)$ to value of m'th output pulse by linear system whose transfer function is $G(s)$.

output is the sum of a sequence of impulse response functions of proper magnitude and spacing. A particular component of the output is the impulsive response resulting from the nth sample $r(nT)$, as shown in Fig. 4.7. Here is shown the contribution to the output resulting from the application of an impulse whose area is $r(nT)$ being sampled at the mth instant. This contribution to the total value of the output sample $c(mT)$ is called $c_n(mT)$ and is given by

$$c_n(mT) = r(nT)g(m - n)T \qquad (4.39)$$

where $g(m - n)T$ is the impulsive response of the system after an elapsed time of $(m - n)T$ sec. The total value of the output at mT is the summation of all the contributions resulting from input pulses ranging from $t = 0$ to $t = mT$. Thus,

$$c(mT) = \sum_{n=0}^{m} r(nT)g(m - n)T \qquad (4.40)$$

It is noted here that the upper limit of the summation can be extended to infinity without effect since the impulsive response $g(m - n)T$ is zero for all negative arguments. Hence,

$$c(mT) = \sum_{n=0}^{\infty} r(nT)g(m - n)T \qquad (4.41)$$

This summation is the analogue of the convolution integral in continuous systems and is referred to as the convolution summation.

Since the pulse transfer function is a relation between the z transforms of the input and output, it is recalled that $C(z)$ is defined by

$$C(z) = \sum_{m=0}^{\infty} c(mT)z^{-m} \tag{4.42}$$

Substituting for $c(mT)$ from (4.41), $C(z)$ becomes

$$C(z) = \sum_{m=0}^{\infty} \sum_{n=0}^{\infty} r(nT)g(m-n)Tz^{-m} \tag{4.43}$$

As an aid in simplifying this double summation, an auxiliary integer k is introduced, such that

$$k = m - n \tag{4.44}$$

Eliminating the integer m by replacing it by its equivalent in (4.44), the summation of (4.43) can be rearranged as

$$C(z) = \sum_{k=-n}^{\infty} \sum_{n=0}^{\infty} r(nT)g(kT)z^{-n}z^{-k} \tag{4.45}$$

It is noted that for physically realizable systems, $g(kT)$ has zero value for all negative values of k so that the lower limit of the first summation in k can have its lower limit replaced by zero. It is also noted that the various elements in (4.45) are functions either of k or n so that they may be separated to yield the following form:

$$C(z) = \sum_{k=0}^{\infty} g(kT)z^{-k} \sum_{n=0}^{\infty} r(nT)z^{-n} \tag{4.46}$$

The second summation in (4.46) is recognized to be the z transform $R(z)$ of the input pulse sequence $r^*(t)$. The first summation is defined as $G(z)$, given by

$$G(z) = \sum_{k=0}^{\infty} g(kT)z^{-k} \tag{4.47}$$

Using this definition, the output z transform $C(z)$ is given by

$$C(z) = G(z)R(z) \tag{4.48}$$

The relation between the output and input z transforms is given by (4.48), and $G(z)$ is called the *pulse transfer function*. The definition of $G(z)$ is contained in (4.47), where it is seen that it is the z transform of the sampled impulsive response $g(t)$. In other words, the pulse transfer function can be found by applying an impulse to the input of a system whose continuous transfer function is $G(s)$ and sampling the output.   The z transform of the resulting sequence is $G(z)$, the pulse transfer function of the system.   *It is emphasized that the pulse transfer function relates only the output pulse sequence to the input pulse sequence.*   It does not relate the continuous output $c(t)$ to the pulse sequence at the input. No information concerning the behavior of the output $c(t)$ between sampling instants is available from the pulse transfer function, although in its modified form indirect information can be obtained, as will be shown in a later chapter.

EXAMPLE

A step function is applied to a system, as shown in Fig. 4.6.   The continuous transfer function $G(s)$ is

$$G(s) = \frac{1}{s + a}$$

The pulse transfer function $G(z)$ is

$$G(z) = \mathrm{Z}\, \frac{1}{s + a}$$

which is, from the table in Appendix I,

$$G(z) = \frac{1}{1 - e^{-aT}z^{-1}}$$

The input z transform $R(z)$ is also obtained from the table and is

$$R(z) = \frac{1}{1 - z^{-1}}$$

The z transform of the output $C(z)$ is the product of $R(z)$ and $G(z)$,

$$C(z) = \frac{1}{1 - e^{-aT}z^{-1}} \frac{1}{1 - z^{-1}}$$

which, upon multiplication, becomes

$$C(z) = \frac{1}{1 - (1 + e^{-aT})z^{-1} + e^{-aT}z^{-2}}$$

If the pulse sequence in the time domain is desired, the z transform $C(z)$ may be inverted either by long division or by the residue method.

It is seen from the foregoing example that the application of the pulse transfer function to sampled-data-system problems is no more complex than the application of the continuous transfer function is to continuous linear systems.

In the previous development, the pulse transfer function was derived for the case where a continuous element was included between the two samplers. Fully digital systems which perform arithmetic operations on number sequences to deliver processed number sequences at their output do not contain such an element. Nevertheless, if the operations which are performed are linear, it is possible to define a pulse transfer function which relates the input and output number sequences. Schematically, the digital system is illustrated as a block diagram in Fig. 4.8.

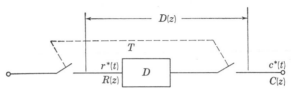

FIG. 4.8. Pulse transfer function of digital system.

In this figure, the block D represents the arithmetic process being carried out. The input and output sampling switches indicate that the input to the digital system is a sequence of numbers and that the output is a sequence of processed numbers. In this simple representation, it is assumed that the switches are synchronous, that is, the output numbers are delivered simultaneously with the intake of a new number. If there is a significant computation delay, the output number will be synchronous but delayed by a fixed time from the input number. This can be taken into account by the insertion, after the output sampler, of a transportation lag or time delay equal to the computation time.

The arithmetic computations carried out in the digital element may be of many different classes, but the usual form used in linear feedback control systems is a linear difference equation relating the input and output pulse sequences. Such an equation or recursion formula is written as follows:

$$c(nT) + b_1 c[(n - 1)T] + b_2 c[(n - 2)T] + \cdots + b_k c[(n - k)T]$$
$$= a_0 r[nT] + a_1 r[(n - 1)T] + a_2 r[(n - 2)T] + \cdots$$
$$+ a_m r[(n - m)T] \quad (4.49)$$

where the various c's are the output numbers at the instant corresponding to the argument, the various r's the input numbers corresponding to the argument, and the b's and a's are constants. This linear relation can be interpreted as a formula through which the present output number $c[nT]$ can be computed by taking weighted sums of a fixed group of input and output numbers. In the strict sense, this computation can be performed by storing $k - 1$ previous output numbers and m input numbers and adding them in the manner prescribed by (4.49).

To obtain a pulse transfer function $D(z)$ which relates the input and output number sequences, an approach is to introduce a "generating function," defined as follows:

$$D(z) = \sum_{k=0}^{\infty} d(kT)z^{-k} \qquad (4.50)$$

where $d(kT)$ is the value of the number occurring at the kth sample and z^{-k} is the ordering variable which establishes the position of the number in the sequence. The similarity to the z transform and the pulse transfer function is obvious; indeed, the generating function and the z transform are identical if $z = e^{Ts}$. The generating function was originally introduced to handle weighting sequences found in mathematical statistics.[9] The input and output sequences are described by generating functions $R(z)$ and $C(z)$, where the significance of z is also that of an ordering variable.

Referring once again to (4.49), it is noted that the relation holds for all positive integer values of n. Thus, iterating the equation for all values of n and taking care to apply the correct ordering variable to each number, there results the following equality:

$$\sum_{n=0}^{\infty} c(nT)z^{-n} + b_1 \sum_{n=0}^{\infty} c(nT)z^{-n-1} + \cdots + b_k \sum_{n=0}^{\infty} c(nT)z^{-n-k}$$

$$= a_0 \sum_{n=0}^{\infty} r(nT)z^{-n} + a_1 \sum_{n=0}^{\infty} r(nT)z^{-n-1} + \cdots$$

$$+ a_m \sum_{n=0}^{\infty} r(nT)z^{-n-m} \qquad (4.51)$$

This complex relationship holds for any instant of time corresponding to a sampling instant. Since the time of the incidence of a particular number is contained in the exponent of z, then the equality at any sampling instant can be set up between numbers having the same power in z. If this is done for any particular value of n, it will be seen that the required relationship between numbers as expressed in (4.49) will be obtained. The lower index in the summations of (4.51) is zero, which indicates the fact that the values of the sequences for negative time are zero.

Factoring out the common summations for each of the terms of (4.51), there results

$$\sum_{n=0}^{\infty} c(nT)z^{-n}(1 + b_1z^{-1} + b_2z^{-2} + \cdots + b_kz^{-k})$$

$$= \sum_{n=0}^{\infty} r(nT)z^{-n}(a_0 + a_1z^{-1} + a_2z^{-2} + \cdots + a_mz^{-m}) \qquad (4.52)$$

The summations which have been factored out are recognized to be the generating functions for the output and input, respectively. Replacing them by $C(z)$ and $R(z)$, (4.52) becomes

$$C(z)(1 + b_1 z^{-1} + b_2 z^{-2} + \cdots + b_k z^{-k})$$
$$= R(z)(a_0 + a_1 z^{-1} + a_2 z^{-2} + \cdots + a_m z^{-m}) \quad (4.53)$$

The pulse transfer function $D(z)$ for the digital system is defined as relating the input generating function $R(z)$ and output generating function $C(z)$ in the following manner:

$$C(z) = D(z)R(z) \quad (4.54)$$

Using the result given in (4.53), the pulse transfer function for a system just described,

$$D(z) = \frac{C(z)}{R(z)}$$
$$= \frac{a_0 + a_1 z^{-1} + a_2 z^{-2} + \cdots + a_m z^{-m}}{1 + b_1 z^{-1} + b_2 z^{-2} + \cdots + b_k z^{-k}} \quad (4.55)$$

The pulse transfer function $D(z)$ was obtained without recourse to the Laplace transform and the impulse approximation. The orders of the various z's serve to place the numbers in the proper position in the sequence and are treated in the same manner as the z's obtained through the Laplace transform and the definition of z as e^{Ts}. It is a fact that the algebraic manipulations are the same whether one deals with the pulsed filter or the digital system. For instance, if a number occurs at time mT, it has associated with it z^{-m}. If this number is to be delayed by one additional sample time, then it should have z^{-m-1} associated with it. It is readily apparent that multiplying z^{-m} by z^{-1}, using the ordinary rules of algebra, produces the correct result. This is equally true when z is interpreted as e^{Ts}, because now e^{-mTs} is multiplied by e^{-Ts} to yield $e^{(-m-1)Ts}$.

The pulse transfer function for a digital system could have been derived in the same manner used for the pulsed filter. The only difference lies in the interpretation of the various steps. For instance, going back to (4.39), $c_n(mT)$ can be interpreted as the number resulting from the weighting of the nth input sample $r(nT)$ by a weight $g(m - n)T$, where $(m - n)$ is the "staleness" of the input sample. Carrying on the same manipulations of (4.40), (4.41), (4.42), and (4.43), one arrives at the convolution summation. The result (4.43) is now interpreted as the sequence in z, $C(z)$, describing the output number sequence, and z^{-m} is the ordering variable which places each number in the correct sampling slot. Finally, (4.47) gives the definition of the pulse transfer function:

$$G(z) = \sum_{k=0}^{\infty} g(kT)z^{-k} \quad (4.47), (4.56)$$

In this context, $G(z)$ is regarded as a *weighting sequence* rather than the z transform of the impulsive response of a linear system. The pulse transfer function $G(z)$ is referred to as $D(z)$ in this application to emphasize the fact that the latter is the result of numerical or arithmetic operations on numbers rather than the result of a linear filter. If $D(z)$, as given in (4.55), is expanded into a power series in z^{-1}, the summation given above will result.

EXAMPLE

To demonstrate how a pulse transfer function can be used to describe a numerical operation, the example of numerical integration will be used. If the integral $y(t)$ of a function $x(t)$ is desired, the following integral must be evaluated:

$$y(t) = \int_0^t x(t)\, dt$$

This can be done numerically, using a number of possible numerical integration rules, such as Simpson's $\frac{2}{3}$ rule. Taking the simplest possible integration rule first, the following steps are taken. First, the integral will be evaluated only at discrete instants of time, a general one of which is nT. Thus,

$$y(nT) = \int_0^{(n-1)T} x(t)\, dt + \int_{(n-1)T}^{nT} x(t)\, dt$$

It is recognized that

$$y(n-1)T = \int_0^{(n-1)T} x(t)\, dt$$

so that

$$y(nT) = y(n-1)T + \int_{(n-1)T}^{nT} x(t)\, dt$$

The integral in the above expression is the contribution to the total integral of the function $x(t)$ over one quadrature interval. Various assumptions of increasing complexity can be made concerning the behavior of $x(t)$ within this interval. The simplest is that $x(t)$ remains constant at the value $x(n-1)T$, just at the beginning of the interval in question. This is equivalent to the action of a clamp circuit in a physical system. With this assumption, the integral has the value

$$\int_{(n-1)T}^{nT} x(t)\, dt = Tx(n-1)T$$

Hence, the relationship between the y's and x's becomes

$$y(nT) - y(n-1)T = Tx(n-1)T$$

This is a recursion formula similar to (4.49). Carrying out the procedure outline in this section or, more simply, "taking the z transform" of both sides,

$$Y(z)(1 - z^{-1}) = (Tz^{-1})X(z)$$

The pulse transfer function which expresses the process $D(z)$ is thus

$$D(z) = \frac{Y(z)}{X(z)} = T\frac{z^{-1}}{1 - z^{-1}}$$

Thus, if an input number sequence has a z transform $X(z)$ and is multiplied by $D(z)$, the output sequence has the transform $Y(z)$. Inversion of the latter will give the values of the integral at the various sampling times.

More complex interpolations of $x(t)$ in the interval under consideration result in more complex pulse transforms. For instance, using known numerical integration formulas,

$$\int_{(n-1)T}^{nT} x(t)\, dt = \frac{T}{2}[x(n-1)T + x(nT)]$$

By a treatment similar to the simple case, this results in a recursion formula given by

$$y(nT) - y(n-1)T = \frac{T}{2}[x(n-1)T + x(nT)]$$

Taking the z transform and evaluating the pulse transfer function for the process,

$$D(z) = \frac{T}{2}\frac{1 + z^{-1}}{1 - z^{-1}}$$

Simpson's $\frac{2}{3}$ rule is stated in the more complex integration formula, in which $x(t)$ is assumed to be fitted by a second-order polynomial in time. This formula states

$$\int_{(n-2)T}^{nT} x(t)\, dt = \frac{T}{3}[x(nT) + 4x(n-1)T + x(n-2)T]$$

Taking the z transform of both sides once again, there results the pulse transfer function for the process:

$$D(z) = \frac{T}{3}\frac{1 + 4z^{-1} + z^{-2}}{1 - z^{-2}}$$

These examples serve to illustrate the fact that a pulse transfer function can describe a purely numerical process in which there is no associated physical system.

In applying these pulse transforms, care should be taken to take into account the error caused by the initial value of the number sequence resulting from the inversion of $Y(z)$. Such an error arises when the integrand $x(t)$ has an initial value $x(0)$ other than zero. For instance, in applying the second pulse transform in this example, the initial value of the output, $y(0)$, can be obtained by application of (4.27) and is found to $T/2x(0)$. The value $T/2x(0)$ is to be subtracted from $y(nT)$ in order to obtain the correct result. The handling of nonzero initial values is treated in Sec. 11.5. As developed here, both $x(0)$ and $y(0)$ or $c(0)$ and $r(0)$ have zero initial values. This is usually the case in the analysis of practical control systems containing digital elements.

Thus, if the output $y(nT)$ of a function which has been operated on by $D(z)$ is to be obtained, the correct inversion of $Y(z)$ is, for relaxed conditions,

$$y(nT) = \frac{1}{2\pi j} \int_\Gamma Y(z) z^{n-1} \, dz - y(0)$$

where $y(0)$ is the initial value of the inversion sequence of $Y(z)$.

Another point is that in inverting the higher-order integration rules, it should be recalled that only values of n compatible with the basic time-domain inversion should be used. For instance, in the simplest integration formulas, n can take on all integral values. On the other hand, in applying Simpson's $\frac{2}{3}$ rule, only every other integral value of n should be used; that is, n can take on only the values of 0, 2, 4, 6, 8, etc., since the process of integration progresses two intervals at a time. The values of $y(nT)$ at n equal to 3, 5, 7, 9, etc., are not valid, as can be seen by inspection of the time-domain recursion formula. Similarly, higher-order integration formulas are valid for every mth ordinate, where m is the order of the polynomial being fitted to the m most recent values of the time function $x(t)$.

The main reason for emphasizing the similarities between the generating function and the z transform and between the digital pulse transfer function $D(z)$ and the pulsed-filter pulse transfer function $G(z)$ is that practical sampled-data control systems contain both types of element in the loop. A digital controller is a small-scale digital computer whose output is applied to a pulsed linear plant. It is extremely convenient to be able to employ the same operational methods and describe both types of element by a unified operational approach, broadly described as the z transform. The inversion theorems, the initial- and final-value theorems, and other manipulative rules to be developed apply equally to digital and pulsed-filter applications.

4.7 Implementation of Pulse Transfer Functions

If the pulse transfer function $G(z)$ is one which results from the application of a pulse sequence to a linear filter and the sampling of its output in synchronism with the input, there is no problem of implementation. If the impulse approximation is acceptable, that is, if the impulsive response of the filter is acceptably similar to the response to the actual pulse, the filter which implements the desired continuous transfer function $G(s)$ is used. Obviously, if $G(s)$ is physically realizable, then $G(z)$ is too and vice versa. Less simple is the implementation of a digital pulse transfer function $D(z)$ in which no linear filter is used but rather a numerical operation.

In the first place, $D(z)$ must be physically realizable; that is, it cannot produce an output prior to the application of an input. This condition is met by allowing that only those forms of $D(z)$ in which the denominator

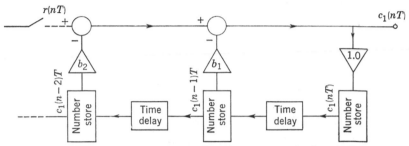

Fig. 4.9. Implementation of digital system to obtain $c_1(nT)$.

has an equal or higher power in z than the numerator. Thus, upon inversion, the sequence in z^{-1} would have no positive powers in z. Properly interpreted, this means that the output would occur at or after the instant of application of the first pulse. Since $D(z)$ is usually expressed in terms of the ratio of a power series in z^{-1} rather than z, the requirement for physical realizability is met with the following form:

$$D(z) = \frac{a_0 + a_1 z^{-1} + a_2 z^{-2} + \cdots + a_m z^{-m}}{1 + b_1 z^{-1} + b_2 z^{-2} + \cdots + b_k z^{-k}} \qquad (4.57)$$

where the important feature is that the denominator contain a term in z^0. If this is the case, expansion of $D(z)$ into a power series in z^{-1} contains no term with z^{-1} to any power higher than the zeroth. It is noted that the numerator of $D(z)$ can contain z^{-1} to any power and that often terms like a_0 or a_1 are zero.

In setting up a block diagram showing the implementation of $D(z)$, an intermediate step is introduced by which $D(z)$ is divided into two factors, $D_1(z)$ and $D_2(z)$, defined as follows:

$$D_1(z) = \frac{1}{1 + b_1 z^{-1} + b_2 z^{-2} + \cdots + b_k z^{-k}} \qquad (4.58)$$

and $\qquad D_2(z) = a_0 + a_1 z^{-1} + a_2 z^{-2} + \cdots + a_m z^{-m} \qquad (4.59)$

The block diagram for $D_1(z)$ has been developed by Barker[1] and is shown in Fig. 4.9. The z transform of the output sequence for this element is $C_1(z)$, and the nth pulse in the time domain is $c_1(nT)$. Tracing the signal through the block diagram it is seen that

$$c_1(nT) = r(nT) - b_1 c_1(n - 1)T - b_2 c_1(n - 2)T - \cdots \qquad (4.60)$$

That this relation between samples is correct can be seen by taking all the r's on one side and all the c_1's on the other side of the equation and then taking the z transform of both sides in the manner used on (4.49). Doing so, this results in

$$R(z) = C_1(z)(1 + b_1 z^{-1} + b_2 z^{-2} + \cdots) \qquad (4.61)$$

which is the required relationship.

The total output $C(z)$ is now obtained by operating on the output $C_1(z)$ by $D_2(z)$. The significance of this operation is that a_0 times the present output sample is added to a_1 times the output sample one sample time previously, etc. These outputs are available in the system shown in Fig. 4.9 and by taking off weighted samples as shown in Fig. 4.10, the total

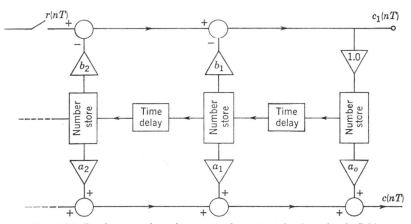

FIG. 4.10. Implementation of system whose transfer function is $D(z)$.

output sequence $C(z)$ is obtained. Thus, the output sample $c(nT)$ at any particular sample time nT is obtained by the addition of weighted samples of the input $r(nT)$ and intermediate output $c_1(nT)$. It is noted that a number of storage elements equal to the order of $D(z)$ must be provided to hold the various numbers and that means for weighting these numbers by the various a's and b's must also be available. If a general-purpose digital computer is used to implement the operations in real time, the operations can be programmed into the computer. If a special-purpose computer is used, combinations of digital and analogue techniques can be used to best advantage. The implementation described in this section uses the minimum number of storage elements, although other methods employing more storage elements have been described in the literature.[3]

4.8 Sum of Squares of Sample Sequence

A useful relation in the application of optimizing design criteria for sampled-data systems is the expression for the sum of the squares of a pulse sequence. This is analogous to the integrated-square integral used in continuous systems. The definition of this sum is given by the following:

$$S^2 = \sum_{n=0}^{\infty} [f(nT)]^2 \qquad (4.62)$$

where $f(nT)$ is the nth sample in the sequence whose z transform is $F(z)$. Using the inversion theorem as given in (4.20),

$$f(nT) = \frac{1}{2\pi j} \int_{\Gamma} z^{n-1} F(z)\, dz \qquad (4.63)$$

and substituting the result in (4.62), there results

$$S^2 = \sum_{n=0}^{\infty} f(nT) \frac{1}{2\pi j} \int_{\Gamma} z^{n-1} F(z)\, dz \qquad (4.64)$$

By interchanging the order of the summation and the integration,

$$S^2 = \frac{1}{2\pi j} \int_{\Gamma} F(z) z^{-1}\, dz \sum_{n=0}^{\infty} f(nT) z^n \qquad (4.65)$$

The summation in (4.65) is recognized to be the z transform of the pulse sequence, of which $f(nT)$ is a typical term except for the fact that the exponents of z are positive instead of negative. In this case, the following identity is recognized:

$$F(z^{-1}) = \sum_{n=0}^{\infty} f(nT) z^n \qquad (4.66)$$

Substituting back into (4.65), the expression for S^2 becomes

$$S^2 = \frac{1}{2\pi j} \int_{\Gamma} F(z) F(z^{-1}) z^{-1}\, dz \qquad (4.67)$$

where it is recalled that the contour Γ is the unit circle since all poles of $F(z)$ are contained therein for stable systems. The advantage of being able to express the sum of the squared samples in the z domain is that evaluation of (4.67) can be readily carried out. In those cases where optimization of the system is sought by adjustment of system parameters which will minimize the sum of the squared error pulses, (4.67) proves to be extremely useful.

EXAMPLE

The z transform of a pulse sequence $F(z)$ is the following:

$$F(z) = \frac{1}{1 - e^{-aT}z^{-1}}$$

To find the sum of the squared pulses described by $F(z)$, the expression is substituted in (4.67), resulting in

$$S^2 = \frac{1}{2\pi j} \int_\Gamma \frac{1}{1 - e^{-aT}z^{-1}} \frac{1}{1 - e^{-aT}z} z^{-1}\, dz$$

This integral can be rearranged into the following form:

$$S^2 = \frac{1}{2\pi j} \int_\Gamma \frac{-e^{aT}}{(z - e^{-aT})(z - e^{aT})}\, dz$$

Evaluating the integral by taking the residue at the pole $z = e^{-aT}$, which is located inside the unit circle Γ, the resultant expression for S^2 is

$$S^2 = \frac{1}{1 - e^{-2aT}}$$

For example, if the constant a were unity and if the sampling interval T were 1 sec, the sum of the squares of all the samples ranging from zero to infinity would be

$$S^2 = \frac{1}{1 - e^{-2}}$$
$$= 1.16 \text{ units square}$$

Evaluation of the integral for more complex expressions is carried out in the same manner.

4.9 The Two-sided Z Transform

In most cases, the behavior of a sampled-data system is required for positive time only. When a systematic input such as a step or ramp function is applied, this restriction is completely satisfactory, just as it is in the case of continuous systems. The input is assumed in these cases to be zero for all negative time. For some situations, however, and particularly those in which the input is a stationary random time function, consideration of the input for all time, positive and negative, is required. The single-sided z transform, as described in previous sections, is unsatisfactory for this class of inputs. To treat systems with inputs of this type, the analogue of the continuous two-sided Laplace transform is used.

The z transform which describes pulse sequences for negative as well as positive time is known as the *two-sided z transform*.

Assuming now that $r^*(t)$ represents a pulse sequence over positive and negative time, its representation in the time domain is

$$r^*(t) = \sum_{n=-\infty}^{+\infty} r(nT)\delta(t - nT) \qquad (4.68)$$

This summation can be split into two summations, one ranging over all negative time and the other over all positive time, as follows:

$$r^*(t) = \sum_{n=-\infty}^{0} r(nT)\delta(t - nT) + \sum_{n=0}^{+\infty} r(nT)\delta(t - nT) - r(0) \quad (4.69)$$

It is necessary to subtract the central term $r(0)$ because it appears twice in the summations, once as the last term of the first summation and once as the first term of the second summation. Taking the z transform of both summations,

$$R(z) = \sum_{n=-\infty}^{0} r(nT)z^{-n} + \sum_{n=0}^{+\infty} r(nT)z^{-n} - r(0)z^0 \qquad (4.70)$$

The first summation will be identified as $R_1(z)$ and the second as $R_2(z)$.

A change of index in $R_1(z)$ from n to m will be made in order to bring the form of $R_1(z)$ to the same as that of $R_2(z)$. The new index is defined as

$$m = -n \qquad (4.71)$$

Making this change,

$$R_1(z) = \sum_{m=+\infty}^{0} r(-mT)z^m \qquad (4.72)$$

Reversing the limits in (4.72) has no effect since it indicates merely that all integral m must be included. Thus,

$$R_1(z) = \sum_{m=0}^{+\infty} r(-mT)z^m \qquad (4.73)$$

The index now can be interpreted as indicating the position of the pulse measured from zero in the *negative* direction. The summation is valid only for positive values of the index m. Thus, the z transform of a two-sided pulse sequence can be expressed as

$$R(z) = R_1(z) + R_2(z) - r(0)z^0 \qquad (4.74)$$

where $R_1(z)$ describes the sequence for negative time and has the form given in (4.73) and $R_2(z)$ describes the sequence in positive time and has the usual form.

For the condition that the pulse sequence $r^*(t)$ is even, that is, $r(nT) = r(-nT)$, then (4.74) becomes

$$R(z) = R_2(z^{-1}) + R_2(z) - r(0)z^0 \qquad (4.75)$$

An interpretation of (4.75) is that for those poles of $R_2(z)$ which lie on or inside the unit circle, the poles of $R_2(z^{-1})$ lie on or *outside* the unit circle, as shown in Fig. 4.11. For instance, if one of the poles is at 0.5 as shown, the other pole lies at 2.0. The significance of this fact can be understood by considering the inversion theorem given by (4.20):

$$r(nT) = \frac{1}{2\pi j} \int_\Gamma R(z)z^{n-1}\, dz \qquad (4.76)$$

where the path of integration Γ is ordinarily taken as a contour or circle about the origin of radius sufficient to enclose all the singularities of $R(z)$.

By evaluating the residues at the various poles of the integrand so enclosed, the pulse sequence can be evaluated for all positive time, or, equivalently, positive n.

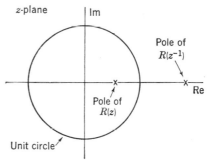

This interpretation of the inversion theorem in the z domain is similar to that of the ordinary Laplace transform on the s plane. The z transform $R(z)$ may contain poles inside and outside the unit circle, particularly if it is a two-sided z transform. This is in many ways analo-

Fig. 4.11. Location of poles of $R(z)$ and $R(z^{-1})$.

gous to the Laplace transform containing poles on the left half or right half of the s plane. In the latter case, the choice as to whether poles on the right half plane represent divergent time functions which are nonzero for positive time or convergent time functions which are nonzero in negative time depends on the choice of contour. In order to produce a time function which is nonzero for all positive time, the contour must be chosen such that it consist of the imaginary axis displaced by a constant c so that all poles lie to the left and a closure is made to encompass the entire left half of the s plane. To produce a time function which is nonzero for all negative time, a displaced imaginary axis and enclosure of the right half of the s plane is made to enclose all poles contributing to the function. Thus, the choice of integration path determines whether positive or negative time is considered.

In the case of the z domain, the integration path is a finite closed contour, which is usually taken as the unit circle. It has been shown in Sec. 4.3 that, for functions having poles outside the unit circle, the pulse sequences in positive time are divergent and, conversely, for functions having poles inside the unit circle, the pulse sequences in positive time are convergent. The pulse sequences for all poles contained inside the unit circle (or, more generally, inside the contour of integration) are zero for negative time. On the other hand, the pulse sequences for all poles contained outside the unit circle are zero for all positive time and convergent for negative time. Just as in the case of the Laplace transform, the selection of the condition of nonzero value for positive or negative real time depends on the selection of the path of integration and the manner in which it divides the poles of $R(z)$ as being within or without the contour. Since the main interest is in pulse sequences which are bounded in both negative and positive time, the unit circle is a natural choice for the integration path, and the inversion formula for a two-sided z transform containing poles inside and outside the unit circle becomes

$$r(nT) = \sum_{\substack{\text{all poles}\\\text{outside}\\\text{unit circle}}} \text{res. } R(z)z^{n-1} \qquad n \leqq 0 \qquad (4.77)$$

and
$$r(nT) = \sum_{\substack{\text{all poles}\\\text{inside}\\\text{unit circle}}} \text{res. } R(z)z^{n-1} \qquad n \geqq 0 \qquad (4.78)$$

The two-sided z transform can thus be used to describe pulse sequences both in the positive and negative time domains, subject to the restrictions and conventions outlined in this section.

EXAMPLE

A two-sided z transform $R(z)$ is given by

$$R(z) = \frac{1}{1 - qz} + \frac{1}{1 - qz^{-1}} - z^0$$

It is assumed that q is a number less than unity, so that the first term in $R(z)$ contains a pole outside the unit circle and the second term contains a pole inside the unit circle. Thus, the first term represents the pulse sequence for negative time and the second term for positive time. Applying the inversion procedure outlined previously and as expressed by (4.77) and (4.78), the positive and negative time pulse sequences can be found. First $R(z)z^{n-1}$ is brought to the form

$$R(z)z^{n-1} = \frac{-z^n(1 - q^2)}{q(z - q^{-1})(z - q)}$$

where the pole inside the unit circle is at q and the pole outside the unit circle is at q^{-1}.

The pulse sequence for positive time, $n \geq 0$, is obtained by taking the residues for all poles inside the unit circle, in this case only one pole, at q.   Thus

$$r(nT) = \frac{-q^n(1 - q^2)}{q(q - q^{-1})}$$
$$= q^n \qquad n \geq 0$$

Now, for negative time, $n \leq 0$, the pulse sequence is obtained by taking the residues at the poles outside the unit circle.   In this case, there is only one, at q^{-1}.   Thus,

$$r(nT) = \frac{-q^{-n}(1 - q^2)}{q(q^{-1} - q)}$$
$$= -q^{-n} \qquad n \leq 0$$

The negative sign resulting from a direct application of the residue method is caused by the fact that the enclosure outside the unit circle is counter to that inside the unit circle, and an additional negative sign must be applied to take this into account.   Thus, the correct value of $r(nT)$ is

$$r(nT) = q^{-n} \qquad n \leq 0$$

In some cases, an equivalent of the method of partial fractions can be applied to the inversion of two-sided z transforms.   This can be done directly on the form used in introducing the problem.   The first fraction, having a pole outside the unit circle, represents the sequence for negative time only.   Hence, it should be expanded into a power series in z.   The second term represents the pulse sequence for positive time only and hence should be expanded into a power series in z^{-1}.   Doing so, there results

$$R(z) = \sum_{n=0}^{+\infty} q^n z^n + \sum_{n=0}^{+\infty} q^n z^{-n} - 1.0 z^0$$

Inverting this summation term by term, the resulting pulse sequence becomes

$$r^*(t) = \sum_{n=0}^{+\infty} q^n \delta(t + nT) + \sum_{n=0}^{+\infty} q^n \delta(t - nT) - 1.0\delta(t)$$

The pulse sequence is seen to cover the entire range of time.   This approach has the same advantages as the partial-fraction method and the long-division method of inversion and is often applicable to problems where the z transforms are ratios of polynomials in z.

4.10 Summary

As in the case of linear continuous systems, transform methods greatly simplify the solution of problems in the analysis and synthesis of linear sampled-data systems. A type of transform calculus which bears the same relation to difference equations as does the Laplace transformation to differential equations can be adapted to the description of sampled-data systems. Known as the z transformation, a set of relations between variables and system constants which are analogous to those of ordinary Laplace transformations can be found. One approach to the z transformation is to consider it as a Laplace transform of impulse sequences, where the value of the function at a particular instant is the area of the impulse. An alternate viewpoint is to consider the exponent of the ordering variable z as the position of the number in a sequence. The resulting expressions are identical if it is assumed that e^{Ts} in the Laplace-transform sequences is replaced by z. The Laplace-transform approach is useful in obtaining the response of pulsed linear systems or filters. In this case, the pulse transfer function relating the input and output impulse sequences is the z transform of the impulsive response of the system. For digital systems, the approach in which the z transform is regarded in the light of generating functions and weighting sequences is more meaningful. A pulse transfer function for a digital system is readily derived, and because of the similarity between this pulse transfer function and that of pulsed linear systems, a unified method of analysis can be applied.

Theorems which are analogous to those of the continuous Laplace transform can be derived. The inversion theorem, the initial- and final-value theorems, and the pulse transfer function are readily derived and applied. The equivalent to the transfer function of continuous systems is the pulse transfer function of sampled systems. The pulse transfer function relates the z transforms of the input and output pulse sequences. It is emphasized that the pulse transfer function relates only the pulse sequences and does not give direct information of the value of the output function between sampling instants. It will be shown later how delayed z transforms can be used to obtain such information indirectly, but this requires special manipulation. For those systems where the linear element is a pulsed filter, the pulse transfer function is the z transform of the pulse sequence resulting from sampling the impulsive response of the filter. In the case of a digital device which implements linear recursion formulas between input and output number sequences, the pulse transfer function is regarded as a weighting sequence. The input and output number sequences are produced by generating functions in which the exponent of z in the transform represents the position of the number in the sequence.

There is a one-to-one similarity between the z transform relations, whether they describe a pulsed linear filter or a digital system. This makes possible a unified analysis and synthesis procedure for mixed systems containing both digital elements and pulsed linear systems.   These are common in the case of digitally compensated sampled-data control systems.   In the optimization of sampled-data feedback control systems, it is often useful to use as a criterion the sum of the squares of the error pulses resulting from the application of some form of systematic input. It is possible to obtain this sum by direct utilization of the z transform of the pulse sequence in a contour integral.

In some problems, the inputs and disturbances to a sampled-data system may be random time functions.   To handle this type of input, which is assumed to extend over negative as well as positive time, a two-sided z transform can be used.   Analogous in all respects to the two-sided Laplace transform for continuous systems, it forms the basis of the theory underlying sampled-data systems with random excitation.

From all viewpoints, the z transformation is a powerful tool in the analysis and synthesis of sampled-data systems.   It is not much more complex than the ordinary Laplace transform when used in similar problems in continuous systems.   In fact, there are many advantages, not the least of which are that inversion can be handled by means of calculating machines and that many continuous problems are reduced to sampled models in order to take advantage of this fact.   Tables of z transforms are available, thus further enhancing its value as a working tool.   Subsequent chapters will make full use of the z transformation and its modifications.

CHAPTER 5

SAMPLED-DATA SYSTEMS

In previous chapters, the individual components which are found in sampled-data systems were discussed and the mathematical relations describing their operation derived. When a number of such elements are interconnected, they constitute a system, and if one or more samplers are included, they are a *sampled-data system*. The configuration may be either open-cycle or closed-cycle, with the latter form being the center of interest in control systems. The rules for combination of elements are somewhat complicated by the presence of samplers. For this reason a direct analogy with the rules of continuous systems cannot be found in all cases, and the tempting possibility that all that need be done is to substitute the z transform for the Laplace transform is not correct. In this chapter the behavior of systems at sampling instants only will be considered. The behavior between sampling instants will be treated later by extensions of the methods used in this chapter.

5.1 Sampled Elements in Cascade

If two linear elements are connected in cascade as shown in Fig. 5.1, it is desirable to be able to relate the over-all input and output sequences in terms of the transfer functions. Figure 5.1 shows two linear elements whose individual pulse transfer functions are $G_1(z)$ and $G_2(z)$. It is important to note that a synchronous sampler is located between the two elements. This distinction is most important because the relations which will be derived depend on its presence. The case where no sampler is included will be taken up later. The over-all output pulse sequence is given by $C_2(z)$, while the intermediate pulse sequence which constitutes the output of the first element and the input of the second is $C_1(z)$.

From the definition of the pulse transfer function given in Sec. 4.6, it follows immediately that

$$C_1(z) \ = \ G_1(z)R(z) \tag{5.1}$$

The sequence $C_1(z)$ is the input to the second element whose pulse transfer function is $G_2(z)$, so that its output $C_2(z)$ is given by

$$C_2(z) \ = \ G_2(z)C_1(z) \tag{5.2}$$

Substituting for $C_1(z)$ its equivalent from (5.1), the over-all relationship becomes

$$C_2(z) = G_1(z)G_2(z)R(z) \qquad (5.3)$$

It is readily deduced that the over-all pulse transfer function is simply the product of the pulse transfer functions of the individual cascaded elements:

$$G(z) = G_1(z)G_2(z) \qquad (5.4)$$

For emphasis, it will be repeated that the over-all pulse transfer function of two elements *which are separated by a synchronous sampler* is the product of the pulse transfer functions of the individual elements.

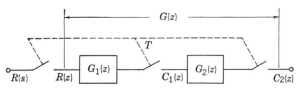

FIG. 5.1. Cascaded sampled elements.

In contrast, two elements may be in cascade with a continuous connection between them, as shown in Fig. 5.2. This case is of significance only when the two elements are themselves continuous elements capable of producing a continuous output between sampling instants. Digital elements are inherently sampled since they can deliver only a number

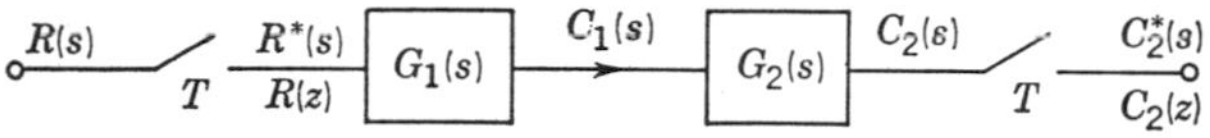

$$R(s) \quad \underset{T}{\diagup} \quad \frac{R^*(s)}{R(z)} \; \boxed{G_1(s)} \; \frac{C_1(s)}{\longrightarrow} \; \boxed{G_2(s)} \; \frac{C_2(s)}{} \quad \underset{T}{\diagup} \quad \frac{C_2^*(s)}{C_2(z)}$$

FIG. 5.2. Cascaded continuous elements.

sequence at their output and do not fall into the category under discussion. For the systems shown in Fig. 5.2, the excitation of the second element is by a continuous time function whose Laplace transform is $C_1(s)$. The relation between this output and the input is

$$C_1(s) = G_1(s)R^*(s) \qquad (5.5)$$

where $R^*(s)$ is the Laplace transform of the impulse sequence at the output of the sampler. The Laplace transform $C_2(s)$ of the final output time function is given by

$$C_2(s) = G_2(s)C_1(s) \qquad (5.6)$$

and the relation between input and output Laplace transforms is obtained by combining (5.6) and (5.5):

$$C_2(s) = G_1(s)G_2(s)R^*(s) \qquad (5.7)$$

This result could have been anticipated by observing that $G_1(s)G_2(s)$ is simply the transfer function of the two continuous elements in cascade.

The relation which is being sought is the one between the final sampled output and the sampled input. The final synchronous switch establishes this pulse sequence, and its Laplace transform $C_2^*(s)$ is obtained simply by replacing all s in $C_2(s)$ by $s + njω_0$ and summing over all n. For simplicity, $G_1(s)G_2(s)$ will be replaced by $G(s)$. Using the result of (5.7) and making this substitution,

$$C_2^*(s) = \frac{1}{T} \sum_{n=-\infty}^{+\infty} G(s + njω_0) \frac{1}{T} \sum_{m=-\infty}^{+\infty} R[s + (m + n)jω_0] \qquad (5.8)$$

A typical term $C_{2,q}(s)$ of this summation is

$$C_{2,q}(s) = G(s + qjω_0) \frac{1}{T} \sum_{m=-\infty}^{+\infty} R[s + (m + q)jω_0] \qquad (5.9)$$

It is noted that the summation in (5.9) is over all integral values of m ad infinitum, and since q is also an integer, the summation is unaffected in the limit by the choice of q. Hence, the summation is not a function of q, or m, for that matter. The summation can be written as

$$\frac{1}{T} \sum_{m=-\infty}^{+\infty} R[s + (m + q)jω_0] = R^*(s) \qquad (5.10)$$

regardless of the value of q. Thus, in (5.8) $R^*(s)$ can be taken out as a common factor and the expression for $C_2^*(s)$ can be rewritten as

$$C_2^*(s) = \left[\frac{1}{T} \sum_{n=-\infty}^{+\infty} G(s + njω_0) \right] R^*(s) \qquad (5.11)$$

The transfer function $G(s + njω_0)$ will now be examined. By definition, it is simply

$$G(s + njω_0) = G_1(s + njω_0)G_2(s + njω_0) \qquad (5.12)$$

The Laplace transform of the output $C_2^*(s)$ contains the summation of these terms over all integral values of n; hence,

$$\sum_{n=-\infty}^{+\infty} G(s + njω_0) = \sum_{n=-\infty}^{+\infty} G_1(s + njω_0)G_2(s + njω_0) \qquad (5.13)$$

It is noted that the summation of the product of terms is not equal to the product of the summations, except under very special conditions.

Thus, it is clearly true that

$$G^*(s) \neq G_1^*(s)G_2^*(s) \qquad (5.14)$$

for elements which are not separated by a sampler. To emphasize the condition, it is conventional to write the transform of two cascaded elements with a continuous connection between them as $G_{12}^*(s)$:

$$G_{12}^*(s) = \frac{1}{T} \sum_{n=-\infty}^{+\infty} G_1(s + nj\omega_0)G_2(s + nj\omega_0) \qquad (5.15)$$

In terms of z-transform notation, (5.15) implies that the over-all pulse transfer function of two cascaded elements which are not separated by a sampler is given by

$$G_{12}(z) = Z[G_1(s)G_2(s)] \qquad (5.16)$$

Stated in words, the pulse transfer function of two cascaded elements not separated by a sampler is the z transform corresponding to the product of

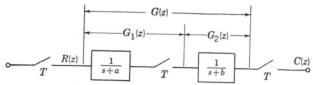

FIG. 5.3. System used in example.

their continuous transfer functions. Where different letters are used for the individual transfer functions, such as $G(s)$ and $H(s)$, the over-all pulse transfer function is written as $GH(z)$. Referring back to (5.11) and using z-transform notation, the output z transform is given by

$$C_2(z) = G_{12}(z)R(z) \qquad (5.17)$$

EXAMPLE

It is desired to find the over-all pulse transfer function for two elements separated by a sampler, as shown in Fig. 5.3. The pulse transfer functions of each of the elements are

$$G_1(z) = Z\frac{1}{s + a}$$

$$= \frac{1}{1 - e^{-aT}z^{-1}}$$

and

$$G_2(z) = Z\frac{1}{s + b}$$

$$= \frac{1}{1 - e^{-bT}z^{-1}}$$

The over-all pulse transfer function $G(z)$ is given by

$$G(z) = G_1(z)G_2(z)$$

which, upon substitution and simplification, becomes

$$G(z) = \frac{1}{(1 - e^{-aT}z^{-1})(1 - e^{-bT}z^{-1})}$$

If the two elements are cascaded *without* a sampler between them, the over-all pulse transfer function is given by

$$G_{12}(z) = \mathcal{Z}[G_1(s)G_2(s)]$$

$$= \mathcal{Z}\,\frac{1}{(s + a)(s + b)}$$

From Appendix I, the z transform is

$$G_{12}(z) = \frac{1}{a - b}\,\frac{(e^{-bT} - e^{-aT})z^{-1}}{(1 - e^{-aT}z^{-1})(1 - e^{-bT}z^{-1})}$$

It is clear that $G_{12}(z)$ differs considerably from $G(z)$, as expected. It could be shown that if the sampling period T were made small, the two expressions would tend to the same limit. Another point is that the two expressions have the same poles but not the same zeros.

5.2 Feedback Sampled-data Systems

The over-all pulse transfer function for a feedback system is not arrived at as directly as that for a continuous system because of the various limitations imposed on the combination of cascaded elements out-

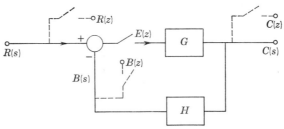

Fig. 5.4. Error-sampled feedback system.

lined in the previous section. There is no unique form of over-all pulse transfer function for closed-loop systems but rather a number of forms dependent on the location of the samplers, as will be seen in this section. To illustrate the methods used to determine the over-all pulse transfer function, several typical forms will be used.

The *error-sampled* system is shown in Fig. 5.4. In this system there is only one sampler, placed at the point in the system where the error signal is generated. The error is in the form of a sequence of error pulses whose z transform is $E(z)$, as seen in the figure. There are two continuous elements whose transfer functions are $G(s)$ and $H(s)$, representing the feedforward and feedback systems, respectively. In the system illustrated, the input and output functions are continuous, and their respective Laplace transforms are $R(s)$ and $C(s)$, respectively. The dashed samplers shown in Fig. 5.4 are fictitious and represent a process of mathematical sampling only. This means that the continuous functions represented by $R(s)$, $C(s)$, and $B(s)$ are examined at sampling instants only, and the pulse sequences so obtained have z transforms given by $R(z)$, $C(z)$, and $B(z)$. The reason for creating these fictitious pulse sequences is that the z transformation relates such pulse sequences in terms of a pulse transfer function.

From Fig. 5.4, it is seen that the error pulse sequence $E(z)$ is given by

$$E(z) = R(z) - B(z) \tag{5.18}$$

Also, the relation between the z transform $B(z)$ and $E(z)$ is given by

$$B(z) = GH(z)E(z) \tag{5.19}$$

where it is recalled that $GH(z)$ represents the z transform corresponding to the Laplace transform $G(s)H(s)$. Substituting (5.19) back into (5.18), there results

$$E(z) = R(z) - GH(z)E(z) \tag{5.20}$$

Solving (5.20) for $E(z)$, the error-sequence z transform becomes

$$E(z) = \frac{R(z)}{1 + GH(z)} \tag{5.21}$$

This error-sequence transform is useful in determining the performance of the system; however, the over-all response is of even more interest. From the figure it is seen that the output-sequence z transform $C(z)$ is related to the error-sequence z transform $E(z)$ by the feedforward pulse transfer function $G(z)$,

$$C(z) = G(z)E(z) \tag{5.22}$$

Substituting (5.21) in (5.22), there results the expression

$$C(z) = \frac{G(z)}{1 + GH(z)} R(z) \tag{5.23}$$

This is the relation between the input and output z transforms of the pulse sequences. The expression is relatively simple and straightforward only because it is restricted to relating the input and output values at sampling instants and not continuously. This relation is listed in the table[49] in Appendix III, along with the resulting relationships for other feedback configurations. Note is made that (5.23) contains the z transform $GH(z)$ corresponding to the loop transfer function $G(s)H(s)$.

Another common and useful structure is the one shown in Fig. 5.5. In this system, the elements G and H are continuous feedforward and feedback components, whose transfer functions are $G(s)$ and $H(s)$, respectively. The element D is a digital controller; that is, it receives a sequence of pulses $e_1^*(t)$ at its input and delivers a processed sequence of pulses $e_2^*(t)$ at its output. Internally, the element contains either a pulsed network or a numerical device such as a digital computer. The

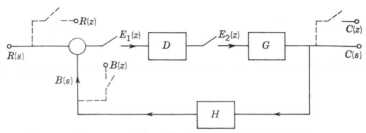

FIG. 5.5. Error-sampled feedback system with digital element.

unit has been referred to at times as a *sampled-data processing unit*,[3] although the term *digital controller*[4] has the advantage of being more compact and more descriptive. It was shown in the previous chapter that such elements, if linear, are characterized by a pulse transfer function $D(z)$ which relates the input and output pulse sequences.

The relations between the various z transforms describing the variables and elements can be obtained directly from the figure. The control error z transform $E_1(z)$ is given by

$$E_1(z) = R(z) - B(z) \qquad (5.24)$$

and
$$B(z) = GH(z)E_2(z) \qquad (5.25)$$

The pulse sequence at the output of the digital controller is related to the control error sequence through the digital-controller pulse transfer function $D(z)$ as follows:

$$E_2(z) = D(z)E_1(z) \qquad (5.26)$$

Solving (5.24), (5.25), and (5.26) for $E_2(z)$,

$$E_2(z) = \frac{D(z)}{1 + D(z)GH(z)} R(z) \qquad (5.27)$$

The output z transform $C(z)$ is given by

$$C(z) = G(z)E_2(z) \qquad (5.28)$$

Substituting (5.27) in (5.28), there results the over-all relation

$$C(z) = \frac{D(z)G(z)}{1 + D(z)GH(z)} R(z) \qquad (5.29)$$

In the compensation of sampled-data systems by means of digital controllers, the problem is to determine the $D(z)$ which will produce a desired relation between output and input sequences.

The over-all response pulse transfer functions for other configurations are found in a similar manner and are tabulated in Appendix III for ready reference. The expressions for any intermediate variables, such as the control error, can be found by application of the rules of combination given in Sec. 5.1. The time-domain pulse sequences are always obtainable by the use of inversion techniques, so that the transient response at the output of a feedback sampled-data system is readily available.

5.3 Stability of Sampled-data Systems

As in the case of continuous systems, the objective of the designer of a sampled-data system is to obtain characteristics which are outlined in a

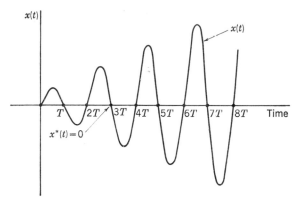

Fig. 5.6. Example of time function with "hidden oscillations."

specification. It is always understood without explicit statement that the system must be stable. For linear systems this implies that the output in response to a bounded input must be bounded. For sampled-data systems, this criterion is altered slightly to state that a sampled-data system is stable if the output pulse sequence is bounded when the input pulse sequence is bounded also. It is recognized that this leaves open the possibility that the continuous output may be unbounded by containing oscillations of increasing amplitude, though a sample sequence derived therefrom may be bounded. This effect is illustrated in Fig. 5.6, where it is seen that even though the oscillation is increasing without bound, the zero crossovers are synchronous with the sampler. This "hidden oscillation" was introduced by Barker[1] and studied by later investigators,[24] but as a practical matter this condition rarely arises; and if it does it is readily detected. In order to remain undetected in an analysis it is necessary that the period of the hidden oscillation match *exactly* the sampling interval or a fraction thereof.

Discarding the possibility outlined above, the definition of stability of a linear sampled-data system can be based on the pulse-to-pulse convergence or divergence. Thus,

A linear sampled-data system is stable if the pulse sequence at its output in response to a bounded sequence at its input is bounded.

Conversely, a sampled-data system is unstable if the pulse sequence at its output in response to a bounded sequence at its input is unbounded.

The problem is to find working criteria by which a system can be tested as to its condition of stability. Toward this end, the system shown in Fig. 5.7 is used as a means of obtaining analytic forms for this determination.

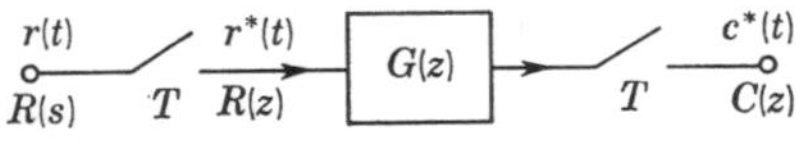

FIG. 5.7. System used to derive stability criterion.

If the pulse transfer function of the system shown in Fig. 5.7 is $G(z)$, then, by definition,

$$G(z) = \sum_{k=0}^{\infty} g(kT)z^{-k} \tag{5.30}$$

where $g(kT)$ is the value of the impulsive response of the system at the kth sampling instant. The output pulses of the system are obtained from the convolution summation

$$c(mT) = \sum_{k=0}^{\infty} g(kT)r[(m-k)T] \tag{5.31}$$

Now, the input $r^*(t)$ is bounded so that it satisfies the relation

$$\text{Max } |r[(m-k)T]| = M < \infty \tag{5.32}$$

where M is some positive number less than infinity. For the system to be stable in accordance with the definition given previously, the output $c(mT)$ must be bounded for all integral values of m. Thus, for stability,

$$|c(mT)| < \infty \tag{5.33}$$

for all integral values of m. The magnitude of $c(mT)$ is given by the magnitude of its equivalent from (5.31),

$$|c(mT)| = \left| \sum_{k=0}^{\infty} g(kT)r[(m-k)T] \right| \tag{5.34}$$

It is readily apparent that the magnitude of a summation is always less than the summation of the magnitudes. Thus,

$$|c(mT)| \leqq \sum_{k=0}^{\infty} |g(kT)| \, |r[(m-k)T]| \qquad (5.35)$$

The second set of terms in the summation is all bounded in view of the fact that it represents the input pulse sequence. Thus, $|r[(m-k)T]|$ is always less than some finite positive number M, and therefore

$$|c(mT)| \leqq M \sum_{k=0}^{\infty} |g(kT)| \qquad (5.36)$$

Hence, $c^*(t)$ is to be bounded if

$$\sum_{k=0}^{\infty} |g(kT)| < \infty \qquad (5.37)$$

Thus, it follows that a sufficient condition for the sampled-data system to be stable is that the summation of the magnitudes of the samples in the sampled impulsive response be bounded.

That the condition given in (5.37) is necessary as well as sufficient can be ascertained by finding at least one bounded input which makes the condition necessary. Such an input is one in which the signs of the various input samples in (5.34) are the same as those of the samples $g(kT)$. In this case, all the terms of (5.34) are positive, and their sum is identically that given by (5.35). Thus, in order for $c(mT)$ to remain bounded for a bounded input, it is *necessary* for the summation of the magnitudes of $g(kT)$ to be bounded since the signs have effectively been all made positive by the choice of signs for the input sequence. The necessary and sufficient condition for the stability of a system is given by (5.37). This summation is the analogue of the one applying to continuous systems which states that the time integral of the magnitude of the impulsive response of the system must be bounded in a stable system.

While the criterion for stability given by (5.37) is rigorous, it is not readily applicable to the problems normally encountered in system synthesis and analysis. It is desirable to relate the condition to characteristics of the pulse transfer function in much the same way as is done in continuous systems. In the latter, satisfaction of the requirement that the integral of the impulsive response be bounded is tested by the presence or absence of poles of the transfer function in the right half of the complex frequency plane. A similar condition must be sought for sampled-data systems whose characteristics are contained in the pulse transfer function.

To relate the condition for stability to the singularities of the pulse

transfer function $G(z)$, the complex variable z is introduced. $G(z)$ is the
pulse transfer function which upon inversion yields the pulse sequence
whose sample values are $g(kT)$ contained in (5.37). Assuming that
$G(z)$ is the pulse transfer function of a *stable* system, it follows that the
inequality

$$\sum_{k=0}^{\infty} |g(kT)| \, |z^{-k}| < \infty \qquad (5.38)$$

is satisfied for the condition that $|z^{-1}| \leq 1$ or, equivalently, that $|z| \geq 1$.
In other words, the inequality given in (5.38) must be satisfied everywhere outside the unit circle of the complex z plane.

It is readily apparent that the following inequality also is true:

$$\sum_{k=0}^{\infty} g(kT)z^{-k} \leqq \sum_{k=0}^{\infty} |g(kT)| \, |z^{-k}| \qquad (5.39)$$

since all the terms on the right-hand side of (5.39) are positive whereas
those on the left-hand side may have mixed signs or be complex. Hence,
a condition for satisfying (5.38) is that, for $|z| \geq 1$,

$$\sum_{k=0}^{\infty} g(kT)z^{-k} < \infty \qquad (5.40)$$

This summation is recognized to be the pulse transfer function $G(z)$ of the
system, and the condition expressed in (5.40) is that $G(z)$ be analytic
everywhere outside the unit circle in the z plane. Thus, a stable system
is characterized by a pulse transfer function satisfying this requirement.
When use is made of the fact that the definition of z is e^{Ts}, it is seen that
this requirement states that the pulse transfer function expressed in
terms of the variable s be analytic in the right half of the s plane, a result
which is not too surprising.

Considering next a system described by a pulse transfer function containing poles which lie outside of the unit circle of the z plane, the condition for *instability* can be found. For such a system there exists a z for
which

$$\sum_{k=0}^{\infty} g(kT)z^{-k} = \infty \qquad (5.41)$$

for $|z^{-1}| \leq 1$ or $|z| \geq 1$. Now the following sequence of inequalities is
readily seen to be true:

$$\sum_{k=0}^{\infty} |g(kT)| > \sum_{k=0}^{\infty} |g(kT)| \, |z^{-k}| > \sum_{k=0}^{\infty} g(kT)z^{-k} = \infty \qquad (5.42)$$

for values of z whose magnitude is greater than unity. The inequality relating the first term of (5.42) and the last term, infinity, satisfies the condition for instability, (5.37). Thus, an unstable system has a pulse transfer function $G(z)$ which contains at least one pole which lies outside of the unit circle in the z plane. To recapitulate:

A stable linear sampled-data system has a pulse transfer function $G(z)$ which contains no poles or other singularities which lie outside of the unit circle of the z plane.

An unstable linear sampled-data system has a pulse transfer function $G(z)$ which contains one or more poles or other singularities outside the unit circle of the z plane.

The pulse transfer functions of the elements generally found in sampled-data feedback control systems have only simple or multiple poles as singularities and are in the form of ratios of polynomials in z or z^{-1}. The conditions for stability of such systems are readily apparent by expanding the pulse transfer function into partial fractions. Thus, if $G(z)$ is of the form

$$G(z) = \frac{a_0 + a_1 z^{-1} + a_2 z^{-2} + \cdots + a_m z^{-m}}{1 + b_1 z^{-1} + b_2 z^{-2} + \cdots + b_n z^{-n}} \qquad (5.43)$$

where conditions of physical realizability require that the term 1 be present in the denominator. If the various roots of the denominator are designated as z_i, then $G(z)$ can be expanded into partial fractions as follows:

$$G(z) = a_0 + \frac{C_1}{1 - z_1 z^{-1}} + \frac{C_2}{1 - z_2 z^{-1}} + \cdots + \frac{C_n}{1 - z_n z^{-1}} \qquad (5.44)$$

If the input to the system is an impulse, then the time-domain pulse sequence which results is simply

$$g(kT) = a_0 + C_1(z_1)^k + C_2(z_2)^k + \cdots + C_n(z_n)^k \qquad (5.45)$$

If the roots of the denominator of (5.43) which are the poles of the pulse transfer function $G(z)$ have magnitudes which are greater than unity, it is evident that the impulsive response $g(kT)$ of the sampled-data system will increase without bound as the various integral values of k increase without bound. The stability condition that $G(z)$ not contain any poles outside the unit circle of the z plane is clearly seen in this approach.

As in the case of continuous systems, it is not convenient to determine the stability of a system by factoring the denominator polynomial of $G(z)$ in order to locate the poles of the function. For simple systems of second or possibly third order this procedure is as direct as any, but for higher-order systems the labor required to factor the polynomials becomes

excessive.   It is desirable to be able to ascertain the presence or absence
of poles outside the unit circle without actually determining their location.
A form of modified Routh-Hurwitz or Nyquist criterion must therefore be
established as a working tool.

5.4 The Modified Routh-Hurwitz Criterion

The Routh-Hurwitz criterion is a test which determines the signs of the
real parts of the roots of a rational polynomial.   This test finds direct
application to determining the condition of stability of a linear continuous
system by applying it to the characteristic equation of the system.   The
presence or absence of roots of this equation with positive real parts is an
indication of instability or stability respectively.   In the case of sampled-
data systems, a direct test of this type would require the determination of
whether or not the magnitudes of the roots of the characteristic equation
are greater than unity, so that a direct application of the Routh-Hurwitz
criterion is not possible.

It is possible, however, to apply a transformation to the characteristic
equation in z which will transform the region outside the unit circle in the
z plane to the right half of an auxiliary plane and the region inside the unit
circle to the left half of this plane.   Such a transformation is the bilinear
transformation which has been applied to problems in the control field by
Oldenbourg and Sartorius.[46]   An auxiliary plane called the λ plane is
defined by the following relation:

$$z = \frac{\lambda + 1}{\lambda - 1} \tag{5.46}$$

or

$$\lambda = \frac{z + 1}{z - 1} \tag{5.47}$$

To show the relation between the z plane and the λ plane, it is noted that
both z and λ are complex, so that

$$z = x + jy$$

and

$$\lambda = u + jv \tag{5.48}$$

Substituting these expressions back in (5.47) and rationalizing the resulting expression, the following is obtained:

$$\lambda = \frac{(x^2 + y^2) - 1}{(x - 1)^2 + y^2} - j \frac{2y}{(x - 1)^2 + y^2} \tag{5.49}$$

In view of the definition of x and y in (5.48), it is seen that $(x^2 + y^2)$ is
the magnitude squared of z, $|z|^2$.   Thus, for all values of z whose magnitude
is greater than unity, the real part of λ is positive, and for all values of z
whose magnitudes is less than unity, the real part of λ is negative.   Thus,
stated differently, the entire region of the z plane which lies outside the

unit circle is transformed into the right half of the λ plane. Similarly, the entire region which lies inside the unit circle of the z plane is transformed into the left half λ plane. This relationship is shown graphically in Fig. 5.8. The regions labeled A and B are corresponding regions in their respective planes.

The procedure which can be used to ascertain whether or not a system is unstable is to express the over-all pulse transfer function $G(z)$ as the

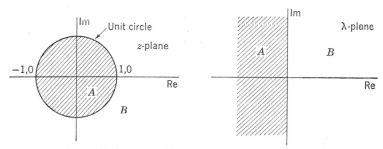

FIG. 5.8. Corresponding regions in z and λ planes.

ratio of two polynomials. The denominator polynomial, when set equal to zero, is the characteristic equation of the system. Each z in this polynomial is then treated by applying the relation for z given by (5.46), and a resultant characteristic equation in λ obtained. The Routh-Hurwitz criterion is then applied directly to this equation in λ.

EXAMPLE

The over-all pulse transfer function $G(z)$ of a system relates the input and output pulse sequence and is given by

$$G(z) = \frac{z^{-1}(1 - 0.5z^{-1})}{1 - 1.6z^{-1} + 0.48z^{-2}}$$

Multiplying both numerator and denominator by z^2,

$$G(z) = \frac{z - 0.5}{z^2 - 1.6z + 0.48}$$

The denominator of $G(z)$ contains the polynomial leading to the characteristic equation

$$z^2 - 1.6z + 0.48 = 0$$

While this simple equation can be solved directly for its roots, the bilinear transformation will be applied to illustrate the method. Using (5.46),

$$\frac{(\lambda + 1)^2}{(\lambda - 1)^2} - 1.6\frac{\lambda + 1}{\lambda - 1} + 0.48 = 0$$

Simplifying and clearing of fractions, this expression becomes

$$0.12\lambda^2 - 1.04\lambda - 3.08 = 0$$

Application of the Routh-Hurwitz criterion to this polynomial will show that there is one root in the left half and one root in the right half of the λ plane. Direct factoring of the characteristic equation in z would show that the roots are 0.4 and 1.2, a direct check.

While simple to apply in principle, the bilinear transformation combined with the Routh-Hurwitz criterion is a fairly tedious process in the case of higher-order systems. In addition, the constants of the original system appear in the transformed expression in a complex manner. For this reason, it is difficult to associate the conditions revealed by the application of the criterion with the constants of the original system. The modified Routh-Hurwitz criterion serves mainly as a check procedure to verify results obtained with some of the mapping procedures outlined in the next section.

5.5 Stability Criterion Using the Transfer Locus

Feedback systems containing one or more samplers are characterized by an over-all pulse transfer function $C(z)/R(z)$, which is called $K(z)$ and is given by

$$K(z) = \frac{G(z)}{1 + GH(z)} \tag{5.50}$$

for the case of an error-sampled system. For other prototypes, the form of $K(z)$ changes except for one characteristic, namely, that the denominator of $K(z)$ contains a polynomial form $1 + F(z)$, where $F(z)$ is the loop pulse transfer function. In the error-sampled case, $F(z)$ is expressed as the z transform corresponding to the continuous transfer function $G(s)H(s)$. In other cases, the relation between $F(z)$ and the transfer functions of the elements comprising the loop may differ. For purposes of discussion, the form $GH(z)$ will be used, though it should be remembered that the loop pulse transfer function, regardless of the form of the system, is implied.

To determine the condition of stability for a feedback system, the roots of the characteristic equation obtained from the denominator polynomial of $K(z)$ must be examined. This characteristic equation is given by

$$1 + GH(z) = 0 \tag{5.51}$$

The problem is to determine if some of the roots of this equation lie outside the unit circle of the z plane by applying the same Cauchy mapping theorem which underlies the Nyquist criterion in continuous systems. It is recalled that this theorem states that if a closed contour Γ encloses poles and zeros of a function, then the number of times the map of this contour encloses the origin on the function plane is equal to the difference between the number of zeros and poles so enclosed.

For the problem at hand, it is necessary to choose a contour on the z plane which encloses the entire region outside the unit circle in order to study the function $1 + GH(z)$. Such a contour is sketched in Fig. 5.9, where the outer radius R is made to approach infinity. The map of this contour on the $[1 + GH(z)]$ plane will indicate by its enclosures of the origin the difference between the zeros and poles of this function. It is

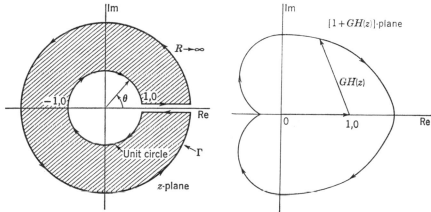

FIG. 5.9. Contour used to enclose poles outside the unit circle.

FIG. 5.10. Typical map of Γ on $[1 + GH(z)]$ plane.

seen that the poles of $1 + GH(z)$ are the same as those of the function $GH(z)$. Thus, if $GH(z)$ is a stable function, that is, if it does not contain poles outside the unit circle, then neither does $1 + GH(z)$. In such an event, the enclosure of the origin by the map of Γ indicates the number of zeros or roots of the characteristic equation. Such enclosures or lack of enclosures indicates a condition of instability or stability respectively.

A typical map resulting from application of this procedure to a practical system is shown in Fig. 5.10, where it is seen that the origin is enclosed once. If the open-loop pulse transfer function is stable, this enclosure indicates that one zero lies outside the unit circle and that the closed-loop system is unstable. As in the case of continuous systems, it is convenient to shift the imaginary axis to the point $(1,0)$, as shown in Fig. 5.11. With this shifted axis it is necessary to plot only $GH(z)$ and to observe the enclosure of the critical point $(-1,0)$ instead of the origin. When plotted on this modified plane, the map is referred to as the *pulse transfer locus*. Essentially, then, the pulse transfer locus is a map of the unit circle only, since the function $GH(z)$ vanishes as z approaches infinity in practical, physically realizable systems. This is shown more clearly in the illustrative example which follows.

In plotting pulse transfer loci, the parameter which is varied from point to point is the angle θ of the complex variable z since the magnitude of the latter is unity. The usual practice is to mark the various corresponding values of θ, as shown in Fig. 5.11. It is seen that $GH(z)$ has conjugate values for positive and negative values of θ of equal magnitude. For pulse transfer functions which are the ratio of rational polynomials in z,

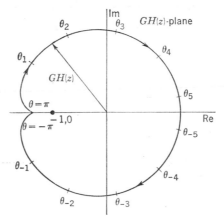

FIG. 5.11. The pulse transfer locus.

the reason for this is that each of the component terms of $GH(z)$ is itself a conjugate and the sums and ratios of conjugate terms are conjugates. As a result of this condition, only half of the pulse transfer locus is plotted in practice.

In most practical applications found in feedback control systems, the feedforward pulse transfer function $G(z)$ contains one or more integrators among the continuous elements. For instance, a typical continuous feedforward transfer function has the form

$$G(s) = \frac{K}{s(1 + T_1s) \cdots} \tag{5.52}$$

This transfer function is expanded into partial fractions in the usual manner,

$$G(s) = \frac{A_0}{s} + \frac{A_1}{1 + T_1s} + \cdots \tag{5.53}$$

Taking the z transform corresponding to $G(s)$, there results

$$G(z) = \frac{A_0}{1 - z^{-1}} + \frac{A_1/T_1}{1 - e^{-T/T_1}z^{-1}} + \cdots \tag{5.54}$$

It is seen that a pole at the origin of the s plane contained by the continuous transfer function $G(s)$ leads to a pulse transfer function $G(z)$ having a pole at $(1,0)$ in the z plane. The presence of this pole would cause a discontinuity in the pulse transfer locus if the contour being mapped were exactly the one shown in Fig. 5.9.

In order to establish a connection between the segments of the pulse transfer locus obtained from the portions of the contour on either side of the pole (1,0), it is necessary to generate a continuous curve around the pole. This is done by taking a small semicircular detour, as shown in Fig. 5.12, so oriented that the pole is included definitely on one side or the

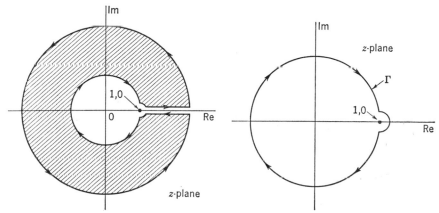

Fig. 5.12. Contour used for pulse transfer functions having poles at (1,0).

Fig. 5.13. Reduced contour used to map practical pulse transfer functions.

other. It is conventional to orient the detour to include this pole *inside* the unit circle, as shown in the figure. The same procedure is followed for any complex poles whose magnitude is exactly equal to unity, although the occurrence of such poles is rare. Since practical pulse transfer functions vanish for infinite values of z and since the portion of the contour along the real axis is self-canceling in the limit, it is customary to map only the unit circle and its detours as shown in Fig. 5.13.

EXAMPLE

A unity feedback sampled-data control system has a feedforward pulse transfer function $G(z)$ given by

$$G(z) = \frac{z^{-1}(0.264z^{-1} + 0.368)}{(1 - z^{-1})(1 - 0.368z^{-1})}$$

It is seen that the loop pulse transfer function contains a pole at (1,0), necessitating the use of the contour shown in Fig. 5.13. For purposes of illustration, however, the full contour of Fig. 5.12 will be used.

Before mapping, the function $G(z)$ will be expressed in positive powers of z by multiplying both numerator and denominator by z^2:

$$G(z) = \frac{0.264 + 0.368z}{(z - 1)(z - 0.368)}$$

This function plane will map the contour shown in Fig. 5.14a. Starting with the point a, which is the value $z = -1.0$, the value of $G(z)$ is seen to be -0.038. As the various values of z are substituted in the range from a to b, a map is generated as shown in Fig. 5.14b. At a phase angle just short of $\pi/2$, the locus again is real and crosses the real axis at about -0.4. At the point b on the contour, the function $G(z)$ is dominated by the behavior of the factor $(z-1)$ in the denominator.

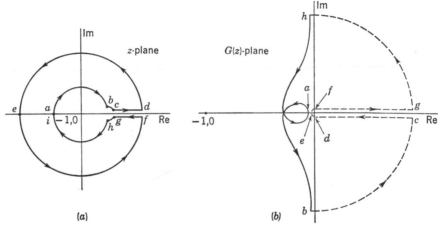

FIG. 5.14. Pulse transfer locus used in example.   (a) Contour used in z plane.   (b) Corresponding points on pulse transfer locus.

As the radius of the detour from b to c becomes increasingly small, this behavior becomes more and more dominant. Thus, to study the transfer locus in this region, $G(z)$ can be approximated by

$$G(z) = \frac{1}{z-1}$$

To study the behavior of the map in the region b-c on the contour, a detail is shown in Fig. 5.15. The complex number $(z-1)$ is represented by a vector extending from the point $(1,0)$ to the contour. The angle of this vector at b is $\pi/2$ and, when substituted into $G(z)$ as approximated in this region, yields,

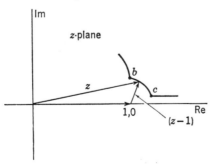

FIG. 5.15. Detail of contour Γ on z plane.

$$G(z) = \frac{1}{r} e^{-j\pi/2}$$

As the contour is traced from b to c, the angle changes from $\pi/2$ to 0 in a clockwise direction, and $G(z)$ has a phase angle which changes from

$-\pi/2$ to 0 in a counterclockwise direction, as shown in Fig. 5.14b.

In mapping from c to d, the variable z takes on larger and larger positive values, and $G(z)$ becomes smaller and smaller until it vanishes when z approaches infinite values. The behavior about the region of zero is only of academic interest since it has no significance in the determination of the enclosure of the point $(-1,0)$ in this case. Thus, the variation of z from d to e is mapped into a point at the origin in Fig. 5.14b. The remainder of the map is obtained by using the conjugate values to corresponding points previously plotted. This part of the map is shown as $efgha$. It is seen that the contour does not enclose the point $(-1,0)$, so that the system is stable. Had the feedforward gain constant been raised to 2.43 times higher than that used in the example, the contour would have enclosed the point $(-1,0)$ and the system would be unstable.

The foregoing example illustrates how the pulse transfer locus is plotted or sketched. The only portion of this locus which is significant is the map of the unit circle and the detours taken about poles of $G(z)$ which lie on the unit circle. Such poles are usually located at the point $(1,0)$ since they arise from integration in the feedforward line. In continuous systems, the margin by which the critical point $(-1,0)$ is avoided is estimated by the use of gain and phase margins or by constant gain loci generally referred to as M circles. While analogous margins can be employed in the design of sampled-data systems, it is not customary to do so. The reason for this is that there is less correlation between the margins and the transient response than in continuous systems. Nevertheless, the larger the margin of avoidance of the critical point, the higher is the degree of damping of the system. Also, a substantial margin is generally accompanied by relatively docile transient response. In view of the fact that it is simpler to invert pulse transfer functions and to obtain time-domain performance characteristics, the use of the pulse transfer locus as a design tool is not as widespread as in the case of continuous systems.

5.6 Root Loci for Sampled-data Systems

The response of a system whose over-all pulse transfer function is $G(z)$ is determined by the poles and zeros of $G(z)$. For instance, if the poles of $G(z)$ are $z_1, z_2, \ldots, z_n$, the transient component of the response, $g_{tr}(kT)$, is given by

$$g_{tr}(kT) = C_1(z_1)^k + C_2(z_2)^k + \cdots C_n(z_n)^k \qquad (5.55)$$

This relationship was derived in Sec. 5.3 and is shown in Eqs. 5.44 and 5.45. While straightforward, there is some difficulty in higher-order

sampled-data feedback systems in obtaining the roots of the characteristic equation which determines the poles of the over-all pulse transfer
function. This problem is analogous to that encountered in continuous
feedback systems where the poles of the feedforward and feedback transfer functions are readily available but the poles of the over-all closed-loop
transfer function are not. The poles of the over-all response pulse transfer function $K(z)$ are the roots of a characteristic equation whose form is
generally

$$1 + GH(z) = 0 \qquad (5.56)$$

where $GH(z)$ is the loop pulse transfer function. It is recalled from a
previous section that the form of the loop pulse transfer function may
differ from that employed in (5.56), depending on the number and locations of the samplers in the system.

The problem is to find the roots of (5.56), knowing readily only the roots
of $GH(z)$. As in the continuous-system problem, a root locus is employed
to either estimate or obtain exactly the root locations of (5.56) in the
complex plane. Stated differently, it is necessary to find all those values
of z in the complex z plane which satisfy the condition

$$GH(z) = 1/\underline{\pi \pm n2\pi} \qquad (5.57)$$

As in all relationships between complex variables, (5.57) implies two
separate equalities, one stating that the amplitudes are equal and the
other that the angles are equal. In view of the fact that most practical
systems either contain or are designed with gain constants which are
adjustable, the amplitude relationship is considered relatively unimpor-
tant. On the other hand, the phase relationship is a property of the
system which reflects the organic characteristics of the components comprising the system and is therefore of prime importance. Thus, a root
locus is desired in which all the points on that locus satisfy the phase relation implicit in (5.57), using the gain as a parameter. The relationship
describing the root locus is

$$\text{Ang } [GH(z)] = \pi \pm n2\pi \qquad (5.58)$$

It is seen that except for a change in variable from s to z and the use of
the z plane instead of the s plane, the problem posed by (5.58) is identical
to that of plotting a root locus of a closed-loop continuous system. The
transfer functions involved, namely, $G(s)$ and $G(z)$, respectively, are
ratios of polynomials in their respective variables, so that the rules
governing the plotting or sketching of the root loci are identical. Since
these rules are well known and available[21] they will not be repeated here.
The only significant difference to be found is that the behavior of the poles
is observed in relation to the unit circle as contrasted to the imaginary
axis. If poles lie inside the unit circle, they represent a stable system,

and if outside, an unstable system. Also, in view of (5.55), the closer the poles approach the magnitude unity, the longer will the transient persist in a system subjected to a sudden input. Generally, proximity to the unit circle has the same effect as proximity to the imaginary axis of poles in a continuous system. The best way of showing these effects is to use an example.

EXAMPLE

To illustrate the rules governing the plotting of root loci for sampled-data systems, the same system used in the illustrative example of the

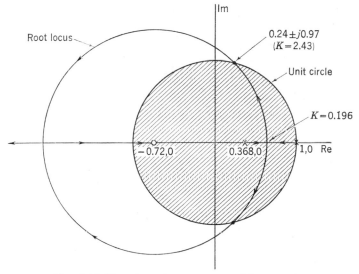

Fig. 5.16. Root locus for system used in example.

previous section will be used. The system considered there has a unity feedback and a feedforward pulse transfer function $G(z)$ given by

$$G(z) = K \frac{0.264 + 0.368z}{(z - 1)(z - 0.368)}$$

The system uses error sampling, resulting in a characteristic equation of the form

$$1 + G(z) = 0$$

whose roots must be determined. The open-loop pulse transfer function $G(z)$ has poles at $(1,0)$ and $(0.368,0)$ and has a zero at $(-0.72,0)$. These poles and zeros are marked on Fig. 5.16.

Starting with the gain constant K at zero, the root loci initiate at the poles of the open-loop transfer function $G(z)$. When the gain K goes to infinity, the loci terminate at the zeros of the open-loop transfer function $G(z)$. In this case, $G(z)$ contains one finite zero and one zero at infinity. The point of departure of the locus from the real axis is found to be at 0.648. It has been shown[21] that for this system the root locus representing the complex closed-loop poles of the system is a circle whose center is at $(-0.72,0)$. The radius of the circle is 1.368 and, using these values, the root locus appears as shown in Fig. 5.16. It should be noted here that more complex systems do not have such a simple form for the root locus and that they must be plotted by identifying those points for which the total angle of $G(z)$ is 180°. Upon reentry into the real axis, the root-locus branches, one branch going to infinity and the other toward the finite zero of the system at $(-0.72,0)$.

A scale drawing of the root locus will show that the intersection with the unit circle occurs at the points $0.24 \pm j0.97$. The gain K required to place the poles at this point is found from the magnitude relationship

$$K \left| \frac{0.264 + 0.368z}{(z-1)(z-0.368)} \right|_{z=0.24 \pm j0.97} = 1.0$$

Solving for K, the gain is found to be 2.43. This result was obtained in the illustrative example of the previous section by consideration of the enclosure of the point $(-1,0)$ by the pulse transfer locus. Thus, to produce a stable system, it is required to have the gain K be less than 2.43. If the gain exceeds this figure, the poles will be located outside the unit circle, resulting in an unstable system. Inversion of the overall response pulse transfer function of the system would show that for the case resulting in complex poles, the response to a step function would be stable, though oscillatory, if K is less than 2.43 and more than 0.196.

An unusual condition obtains in sampled-data systems for which no comparable or analogous situation exists in continuous systems. There may be stable sampled-data systems which have poles in the over-all pulse transfer function $K(z)$ that are both *real* and *negative*. For instance, in the system giving rise to the pulse transfer function $G(z)$ of the system used in the preceding example, this condition will be realized if the sampling interval T is halved. If this happens, the root locus will appear as shown in Fig. 5.17, where it is evident that for some value of K two real negative roots will result. Such negative real roots will produce an oscillatory response, as can be seen by considering the transient produced by such a root. The transient contribution of a root of this type is

$$c_{tr}(kT) = A(-z_1)^k \tag{5.59}$$

where A is an arbitrary constant and z_1 is a positive number, the sign of the root being explicitly written. For negative real roots, the sequence is alternating, being positive for even values of k and negative for odd values of k. So long as z_1 has a magnitude less than unity, the sequence is stable; that is, it converges as k tends toward infinity. Thus, in sampled-data systems it is not necessary that the poles of the over-all transfer function be complex in order to obtain an oscillatory solution. If the poles of the over-all pulse transfer function are real and positive, then the system is nonoscillatory, as can be seen readily from (5.59).

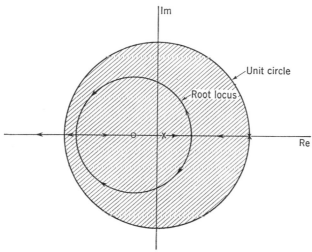

FIG. 5.17. Root locus for stable system containing poles on negative real axis.

Generally, the proximity of the poles of the over-all pulse transfer function to the unit circle is indicative of a pronounced transient response. For instance, if the poles are complex and close to the unit circle, the oscillatory transient which results when the system is excited will have significant values many sample times later since a magnitude slightly less than unity raised to a power will not be significantly less than unity unless the power is very high. Thus, considerable overshoot and oscillation can be expected from a system of this type. Similarly, if the roots are real and negative and lie close to the unit circle, a heavy oscillatory response can also be expected. If the roots are real and positive and lie close to the unit circle, the response is monotonic but the approach to steady state requires many sample times. In the design of sampled-data systems having moderate transient response and minimum overshoot, it is necessary that the poles of the system lie well within the unit circle. Quantitative criteria as to pole locations cannot be given any more than they can for continuous systems, except for specific cases. Dominant poles are characterized by their proximity to the unit circle, as contrasted to all the other poles of the system.[21] For instance, if a pair of complex poles lies close to the unit circle, say, with a magnitude of 0.9, and all other poles lie well within the unit circle, say, with magnitudes of 0.2 or less, the former are dominant poles and determine the transient response of the system.

5.7 Frequency Response of Sampled-data Systems

While not as useful as in the analysis of continuous systems, frequency-response methods can be applied to sampled-data systems also. In fact, the pulse transfer locus which is a map of the unit circle may be regarded as a frequency locus since, by definition, $z = e^{Ts}$, and as z traces the unit circle on the z plane it is equivalent to tracing the imaginary axis on the s plane. Frequency-response concepts can be applied to the over-all response pulse transfer function $K(z)$ of a sampled-data system. Referring to Fig. 5.18, the block represents a sampled-data system whose internal configuration may be either open- or closed-cycle. The frequency response of this system is obtained by applying a sinusoidal signal at the input, shown as $R(s)$, and determining the phase and amplitude of an equivalent sinusoidal envelope passing through the resulting sequence of samples at the output, shown as $C(z)$. It is recognized that the actual output of the system before sampling, shown as $C(s)$, is not sinusoidal but that it contains many frequency components at sampling frequency and related frequencies; however, it will be shown that the sampled output can describe an envelope which is sinusoidal.

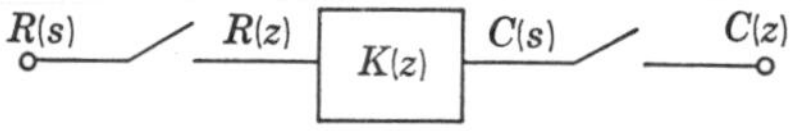

FIG. 5.18. System used to define frequency response of sampled-data device.

To determine analytic expressions for the frequency response, it will be assumed that the input is

$$r(t) = e^{j\omega t} \tag{5.60}$$

The z transform of $r(t)$ is obtained in the usual manner or from the tables, resulting in

$$R(z) = \frac{1}{1 - e^{j\omega T}z^{-1}} \tag{5.61}$$

If the pulse transfer function of the system is $K(z)$, then the output sequence is given by the relationship

$$C(z) = K(z)R(z) \tag{5.62}$$

Inverting $C(z)$ by means of the inversion integral, $c(nT)$ becomes

$$c(nT) = \frac{1}{2\pi j} \int_\Gamma K(z) \frac{z^n}{z - e^{j\omega T}} \, dz \tag{5.63}$$

Since the frequency response represents only that component of the output which exists in the steady state and the transient terms which result from the poles of $K(z)$ vanish as time approaches infinity, only the residues at the pole of the integrand introduced by the forcing function need be evaluated. Thus, the steady-state component of the output is given by

$$c_{ss}(nT) = K(e^{j\omega T})e^{jn\omega T} \qquad (5.64)$$

An envelope which produces a pulse sequence such as that in (5.64) is a sinusoidal function $c(t)$, which is given by

$$c(t) = K(e^{j\omega T})e^{j\omega t} \qquad (5.65)$$

It is understood that this envelope is not unique since any number of other components may be included so long as they correspond to the value of the output at sampling instants. However, the envelope which has been selected is the simplest and lowest-frequency time function which fits these points. The frequency-response function is that complex function of frequency which relates the amplitude and phase of the output sinusoid in terms of the input sinusoid. In this case, referring to the frequency-response function as $K(\omega)$, it is seen to be

$$K(\omega) = \frac{C(\omega)}{R(\omega)} = |K(z)|_{z=e^{j\omega T}} \qquad (5.66)$$

Since $K(z)$ is periodic in ω_0, where ω_0 is $2\pi/T$, it follows that the frequency-response function $K(\omega)$ is also periodic in ω_0.

EXAMPLE

A pulsed network has a pulse transfer function $G(z)$ given by

$$G(z) = \frac{1}{1 - e^{-aT}z^{-1}}$$

It is desired to determine the frequency response $G(\omega)$ of this pulsed network. Applying (5.66), there results

$$G(\omega) = \frac{1}{1 - e^{-aT}e^{-j\omega T}}$$

Typically, this frequency-response function plots as shown in Fig. 5.19. It is seen that the response is periodic in ω_0.

The periodicity of the frequency-response function of sampled-data systems is disconcerting since it is not readily comparable to the common and familiar response functions found in continuous systems. A clearer understanding of the significance of these response functions is obtained by going back to the pole distributions of the pulse transfer functions in the z plane. If an over-all pulse transfer function $K(z)$ is a ratio of polynomials in z given by

$$K(z) = \frac{(z - z_{01})(z - z_{02}) \cdots (z - z_{0n})}{(z - z_{p1})(z - z_{p2}) \cdots (z - z_{pk})} \tag{5.67}$$

then its pole and zero distributions will be as shown in Fig. 5.20. If z is taken equal to $e^{j\omega T}$, it traces a path in the z plane which is the unit circle. In that case, the denominator will consist of the complex numbers represented by the sinors $z - z_{pk}$ indicated in Fig. 5.20. It is readily seen that if any poles are near the unit circle, the magnitude of this sinor becomes very small, with the result that the magnitude of $K(\omega)$ becomes very large at this frequency. Thus, if poles are very close to the unit circle,

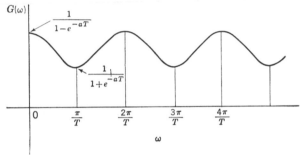

FIG. 5.19. Frequency-response function for system used in example.

they produce a pronounced frequency overshoot. The frequency at which this overshoot occurs depends on the angular location of the poles in question. For instance, a pole which is near the unit circle at an angle of 45° indicates a frequency overshoot at one-eighth of the sampling frequency. This condition is analogous to the condition of dominance of poles in determining the time-domain response. A pole located near the unit circle will have a dominant effect on the transient response.

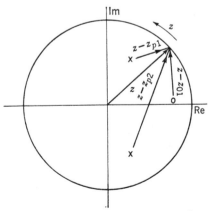

FIG. 5.20. Component sinors contributing to frequency-response function.

Indirectly, the frequency response can indicate the location of poles of the over-all pulse transfer function, and all the properties associated with frequency response in continuous systems can be transferred to sampled-data systems. The fact that the frequency response of a sampled-data system is periodic causes no concern since the repeated spectra are merely reproductions of the first significant spectrum. The periodicity of the frequency-response function merely reflects the fact that a sampled-data system is limited in its capacity to transmit a useful spectrum by the sampling frequency. A typical sequence of spectra is reproduced from the literature[15] for a second-order sampled-data servomechanism in Fig.

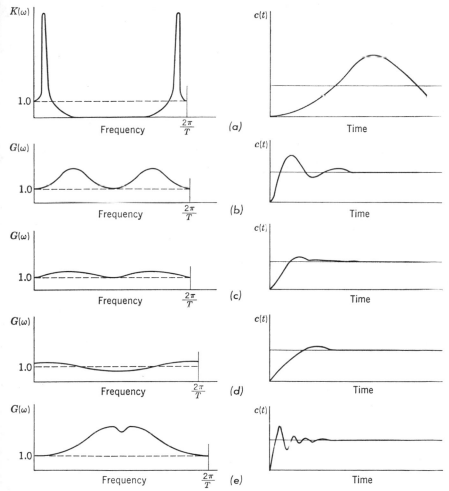

FIG. 5.21. Frequency-response functions and related time-domain response to unit step function.

5.21. In Fig. 5.21a there is a pole located very near the unit circle at about one-twentieth the sampling frequency. This means that the pole is located on the z plane, with polar coordinates at a radius of almost unity and an angle of $\pm18°$. The time-domain response to a unit step input is experimentally obtained and appears adjacent to the corresponding frequency-response curve. It is seen that the response to a unit step input is slow and that there is considerable overshoot.

In the other frequency-response functions plotted in Fig. 5.21, there is a distinct correlation between the frequency-response characteristics and the time-domain response. Relatively flat frequency response indicates a time-domain response with relatively little overshoot, as seen in Fig. 5.21c and d. Peaked frequency response at the high end of the spectrum indicates some overshoot, with oscillation at higher frequencies. It is emphasized that while it is theoretically possible to deduce the performance of a sampled-data system from the complete frequency-response characteristics, this can rarely be done in practice. Only qualitative ideas of how the system is likely to behave can be obtained from the more obvious features of the frequency response. Because of the relative ease with which time-domain performance can be obtained for sampled systems using methods of long division or other machine computation, the frequency response is rarely plotted. As a concept, however, it serves the useful purpose of tying together the time domain, pole and zero locations, and frequency characteristics. As will be seen later, design in the time domain is feasible in sampled-data systems.

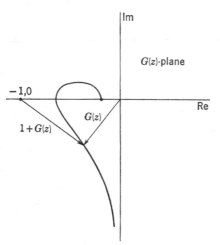

FIG. 5.22. Relation of pulse transfer locus to frequency-response function.

The foregoing discussion serves also to substantiate the statement that the proximity of the pulse transfer locus to the critical point $(-1,0)$ is indicative of a tendency of the system to have an oscillatory, though stable, response. This can be seen by reference to Fig. 5.22, where a typical pulse transfer locus is sketched. Each point on the pulse transfer locus represents a point on the unit circle of the z plane. Viewed from the frequency domain, each point on the unit circle represents a particular frequency. It is recalled that for a unity feedback system, the over-all pulse transfer function $K(z)$ is

$$K(z) = \frac{G(z)}{1 + G(z)} \tag{5.68}$$

From Fig. 5.22, it is seen that $K(z)$ can be obtained for various values of frequency by taking the ratio of the sinors indicated. Now, if the pulse transfer locus passes close to the critical point $(-1,0)$, the sinor $1 + G(z)$

becomes very small and the frequency-response function $K(\omega)$ becomes large. This peak in frequency response reflects the fact that a pole lies near the unit circle and that the transient response will be relatively oscillatory. Thus, avoidance of the critical point $(-1,0)$ by the pulse transfer locus by a substantial margin is a means of obtaining an over-all response which is docile in the time domain.

5.8 Summary

Sampled-data systems are structures of interconnected linear elements characterized by the fact that samplers may be located at one or more points. The rules of combination of sampled systems are not entirely analogous to those relating to continuous linear systems but depend on the locations of the samplers in the structure. In the simple case of two cascaded elements which are separated by a sampler, the pulse transfer function of the combination is simply the product of the pulse transfer functions of the elements. On the other hand, in the case of the pulse transfer function of cascaded elements which are not separated by a sampler, the pulse transfer function of the combination is the z transform corresponding to the product of the continuous transfer functions of the two elements. The over-all pulse transfer function in this case is not equal to the product of the two individual pulse transfer functions.

The over-all pulse transfer functions of closed-loop systems can be obtained by applying the rules developed for combining individual elements. There is no one form for the over-all pulse transfer function of a closed-loop system since it depends on the location of the samplers in the system. Thus, for each configuration, an over-all pulse transfer function must be derived. For convenience, the forms for a number of common configurations are recorded in tables. Regardless of the detailed form, however, a characteristic equation in z which describes the condition of stability of the system can be found. This relation equates a general form $1 + F(z)$ to zero, where $F(z)$ is the loop pulse transfer function of the system which is dependent on the exact distribution of continuous elements and sampling switches.

If the magnitude of the roots of the characteristic equation is greater than unity, a sampled system is unstable. More generally, if the summation of the magnitudes of the samples obtained by sampling the impulsive response of the system is bounded, the system is stable. This necessary and sufficient condition for stability is met if the poles of the over-all pulse transfer function, or equivalently, the roots of the characteristic equation, lie within the unit circle of the z plane. A test for stability is one in which a modified Routh-Hurwitz criterion is applied. By using the bilinear transformation on the characteristic equation, the resultant transformed equation can be tested for stability by applying the standard Routh-Hurwitz criterion.

While perfectly rigorous, the modified Routh-Hurwitz test is of limited practical utility since the effects of parameters in the system are disguised. More direct is the mapping method resulting in the pulse transfer locus. By observing the enclosure of the critical point $(-1,0)$ in the function plane, the condition of stability can be readily determined. The same rules governing the plotting of the continuous transfer locus apply in sampled system, except that the unit circle is used instead of the imaginary axis. A difficulty found in shaping the pulse transfer locus is that the rules for cascaded elements depend on the location of samplers and simple techniques for shaping cannot be generally applied.

The location of the roots of the sampled-data-system characteristic equation largely determine the transient response of the system. The root locus is useful in observing the migrations of these roots as either the system gain or other parameters are varied. The rules for the construction of the root locus in the z plane are identical to those for the s plane since the functions governing the locations of the poles are ratios of polynomials in either z or s, respectively. The only difference is that in sampled systems the behavior of the root loci relative to the unit circle, rather than the imaginary axis, is observed. Generally, the closer the roots lie to the unit circle, the less damped will a sampled system be. On the other hand, if roots lie close to the origin of the z plane, the system will tend to be "dead beat."

Another way of representing the performance of sampled-data systems is by means of the frequency-response function, which relates the sinusoidal envelope of the output pulse sequence to the sinusoidal input. Frequency-response functions for sampled systems are periodic at sampling frequency, a unique characteristic not found in continuous systems. Peaked frequency-response functions indicate that poles of the over-all pulse transfer function lie close to the unit circle and that the time-domain response is oscillatory in nature. While not as useful in the analysis of sampled-data systems as in continuous systems, frequency-response functions are valuable in relating the transient response and root locations. For that reason, frequency response in sampled-data systems is a useful concept. The combination of the three viewpoints, namely, transient response, root locations, and frequency response, serve to give a full understanding of the behavior of sampled-data systems.

CHAPTER 6

APPLICATION OF CONVENTIONAL TECHNIQUES TO THE DESIGN OF SAMPLED-DATA CONTROL SYSTEMS

After the techniques of analysis as described in the previous chapters have been applied to a sampled-data system, one's attention naturally turns to the problems of design or synthesis. With reference to Fig. 6.1, the design problem for a single-loop system may be described as that of specifying the operation of the digital controller, D, and the continuous network, N, such that the over-all system performance meets the designer's requirements. The approach used to solve this problem depends to a large degree upon the basic performance specification and upon the system constraints in terms of plant characteristics and controller limitations. It is neither possible nor practical to enter into a detailed discussion of all these factors here because of the enormous variation among individual cases and the lack of a unique solution of even one of these cases. It is possible, however, to indicate several alternative approaches which have promise in a fairly broad class of problems and thereby to aid the individual designer select that method which most nearly fits his particular needs. Since this is a book on sampled-data control systems, the primary emphasis here is placed on those particular characteristics of the problem which are introduced by the sampling process. In order to meet this aim with the least possible confusion, attention will be centered on the single-loop error-sampled system of Fig. 6.1, and no extension of these techniques to more complicated cases will be attempted. In general, so long as only linear control systems are considered, the single-loop case displays almost all of the essential peculiarities of the sampled-data design problem.

Two specific aspects of the design problem will be postponed until later chapters. These are the ripple, or intersample behavior, of the output and multirate systems where T_1 and T_2 in Fig. 6.1 are not equal. Each of these problems requires special techniques and is treated separately from the basic single-rate design problem. Of course every design requires satisfactory performance between sampling instants, but, as shown in the next chapter, this problem can be handled by proper design at sampling instants.

117

Within the restriction of design of the single-loop system shown in Fig. 6.1 for $T_1 = T_2 = T$, there are two fundamentally different approaches, based upon the restriction placed on the characteristics of the controller available to the designer. In the application of conventional feedback-system-design techniques usually implied by the frequency methods associated with the names Nyquist, Bode, or Nichols, the designer typically selects a specific network, such as lead, lag, or lag-lead, and tries the resulting design against his specifications. A series of such cut-and-try steps leads, hopefully, to satisfactory performance. The present chapter will outline the extension of these conventional techniques to sampled-data-system design.

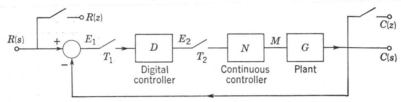

FIG. 6.1. Single-loop error-sampled control system.

A technique for the realization of arbitrary pulse transfer functions for purposes of controller design by the use of essentially conventional RC networks is also presented. This technique was originally suggested by Barker[1] and developed by Sklansky.[59] In the following chapter a method of direct time-domain synthesis will be presented which can be applied, provided that the necessary complexity of controller is available.

6.1 Limitations to the Application of Conventional Techniques to Sampled-data-system Design

A direct attempt to apply conventional frequency techniques to the design of shaping networks for the error-sampled system leads to the block diagram shown in Fig. 6.2. In this case the form of the transfer

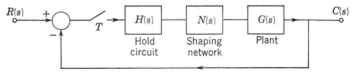

FIG. 6.2. A block diagram for the application of conventional techniques to design.

function of the shaping network $N(s)$ is chosen at the outset as, for example, $(1 + \alpha \tau s)/(1 + \tau s)$, and one wishes to choose α and τ in such a fashion that the system gives satisfactory performance. The reasons for the rather widespread use of frequency techniques are fairly easy to understand. The methods guarantee at the outset that the compensating network will be of a realizable form and, furthermore, successive applications of the cut-and-try procedure are simply and quickly made. In the case of sampled-data systems, only the first of these recommendations can be made without reservation.   Unfortunately, the cut-and-try procedure is neither simple nor quick in the sampled-data case, so that one is typically forced to adopt approximate schemes which have limited ranges of validity.   The source of the difficulty may be readily seen from an analysis of Fig. 6.2.   Using the methods of Chap. 5, one can write

$$\frac{C(z)}{R(z)} = \frac{HNG(z)}{1 + HNG(z)} \tag{6.1}$$

where $HNG(z)$ is the pulse transfer function corresponding to the product $H(s)N(s)G(s)$.   The stability and general performance of the system depends upon the location of the roots of this pulse transfer function, and design depends upon the modification of these root locations by changes in $N(s)$.   The relation between the roots of $1 + HNG(z)$ and the parameters of $N(s)$ is very complicated, and it is this complication which is the source of the difficulty.   In terms of the frequency domain the transfer function can be written as

$$\frac{C(j\omega)}{R^*(j\omega)} = \frac{H(j\omega)N(j\omega)G(j\omega)}{1 + HNG^*(j\omega)}$$

$$= \frac{H(j\omega)N(j\omega)G(j\omega)}{1 + \frac{1}{T}\sum_{-\infty}^{\infty} H(j\omega + jn\omega_0)N(j\omega + jn\omega_0)G(j\omega + jn\omega_0)} \tag{6.2}$$

The function which must be plotted for a Nyquist- or Bode-type analysis and shaping is

$$F(j\omega) = \frac{1}{T}\sum_{-\infty}^{\infty} H(j\omega + jn\omega_0)N(j\omega + jn\omega_0)G(j\omega + jn\omega_0) \tag{6.3}$$

The expression (6.3) shows immediately that no simple product of vectors or addition of logarithms will suffice, in general, to show the effect of a change in $N(j\omega)$ on the over-all plot.   In other words, each new compensating network parameter requires a completely new frequency plot to display its effect on relative stability and other performance characteristics.

   In preference to an exact replotting of the frequency transfer function, the design engineer may take advantage of several alternatives and approximations.   Although it is difficult to give a quantitative measure of the range of validity of the approximate methods, it is clear that qualitatively the determining factor is the ratio of sampling frequency f_0 to system cutoff frequency. In other words, from inspection of (6.2) and (6.3), the source of difficulty introduced by the sampling operation lies in the production of harmonics or sidebands at integral values of f_0. If these sidebands are negligible, then the sampling can be ignored, and, conversely, the extent to which the sampling aspects of the problem must be considered depends upon the extent to which the sidebands are *not* negligible.

In the present chapter a few examples will be studied and an attempt made to develop an experience and "feel" for the extent of the difficulty.

6.2 Summary of Alternative Design Methods

Before describing any of the design alternatives in detail it will be instructive to list the various possibilities and discuss briefly their important characteristics. Although the list which follows is by no means exhaustive, it is felt that the procedures included in this list hold the greatest promise for the practical applications of conventional techniques to the design problem presented by sampled-data control systems.

Method 1. Approximation of sampled-data system with continuous system.

Design step 1.1. Replace the sample and hold operations with a continuous approximation.

Design step 1.2. Design the approximate system on a continuous basis.

Design step 1.3. Check the exact response of the compensated system by z-transform analysis techniques and repeat the design if necessary.

This procedure for the design of sampled-data systems is the simplest possible approach for those familiar with continuous-control-system design, and the method is effective when the sampling rate is relatively high. The simplest approximation to take for the sampler and hold circuit is a through connection. In other words, when the sample rate is very high, one can ignore the fact that the system is sampled at all. This "approximation" is common practice, of course, in many pulsed radar systems and digital-computer or so-called numerical control loops, where it is fairly obvious that the data rate is sufficiently high to permit the designer to ignore the discrete character of some of the data in the system. The development and use of a more sophisticated approximation will be examined later, along with an example problem using the proposed method.

Method 2. Approximation of the effects of the sampler by use of low-order sidebands only.

Design step 2.1.   Make a polar plot of $H(j\omega)G(j\omega)$.

Design step 2.2.   Approximate the sampled loop transfer function $\frac{1}{T} \sum_{-\infty}^{\infty} H(j\omega + jn\omega_0)G(j\omega + jn\omega_0)$ by a vector addition of a few sideband terms to the fundamental plot obtained in step 2.1.

Design step 2.3.   Select a network transfer function $N(j\omega)$ by conventional methods, using such aids as M circles if desired, and replot the compensated loop transfer function

$$\frac{1}{T} \sum_{-\infty}^{\infty} N(j\omega + jn\omega_0)G(j\omega + jn\omega_0)H(j\omega + jn\omega_0)$$

using again only a few terms in the expansion.

Design step 2.4.   After repeated application of step 2.3 indicates a probably satisfactory design, check the performance by conventional z-transform techniques or by experimentation.   Repeat the last two steps until the specifications are met.

The accuracy as well as the difficulty of application of this method, which was first proposed in detail by Linvill,[38,39] increases with the number of terms included in the approximation to (6.3).   The principal virtue of the method lies in its immediate use of well-known design techniques with a modification of the plots to include what might be called the "first-order" effects of sampling.

A rough check on the accuracy of the method is possible by comparing the approximate plot of $\frac{1}{T} \sum_{-\infty}^{\infty} G(j\omega + jn\omega_0)H(j\omega + jn\omega_0)$ with the exact plot obtained with z-transform methods.   A specific example is used for illustration later in this chapter.

Method 3.   Introduction of a sampling switch between plant and network.

Design step 3.1.   Approximate the continuous connection between the network and the plant by a fictitious sampler and hold (see Fig. 6.3).

Design step 3.2.   Design for the pulse transform of the shaping network $N(z)$, using either frequency- or time-domain (Chap. 7) methods.

Design step 3.3.   Obtain the continuous transfer function $N(s)$ which corresponds to $N(z)$.

Design step 3.4.   Check the design with exact analysis techniques.

This method, which was originally proposed by Sklansky,[59] aims to use a fictitious sampler to perform the separation of transfer functions necessary to apply conventional shaping techniques directly. The mathematical sampling represented by T_2 in Fig. 6.3 is usually taken as a higher rate than the basic sampling rate T, in which case the system is a multirate problem, which will be treated in a later chapter. The hold operation indicated by H_2 is part of the numerical or mathematical approximation to a continuous connection between plant and shaping network and

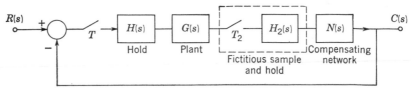

FIG. 6.3. Block diagram for approximate design procedure, using mathematical sampling between plant and network.

consequently need not be physically realizable. The use of nonphysical extrapolators permits considerably greater freedom in the choice of hold and consequently greater accuracy in the approximation. This method is comparable to method 2 (Linvill's method) in range of applicability and accuracy.

Method 4. Time-domain solution for continuous network compensation.

Design step 4.1. From considerations of the over-all transfer function from input to output specify the pulse transfer function $HNG(z)$.

Design step 4.2. Find a continuous transfer function $F(s)$ corresponding to the pulse transfer function obtained in step 4.1.

Design step 4.3. Solve for $N(s)$ as

$$N(s) = \frac{F(s)}{G(s)H(s)}$$

This method, originally proposed by Truxal[64] as an extension of Guillemin's control-system synthesis procedure to sampled-data systems, has great intuitive appeal but has not yet been satisfactorily applied in many practical cases. Because of the complicated relation between $N(s)$ and the pulse transfer function of the system, no simple criterion exists to guide the initial choice of pulse transfer function in such a manner that the final network will be practical. The cut-and-try process is rather like a random search because failure at one step does not point toward success at later steps. Cut and try does not converge in this method. This peculiarity will be demonstrated with examples later in the chapter.

Method 5. Pulsed-network compensation.

Design step 5.1.   Represent the pulse transfer function $HG(z)$ in the form (polar plot or root locus) which is most familiar to the designer.

Design step 5.2.   A pulse transfer function of a form realizable by practical networks (to be discussed in detail later) is selected and the new plot or locus drawn for $N(z)HG(z)$ and evaluated directly or by time-response calculation.

Design step 5.3.   The selected network is realized by a continuous network (RC) *separated* from the plant and hold by a switch.

This method, which was also proposed by Sklansky,[59] truly applies conventional methods to sampled-data systems.

The fundamental procedure of plotting frequency data and shaping by forming the product of the plant and network pulse transfer functions is exactly analogous to conventional continuous-design techniques.   One may even apply constant magnitude "M circles" to the design to ensure a specific maximum response for real frequencies.   In terms of the root locus, the rules[64] for loci construction are exactly the same as in the continuous case, although for sampled-data systems the unit circle replaces the imaginary axis as the boundary of stability and the negative real axis and origin in the z plane have significance not ordinarily found in the s plane.

6.3 Design by Continuous Approximation of Sample and Hold. *Method* 1

The fundamental step in the application of this method lies in determining a useful and realistic continuous approximation to the sample and hold operation.   Such an approximation may be derived and evaluated either by time- or frequency-domain considerations, but it is essential that the approximation be as simple as possible.   The first application of the method will be made to the most common hold circuit, which is the clamp, or zero-order hold.   This circuit was discussed in some detail in Chap. 3 and is described by the transfer function

$$H(j\omega) = Te^{-j\omega T/2} \frac{\sin \omega T/2}{\omega T/2} \tag{6.4}$$

If this element is followed by a plant with the transfer function $G(j\omega)$, then the over-all loop pulse transfer function is

$$HG^*(j\omega) = \frac{1}{T} \sum_{-\infty}^{\infty} Te^{-jT\frac{(\omega + n\omega_0)}{2}} \frac{\sin\left[\left(\frac{\omega + n\omega_0}{2}\right)T\right]}{\frac{[(\omega + n\omega_0)T]}{2}} G(j\omega + jn\omega_0) \tag{6.5}$$

If T is sufficiently small, or, equivalently, if ω_0 is high, and $G(j\omega)$ is low-pass, all harmonics can be neglected, and the transfer function in (6.5) reduces to

$$HG^*(j\omega) \cong e^{-jT\omega/2}\frac{\sin \omega T/2}{\omega T/2} G(j\omega) \tag{6.6}$$

Actually, for low frequencies, $\dfrac{\sin \omega T/2}{\omega T/2}$ is approximately unity, so that finally

$$HG^*(j\omega) \cong e^{-j\omega T/2}G(j\omega) \tag{6.7}$$

In words, the loop transfer function is approximately the equivalent of replacing the sample and hold operation by a pure time delay of half a

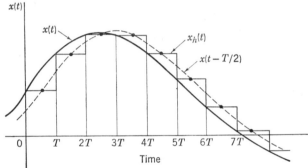

Fɪɢ. 6.4. Sketch showing the delay of $T/2$ sec introduced by the zero-order hold.

sampling period. This approximation may also be quickly obtained by consideration of time-domain plots of a signal and its sampled and clamped resultant as shown in Fig. 6.4. The boxcar output of the zero-order hold seems to follow the input curve delayed by $T/2$ sec. In terms of block diagrams the system of Fig. 6.5a is replaced or approximated by the continuous system of Fig. 6.5b. The applications of standard frequency design methods to the approximate system are straightforward, as will be illustrated by an example.

EXAMPLE   *Method* 1

As an illustrative example of the application of the approximating technique outlined above, the compensation of the system shown in Fig. 6.6 will be considered. For the purposes of this example the sampling rate will be taken to be 1 per second, and the Bode diagram or logarithmic frequency plots used to suggest the compensation required. A polar plot or Nichols chart could be as easily used, of course. The separate logarithmic plots of gain and phase are chosen arbitrarily to illustrate the use of a conventional technique with this particular approximation. The plots of the uncompensated gain and phase are shown in Fig. 6.7 for a value of loop gain constant of unity. For the purposes of this example let it be supposed that the objectives of the design are to maintain the low frequency gain at unity and to increase the phase margin from the indicated 17° to approximately 50° to ensure satisfactory performance. The time response will be checked to evaluate the final design in terms of overshoot and general transient behavior.

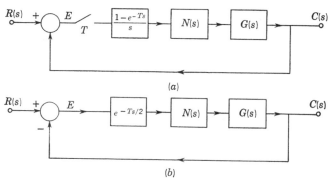

(a)

(b)

Fig. 6.5. A sampled-data system and the approximating continuous system.

The first network one might apply for the stated purposes is a lag network. In general terms, one can say from a consideration of the Bode plot that greater benefit can be derived from a lag network than

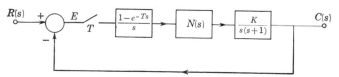

Fig. 6.6. Block diagram for illustrative example.

from a lead network because of the very rapid increase in phase—fall of phase margin—as the linear phase from the delay $e^{-s/2}$ begins to be effective. A lead network has only limited effectiveness against this rapidly increasing lag angle. The exact location of the lag network and the separation of break frequencies are matters for individual judgment and component size requirements. As a first attempt, the network transfer function

$$N(j\omega) = 0.3 \frac{j\omega + 0.2}{j\omega + 0.06}$$

will be tried. The modified plots of gain and phase are shown in Fig. 6.8, where it may be observed that the phase margin at 0-db gain, "gain crossover," has been increased to about 47°. A slight additional improvement can be effected by the use of a lag-lead network as described by the transfer function

$$N(s) = 0.9 \frac{(j\omega + 0.2)(j\omega + 1)}{(j\omega + 0.06)(j\omega + 3)}$$

The total gain and phase characteristics of the compensated system are shown in Fig. 6.9, where it is observed that the phase margin has

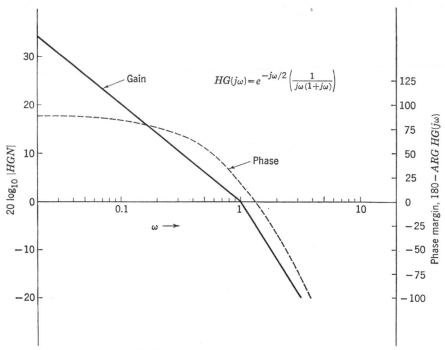

Fig. 6.7. Bode plot for uncompensated system.

been further increased to 60°. The introduction of networks having different transfer characteristics than those described above is easily accomplished on the gain and phase curves, and any conventional rules observed by a particular designer can be applied to this approximate model. The ultimate limitation on the use of the method is exactly the same as that which applies to the use of frequency methods in the design of continuous systems. The designer does not know in advance the exact effect of a change in the frequency characteristics on the time response. The closed-loop step responses which correspond to the frequency plots of Figs. 6.7, 6.8, and 6.9 are sketched in Fig. 6.10. Examination of these time-response plots indicate that application of very simple conventional frequency-response ideas leads to an improvement in the time response but that the extent of the improvement is not included in the design method and is not known until after a tentative design is completed.

Although the clamp, or zero-order hold, is the most common hold circuit used in sampled-data control systems, the method of approximat-

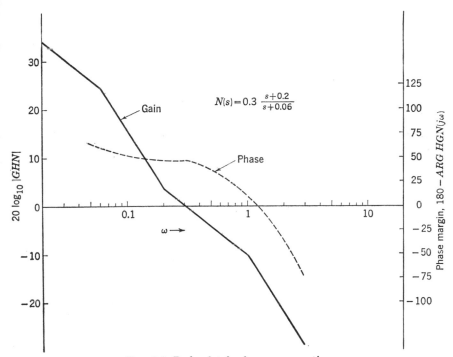

$$N(s) = 0.3 \frac{s+0.2}{s+0.06}$$

FIG. 6.8. Bode plot for lag compensation.

ing the sample and hold operation by a continuous network is obviously not limited to that case. As a matter of fact, the higher-order-hold networks lead to generally simpler approximate continuous networks than that necessary for the clamp. The transfer function of the first-order hold, for example, is

$$H_1(s) = T(1 + Ts)\left(\frac{1 - e^{-Ts}}{Ts}\right)^2 \tag{6.8}$$

which may be reduced to

$$H_1(j\omega) = T(1 + j\omega T)e^{-j\omega T}\left(\frac{\sin \omega T/2}{\omega T/2}\right)^2 \tag{6.9}$$

for real frequencies. If this hold circuit is followed by a plant with the transfer function $G(j\omega)$, then the pulse transfer function of the combina-

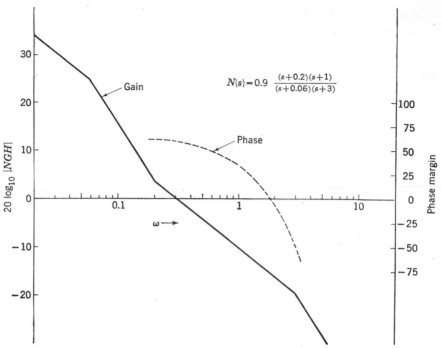

$$N(s) = 0.9 \ \frac{(s+0.2)(s+1)}{(s+0.06)(s+3)}$$

FIG. 6.9. Bode plot for lag-lead compensation.

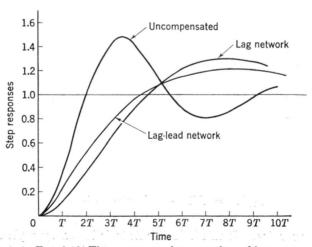

FIG. 6.10. Time responses for example problems.

tion is given by

$$H_1G^*(j\omega) = \sum_{-\infty}^{\infty} (1 + j\omega T + jn\omega_0 T)e^{-j\omega T - jn\omega_0 T} \left\{ \frac{\sin\left[(\omega + n\omega_0)T/2\right]}{(\omega + n\omega_0)T/2} \right\}^2$$

$$G(j\omega + jn\omega_0) \quad (6.10)$$

If all harmonics are ignored and the $(\sin x/x)^2$ term approximated by unity,

$$H_1G^*(j\omega) \cong (1 + j\omega T)e^{-j\omega T}G(j\omega)$$

$$\cong G(j\omega)\frac{(1 + j\omega T)}{e^{j\omega T}}$$

$$\cong G(j\omega) \quad (6.11)$$

From (6.11) it is evident that the first-order hold and the sampler may be replaced by unity to the same degree of approximation that requires a delay to represent the clamp. Although this approximation is crude, it

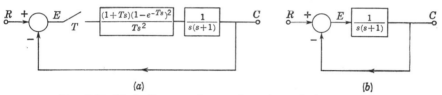

(a)   (b)

FIG. 6.11. Block diagram of approximately equivalent systems.

is useful if the transmission of $G(j\omega)$ is very small at frequencies above π/T radians/sec. As an example of the nature of the approximation, consider the system shown in Fig. 6.11, where the continuous system of Fig. 6.11b results if the sampler and hold of the system of Fig. 6.11a are replaced by a through connection. The step responses of these systems are plotted in Fig. 6.12, where it is obvious that the equivalence between the two systems is not impressive. Actually, the sampled-data-system response closely resembles the response of the continuous system with a gain of 4, rather than a gain of 1. It is not evident from the expression for the first-order hold, (6.10), however, that this should be so.

Only the simplest possible approximation to the zero- and first-order-hold circuits has been considered in this outline of one method for the design of sampled-data control systems. The extension of the method to establish more sophisticated approximations suitable to a wider range of devices is obviously possible but has limited value. When the simplest approximation derived above is not valid, then the system designer would be best advised to abandon the method altogether rather than try to refine it with more complicated approximations.

6.4 Design by the Use of the Most Important Sidebands Due to Sampling. *Method 2*

As was mentioned in Sec. 6.2, method 2, which was first proposed by W. K. Linvill,[38] lends itself most easily to the use of the polar plot or Nyquist diagram as a design tool. Application of the design steps out-

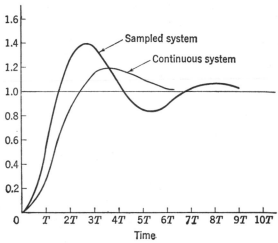

FIG. 6.12. Step responses of systems of Fig. 6.11.

lined in Sec. 6.2 is straightforward and will be illustrated shortly by the same example used for method 1. Method 2 has two principal advantages over method 1. The first of these is the fact that by using more and more sidebands it is possible in a perfectly straightforward manner to improve the accuracy of the method. Obviously, there is a limit, determined by the amount of labor involved, to how far this process can be carried, but the fact remains that if a particular part of the frequency response is critical, an improvement in the approximate plot of those frequencies can be made. The second advantage of this method is that a measure of the validity of the approximation can be made relatively quickly by plotting the exact polar plot for the loop transfer function from the pulse transfer function of the system. This check procedure is simple to apply on a polar plot but rather obscure on the Bode diagram.

The basic idea of this method is the approximation of

$$G^*(j\omega) = \frac{1}{T} \sum_{-\infty}^{\infty} G(j\omega + jn\omega_0) \tag{6.12}$$

by a few terms of the summation. The construction of the approximate plot of (6.12) can be considerably simplified by the observation of the following facts.   First, $G^*(j\omega)$ is periodic, with period ω_0, so that the approximate plot need be constructed over a range of width ω_0 only. Secondly, $G^*(-j\omega)$ is the conjugate of $G^*(j\omega)$, which permits the designer to construct the entire plot from the half obtained for positive frequencies. In other words, one need consider $G^*(j\omega)$ only over the range $0 \leqq \omega \leqq \omega_0/2$.   The number of terms required to give a reasonable approximation depends upon the accuracy required and the speed with which the series (6.12) converges.   For the method to be effective, it is necessary that $G(j\omega)$ approach zero at least as rapidly as $1/\omega^2$ for frequencies above ω_0, and it is preferable if the cutoff is even more rapid.   As an example of the limitation of the method, consider the system shown in Fig. 6.13.   In this example, the plant is of first order only, and the series (6.12) does not converge sufficiently rapidly to make the approximate method useful.

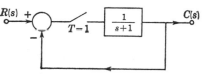

FIG. 6.13. Block diagram for example illustrating limitation on use of method 2.

The plot of $G(j\omega)$ for this example is shown in Fig. 6.14, along with the exact $G^*(j\omega)$.   The construction of three terms of the series for $G(j1)$ is shown, and it is obvious from this construction that an accurate approximation cannot be made in this case.   Although the higher-sideband terms are very small in amplitude, they converge so slowly that poor accuracy results.   The difficulty is obvious in the simple example used here for

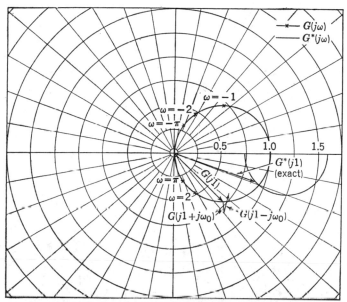

FIG. 6.14. Polar plots showing construction of approximate plots.

illustration, but in more complicated problems considerable care must be exercised to ensure that the approximation is near enough to the exact plot. A more practical design problem is given in the next example, where the sideband contribution is actually negligible.

EXAMPLE   *Method 2*

The method of Linvill will be applied to the same system used for illustrating method 1. The block diagram of the system is shown in Fig. 6.6. The pulse transfer function for this system is given by

$$HG^*(j\omega) = \sum_{-\infty}^{\infty} e^{-j(U_n/2)} \frac{\sin U_n/2}{U_n/2} \frac{1}{jU_n(1 + jU_n)} \qquad (6.13)$$

where $U_n = \omega + n\omega_0$. A plot of the first term in (6.13), which is $H(j\omega)G(j\omega)$, is shown in Fig. 6.15, with points on the exact $HG^*(j\omega)$ indicated. From these points it is obvious that all sideband terms may be ignored in the design of the system.

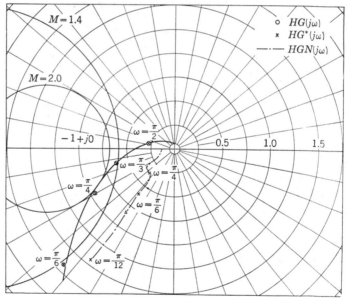

FIG. 6.15. Polar plot for illustrative example 2.

From the polar plot it is seen that a smaller frequency peak will require a lead network near 1 radian/sec, and a lag network, if added, should be at frequencies below about 0.3 radian/sec. The plot of the compensated system with the network

$$N(j\omega) = 0.9 \frac{(j\omega + 0.2)(j\omega + 1)}{(j\omega + 0.06)(j\omega + 3)} \qquad (6.14)$$

is shown in dashed lines on Fig. 6.15. The compensation has reduced the frequency overshoot from 2.0 to approximately 1.25, which is probably satisfactory. A transient response test could be made to determine the exact nature of the system response to a particular type of input if that is necessary. For this example, the pertinent step responses are shown in Fig. 6.10.

The two examples used here to illustrate Linvill's method lie almost at opposite extremes as far as the applicability of the method is concerned. The first-order example plotted in Fig. 6.14 does not permit use of the method at all for reasonable ease and accuracy, and the second example required only one term for satisfactory accuracy. The evaluation of the method for any particular system can be quickly made by a comparison of the loop transfer function $1/TG(j\omega)$ with the exact pulse transfer function $G^*(j\omega)$. Without this check, the designer is not able to say with confidence that one or two or even ten terms satisfactorily approximate the true loop transfer function.

Method 3, in which the continuous network $N(s)$ is separated from the plant by a fictitious sampler and hold as shown in Fig. 6.3, is most useful only when the sampling period T_2 of the fictitious sampler is considerably smaller than that of the first actual sampler. If the sampling periods T and T_2 are the same, this technique is no more accurate than that of method 1. In choosing T_2 to be a fraction of T, the system becomes a multirate system, which is treated in Chap. 9, so that no detailed example will be given until the theory is more fully developed. The design steps outlined in Sec. 6.3 are self-explanatory for the case of equal sampling periods and can be extended to the case of multirate systems using the techniques developed in Chap. 9.

6.5 Design of Continuous Network by Time-domain Specifications.
Method 4

This design method is based upon the following calculations. For the single-loop feedback system shown in Fig. 6.2 one can write

$$\frac{C(z)}{R(z)} = \frac{HNG(z)}{1 + HNG(z)} = K(z) \tag{6.15}$$

and, consequently,

$$HNG(z) = \frac{K(z)}{1 - K(z)} \tag{6.16}$$

If now, one were to specify $K(z)$, the *closed-loop* pulse transfer function from input to output, then, from (6.16) one can calculate the open-loop transfer function $NHG(z)$. From this open-loop pulse transfer function the designer may then specify an open-loop *continuous* transfer function which has the desired characteristics and solve for the necessary compensating network. The difficulty with the method lies in the initial selection of a $K(z)$ such that the resulting continuous network is realizable and practical. There does not seem to be a simple method for introducing the necessary constraints on $K(z)$ for this purpose. It should be mentioned, however, that this particular problem has not been seriously studied because of the development of the more attractive time-domain design methods for digital controllers which are described in Chap. 7.

The nature of the difficulty in the application of method 4 is best illustrated by example. Consider the basic system shown in Fig. 6.2 and assume a zero-order-hold circuit. A typical specification on the over-all transfer function $K(z)$ might be that the system follow a first-order polynomial in time (ramp) with zero steady-state error. That is, the steady-state value of the error is to be zero. For the system being considered, the error transform is

$$
\begin{aligned}
E(z) &= R(z) - C(z) \\
&= R(z)[1 - K(z)] \\
&= \frac{Tz^{-1}}{(1 - z^{-1})^2}[1 - K(z)]
\end{aligned}
$$ (6.17)

From the final-value theorem and (6.17)

$$
\lim_{n \to \infty} e(nT) = \lim_{z \to 1} (1 - z^{-1}) \frac{Tz^{-1}}{(1 - z^{-1})^2}[1 - K(z)]
$$ (6.18)

Inspection of (6.18) shows that, if the final value of $e(nT)$ is to be zero, then $1 - K(z)$ must contain factor $(1 - z^{-1})^2$. The simplest possible transfer function which satisfies this condition is

$$
K(z) = 2z^{-1} - z^{-2}
$$ (6.19)

For the control system shown in Fig. 6.2, direct analysis shows that if $H(s)$ is a zero-order hold,

$$
\begin{aligned}
(1 - z^{-1})\mathcal{Z}\frac{NG}{s} &= \frac{K(z)}{1 - K(z)} \\
&= \frac{2z^{-1} - z^{-2}}{(1 - z^{-1})^2}
\end{aligned}
$$ (6.20)

Therefore, the transfer function of the compensating network must satisfy the relation

$$
\begin{aligned}
\mathcal{Z}\frac{NG}{s} &= \frac{2z^{-1} - z^{-2}}{(1 - z^{-1})^3} \\
&= \frac{z(2z - 1)}{(z - 1)^3}
\end{aligned}
$$ (6.21)

if the over-all pulse transfer function is to be given by (6.19).   There is no unique continuous transfer function which satisfies (6.21).   The time function corresponding to the transform NG/s must have a specified set of values at sample instants to satisfy (6.21) but may take any shape between sample values of time without affecting (6.21) at all.   However, there are only a limited number of admissible or *practical* forms for NG/s. In order to exercise some control over the behavior of the output between sampling instants it is desirable that the selected continuous transform be as nearly "low-pass" as possible.   The simplest and most direct method of obtaining such a transform is to do a partial-fraction expansion of the pulse transform into elements which can be looked up in a table of transform pairs.   For example, the poles of (6.21) are all located at unity, so that the continuous transform has all its poles at zero.   Therefore, one should write

$$ \mathcal{Z} \frac{NG}{s} = \frac{AT^2}{2} \frac{z(z+1)}{(z-1)^3} + \frac{BTz}{(z-1)^2} + \frac{Cz}{(z-1)} \qquad (6.22) $$

Simple matching of coefficients between (6.22) and (6.21) shows that in this case

$$ A = \frac{1}{2T^2} $$
$$ B = \frac{3}{2T} $$
$$ C = 0 $$

and, consequently, associating the Laplace transforms and z transforms from the table in Appendix I and simplifying,

$$ \frac{N(s)G(s)}{s} = \frac{1+3Ts}{2T^2s^3} \qquad (6.23) $$

If the plant $G(s)$ happens to be a pure integration then this problem is nicely solved with the compensation network

$$ N(s) = \frac{1+3Ts}{s} \qquad (6.24) $$

which is a practical transfer function.   However, if $G(s)$ has a greater excess of poles over zero than unity, then the compensation network will have more zeros than poles and the system will not be practical.   In addition to the difficulties attendant on the realization of networks having more zeros than poles, in the present case such a compensation network would cause impulses and possibly higher-order singularity functions to be applied to the plant.   A possible way to increase the number of poles in the compensating network would be to add to the transform given by

(6.23) other terms which would not add to the pulse transfer function. For example, one could add terms of the form

$$\frac{\alpha_i}{(s + a_i)^2 + (\pi/T)^2}$$

with arbitrary a's and α's without changing the pulse transfer function since the z transform of all these addition terms is zero. This method is treacherous, however, because these terms add to the intersample ripple and can cause enormous "hidden oscillation" in the output of the system, as shown in Sec. 8.5. There is a certain arbitrariness to the selection of the $K(z)$ given by (6.19), but no other method seems to lead to a specification which can be realized by a practical tandem network. In particular, the methods of Chap. 7 for the design of digital controllers are not satisfactory for the problem of tandem network compensation. However, by a slight modification of the structure and the possible introduction of an additional sample and hold circuit, one can avoid the problem completely, as shown in the next section.

6.6 Design of Pulsed-network Compensators. *Method 5*

The original work on pulsed networks for sampled-data control systems was done by Sklansky,[59] and the treatment here follows that work. A block diagram of the basic system being considered is shown in Fig. 6.16.

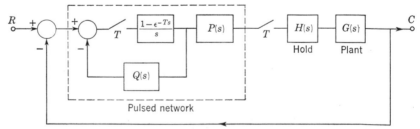

FIG. 6.16. Pulsed network compensation of sampled-data system.

In this figure, the transforms $P(s)$ and $Q(s)$ represent the transfer functions of RC networks and supply the shaping or compensating action in the control loop. The design of the pulsed network for a control application may follow either of at least two directions. In the first place, the designer may select a specific form for the pulsed network and obtain the best design of the system in terms of the best parameter values of his chosen network. This is referred to as conventional design. A second alternative is to select at the outset the over-all transfer function which satisfies his needs and to calculate the transfer function of the network which will do the job. This alternative is the time-domain synthesis which failed in method 4 but which succeeds here because of the sampling switch which separates the network from the plant. With pulsed networks the designer can control both the poles and the zeros of the compensating network and ensure success of the design at the outset. These ideas are developed in some detail in Chap. 7. For the present purpose it will suffice to show later in this section that any realizable linear digital-controller pulse transfer function can be realized with a pulsed RC network.

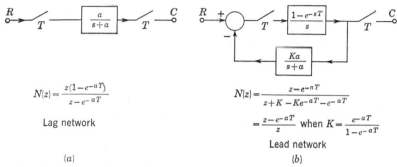

$$N(z) = \frac{z(1-e^{-aT})}{z-e^{-aT}}$$

Lag network

$$N(z) = \frac{z-e^{-aT}}{z+K-Ke^{-aT}-e^{-aT}}$$

$$= \frac{z-e^{-aT}}{z} \text{ when } K = \frac{e^{-aT}}{1-e^{-aT}}$$

Lead network

(a)   (b)

FIG. 6.17. Block diagrams for typical pulsed-network transfer functions.

The application of conventional techniques to the design of pulsed-network compensators requires the analysis of a few simple examples to give the designer a selection of tools for various requirements. Figure 6.17 shows symbolically a few examples with their corresponding pulse

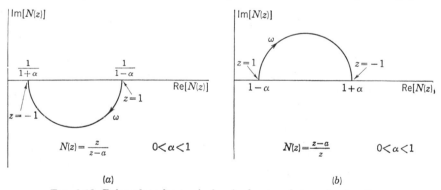

$$N(z) = \frac{z}{z-a} \qquad 0 < \alpha < 1$$

$$N(z) = \frac{z-a}{z} \qquad 0 < \alpha < 1$$

(a)   (b)

FIG. 6.18. Polar plots for typical pulsed-network transfer functions.

transfer functions. The polar plots of the variations of these transfer functions as z moves around the upper half of the unit circle are shown in Fig. 6.18. It is clear from these diagrams that the configurations shown behave like lag and lead networks, respectively, and the application of these plots to polar-diagram design is obvious. Pulsed networks can also be used with pole-zero design methods using the root-locus method.

EXAMPLE   *Method 5*

The design of a pulsed network to compensate the system shown in Fig. 6.6 may be easily done from root-locus or pole-zero considerations. The pulse transfer function of the plant and hold combination is

$$HG(z) = 0.368 \frac{z + 0.719}{(z - 1)(z - 0.368)} \tag{6.25}$$

which may be represented by the pole-zero constellation and corresponding root locus shown in Fig. 6.19.   The relative damping of

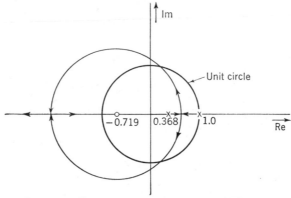

FIG. 6.19. Gain root locus for system of Fig. 6.6.

the transient terms corresponding to the poles of the closed-loop transfer function depends upon the distance of these poles from the unit circle.   Poles on the unit circle correspond to transients which do not decay with time, and poles at the origin of the z plane correspond to transient terms which vanish completely in a finite time.   In general terms, the objective of the design is to bring the closed-loop roots close to or exactly to the origin.   Any of the well-known techniques of root-locus modification may be used toward this end, using either the simple networks shown in Fig. 6.17 or more complicated structures.   In the present example, a very satisfactory result can be obtained by use of the "lead" structure of Fig. 6.17b to cancel the zero and the pole of the $GH(z)$ transfer function at 0.368.   To accomplish this end, it is necessary to select the gain K and the time constant a of the compensating network in such a fashion that

$$\begin{aligned} N(z) &= \frac{z - e^{-aT}}{z + K - Ke^{-aT} - e^{-aT}} \\ &= \frac{z - 0.368}{z + 0.719} \end{aligned} \tag{6.26}$$

The necessary values are, for $T = 1$ sec,

$$a = 1$$
$$K = 1.72$$

With the compensating network so chosen, the loop pulse transfer function reduces to

$$N(z)HG(z) = \frac{0.368}{z - 1} \qquad (6.27)$$

and, from elementary root-locus considerations, it may be seen that increasing the forward gain by a factor of 2.72 to unity moves the pole of the closed loop to the origin. The over-all pulse transfer function $K(z)$ is thus reduced to

$$\frac{C(z)}{R(z)} = z^{-1} \qquad (6.28)$$

which describes a system which, at sampling instants, represents a pure delay of one sampling period and *no* transient beyond one sampling period. The extension of these ideas of cancellation compensation and the limitations on the method will be developed in some detail in the next chapter.

The use of pulsed RC networks to provide the necessary compensating transfer functions for sampled-data systems is considerably more general and more flexible than is indicated by the special examples worked out in Fig. 6.17. As a matter of fact, Sklansky[59] has shown that any linear realizable pulse transfer function may be realized by a pulsed RC network, of the general form shown in Fig. 6.16. The proof of this important result follows from a consideration of the characteristics of the basic pulse network transfer function and the general form of the realizable pulse transfer function of a finite system. The latter is

$$D(z) = \frac{\sum\limits_{i=0}^{p} a_i z^{-i}}{\sum\limits_{j=0}^{q} b_j z^{-j}} \qquad (6.29)$$

where the a_i and b_j are real and $b_0 \neq 0$. As shown in Chap. 4, the restriction on b_0 is necessary to ensure that the linear system described by (6.29) operates only on present and past and not on future samples. The system is finite (stores a finite number of past-input and past-output data values) if p and q are finite. From an elementary analysis of the pulsed network in Fig. 6.16 it is clear that

$$N(z) = \frac{(1 - z^{-1})Z[P(s)/s]}{1 + (1 - z^{-1})Z[Q(s)/s]} \qquad (6.30)$$

is the pulse transfer function of the network. The expression (6.30) can be factored into two terms:

$$N(z) = D_s(z)D_f(z) \qquad (6.31)$$

where

$$D_s(z) = (1 - z^{-1})Z\frac{P(s)}{s} \qquad (6.32)$$

and

$$D_f(z) = \frac{1}{1 + (1 - z^{-1})Z[Q(s)/s]} \qquad (6.33)$$

The factor $D_s(z)$ is basically the result of the series RC network, $P(s)$, and $D_f(z)$ is the result of the feedback network, $Q(s)$. The proof of the theorem that (6.29) can always be realized with the form of (6.30) depends upon the demonstration that $D_s(z)$ can be realized with essentially arbitrary zeros and $D_f(z)$ can be realized to provide arbitrary poles.

If $P(s)$ is a realizable RC transfer function, then all the poles of $P(s)$ are simple and lie on the negative real axis of the s plane. A partial-fraction expansion of $P(s)/s$ is thus of the form

$$\frac{P(s)}{s} = \sum_i \frac{k_i}{s + s_i} \qquad s_i \text{ real}, \ -\infty < s_i \le 0 \qquad (6.34)$$

where the k_i are arbitrary, except for a constant multiplying factor, and one of the s_i is zero. The z transform of $P(s)/s$ is therefore

$$Z\frac{P(s)}{s} = \sum_i \frac{k_i}{1 - \alpha_i z^{-1}}$$

$$= \sum_i \frac{k_i z}{z - \alpha_i} \qquad (6.35)$$

where $\alpha_i = e^{-s_i T}$ and one of the α_i is unity. Therefore, the form of $D_s(z)$ is, from (6.32)

$$D_s(z) = \frac{z - 1}{z} Z\frac{P(s)}{s}$$

$$= \sum_i \frac{k_i(z - 1)}{z - \alpha_i} \qquad (6.36)$$

The expression (6.36) has the following properties:
1. The poles of $D_s(z)$ are in the range $0 < z_i < 1$.
2. The zeros of $D_s(z)$ are arbitrary.

The transfer function for the feedback portion of the pulsed network can be shown from (6.33) to satisfy the relation

$$\frac{z-1}{z} \, \mathrm{Z} \, \frac{Q(s)}{s} = \frac{1}{D_f(z)} - 1 \tag{6.37}$$

Since the left-hand side of (6.37) is of exactly the same form as the right side of (6.36), it is immediately possible to say:
1. The zeros of $D_f(z)$ are in the range $0 < z_i < 1$.
2. The poles of $D_f(z)$ are arbitrary.

From the two sets of conditions on the characteristics of $D_f(z)$ and $D_s(z)$ given above it is possible to state rules for the realization of an arbitrary physically realizable transfer function in the form of a pulsed network as follows:

Step 1.   Factor the desired $D(z)$ into $D_s(z)D_f(z)$ so that all finite zeros outside the range $0 < z_i < 1$ are contained in $D_s(z)$ and all poles outside this range are in $D_f(z)$.

Step 2.   Assign poles and zeros of $D(z)$ which fall inside the range $0 < z_i < 1$ to either $D_s(z)$ or $D_f(z)$, respectively, so that $D_s(z)$ has no poles and $D_f(z)$ has no zeros for infinite values of z.   This is necessary in order to prevent the resultant network from being physically unrealizable in that it would be required to predict future values of the sample sequence.   If there are not enough such factors in the desired pulse transfer function $D(z)$, add arbitrary poles in the range $0 < a_i < 1$ to $D_s(z)$ and identical corresponding zeros to $D_f(z)$ until $D_s(\infty)$ and $1/D_f(\infty)$ are both less than infinity.

Step 3.   Determine $P(s)$ from the inverse relation

$$P(s) = s\mathrm{Z}^{-1} \frac{zD_s(z)}{z-1} \tag{6.38}$$

and find $Q(s)$ from

$$Q(s) = s\mathrm{Z}^{-1} \left[\frac{z}{z-1} \frac{1 - D_f(z)}{D_f(z)} \right] \tag{6.39}$$

where Z^{-1} signifies the Laplace transform corresponding to the z transform.

The simplest way to perform the inversions indicated in (6.38) and (6.39) is to expand $D_s(z)/(z-1)$ in partial fractions, multiply by z and look up, or write by inspection, the corresponding continuous transform.

As an example of the synthesis of a pulse transfer function, first consider $D(z) = z^{-1}$.   This function has a pole at zero which, from step 1, must be contained in $D_f(z)$.   Therefore, after the first step, the two factors are

$$D_s(z) = 1$$
$$D_f(z) = \frac{1}{z}$$

Although all the factors of $D(z)$ have been used, the reciprocal of $D_f(z)$ is not bounded at infinity, so that a common factor must be added, such as $z - \alpha$. One such factor is sufficient, and the final results are

$$D_s(z) = \frac{1}{z - \alpha}$$
$$D_f(z) = \frac{z - \alpha}{z} \qquad (6.40)$$

From (6.38),

$$\mathcal{Z}\frac{P(s)}{s} = \frac{z}{(z - 1)(z - \alpha)}$$
$$= \frac{1}{1 - \alpha}\frac{z}{z - 1} - \frac{1}{1 - \alpha}\frac{z}{z - \alpha}$$

and, from the tables in Appendix I,

$$\frac{P(s)}{s} = \frac{1}{1 - \alpha}\frac{1}{s} - \frac{1}{1 - \alpha}\frac{1}{s + a}$$
$$P(s) = \frac{a}{1 - \alpha}\frac{1}{s + a} \qquad (6.41)$$

where $\alpha = e^{-aT}$.
From (6.39),

$$\mathcal{Z}\frac{Q(s)}{s} = \frac{z}{z - 1}\frac{\alpha}{z - \alpha}$$
$$= \frac{\alpha}{1 - \alpha}\left(\frac{z}{z - 1} - \frac{z}{z - \alpha}\right)$$

and

$$Q(s) = \frac{\alpha}{1 - \alpha}\frac{a}{s + a} \qquad (6.42)$$

for $\alpha = e^{-aT}$.

As a second example consider $D(z) = z/(z - 1)$, which is a pure integrator. In this case the transfer function has a zero at the origin which must be assigned to $D_s(z)$ and a pole at unity which must be assigned to $D_f(z)$. Therefore, after the first step,

$$D_s(z) = z$$
$$D_f(z) = \frac{1}{z - 1}$$

Neither of these preliminary functions has satisfactory behavior at infinity, so that a common factor $z - \alpha$ is added to give

$$D_s(z) = \frac{z}{z - \alpha}$$

$$D_f(z) = \frac{z - \alpha}{z - 1} \tag{6.43}$$

The use of (6.38) and (6.39) is straightforward and leads to the results

$$P(s) = \frac{1}{1 - \alpha} \frac{(1 - \alpha)s + a}{s + a}$$

$$Q(s) = -\frac{a}{s + a} \tag{6.44}$$

where $e^{-aT} = \alpha$ as before. The selection of the time constant $1/a$ introduced in the procedure outlined above is arbitrary and can be chosen from the practical considerations of size and impedance level. It should be emphasized that the synthesis procedures given here for pulsed RC networks require, in general, a gain factor in series with $Q(s)$ and $P(s)$. This additional gain can, in most practical situations, be associated with the zero-order-hold circuits which follow the two sampling switches. It should also be noticed that no restriction is placed by this design procedure on the hold circuit which precedes the plant. In practice, one can frequently arrange the design so that all the zeros of $N(z)$ are in the restricted range $0 < z < 1$ and can be realized by a pulsed network with $P(s) = 1$. In this case, only one sampling switch and one hold circuit are required for the design.

The complete development of specifications for digital controllers is given in the next chapter. Obviously, any of the designs given there can be realized by the pulsed networks described here if that is desirable.

6.7 Summary

This chapter has outlined five methods for the design of sampled-data control systems by the use of conventional servo techniques, which include the frequency-response methods associated with the names Nyquist, Bode, and Nichols, and the root-locus methods introduced by Evans. The design of continuous tandem networks to provide the compensating action is difficult because of the complicated effects of such an element on the closed-loop pulse transfer function. The first three methods of design presented in this chapter are approximate methods which attempt to unscramble these effects or use only the most significant parts of them. The last two methods are exact design methods. The fourth method is a procedure for the specification of a continuous network to realize a time response specification. This method has great intuitive appeal but fails to be practical, partly because of the lack of basic work needed to develop the method. The last method, which appears at this time to hold the greatest promise of all, uses a physical sampler to separate the network from the plant. This structure permits the immediate use of the various conventional techniques without approximation and, in fact, it is shown that any physical pulse transfer function can be realized with a pulsed RC network of a particular form. This proof permits the designer who must use such networks for compensation to avail himself of all the attractive time-domain synthesis procedures developed in the next chapter.

CHAPTER 7

DIGITAL COMPENSATION OF SAMPLED-DATA SYSTEMS

In the preceding chapter, the stabilization and compensation of sampled-data systems are accomplished by the insertion of a continuous element in cascade with the plant. This element is not separated by a sampler, so that its effect is that of altering the continuous transfer function to produce some over-all desirable characteristic in the sampled-data system. This procedure is relatively obvious since it is analogous to that employed in completely continuous systems. Analytically, it is difficult to apply, mainly because the over-all pulse transfer function is not simply related to the cascaded continuous transfer functions. This difficulty is, of course, no justification to seek other means of compensation, but it so happens that better results can be achieved by means of pulsed or digital compensators. Such compensators can be pulsed networks, that is, networks having a sampler at both their input and output. Alternatively, active linear digital controllers can be designed such that they accept a number sequence and deliver a processed number sequence at their output. Such a controller has a sampler at both its input and output, and its performance is described by a pulse transfer function. In general, any active or passive compensating device which is preceded and followed by synchronous samplers is referred to here as a *digital controller*. This chapter will be devoted to the theory and design of such digital controllers as compensators in sampled-data feedback control systems.

7.1 The Digital Controller

An approach to the concept underlying the digital compensation of sampled-data systems may be arrived at by the reasoning which follows. Referring to Fig. 7.1, it is seen that a continuous network is employed to compensate the sampled-data feedback system. In this case, the sampled error sequence E^* is reconstructed into an approximation of the continuous error E by means of the data hold. The compensating network whose transfer function is $N(s)$ then operates on the reconstructed error signal E_h to form the command input M, which is applied to the plant. The viewpoint taken here is that the error signal is first reconstructed and then altered by the compensating network to produce a desirable over-all system.

In contrast to this approach, an alternative method is shown in Fig. 7.2. In this case, the sampled error E_1^* is applied to a unit identified here as the digital controller. This unit computes or generates a sequence of output numbers E_2^* which are linearly related to the input number sequence E_1^*. The sequence E_2^* is then reconstructed into a continuous

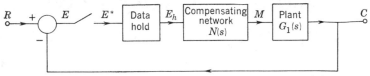

FIG. 7.1. Sampled-data feedback control system using continuous network compensation.

command function M, which is applied to the plant. The difference is apparent when it is noted that continuous compensation first reconstructs and then modifies the error signal, while the digital controller first modifies the error sequence and then reconstructs the modified error function. The compensating element which carries out the number-sequence reconstruction is called the digital controller.

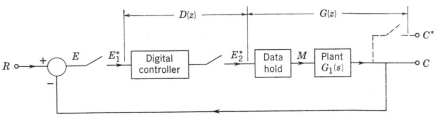

FIG. 7.2. Sampled-data feedback control system using digital controller.

The digital controller may contain a pulsed network which is merely a passive network to which is applied a sequence of samples. The output sequence of numbers or pulses is related to the input sequence by the pulse transfer function of the network $N(z)$. On the other hand, the digital controller may contain an active element such as a numerical processing unit or a program on a digital computer. In this case, the restrictions which are imposed on the pulse transfer function of networks can be overcome and more complete freedom in the choice of stabilizing functions can be achieved. One of the more interesting aspects of sampled-data systems is the possibility of using a digital computer to compensate the system. It should be mentioned here that a digital controller need not have any resemblance to a large-scale digital computer since it is a special-purpose device and can be constructed much more simply than the general-purpose computer. In addition, the digital controller can be implemented entirely in analogue form if it is considered desirable. More detailed discussions of implementation will be covered in later sections.

7.2 Basic Principle of Linear Digital Compensation

If it is assumed that the digital controller is linear, it follows that the relation between the input number sequence and the output number sequence is linear. Furthermore, a desirable system will require the storage of only a finite number of input and output samples. A general linear relation subject to these conditions will relate the input and output sequences, $e_1^*(t)$ and $e_2^*(t)$, respectively, in the following manner:

$$e_2(nT) + b_1 e_2[(n-1)T] + b_2 e_2[(n-2)T] + \cdots b_k e_2[(n-k)T]$$
$$= a_0 e_1(nT) + a_1 e_1[(n-1)T] + \cdots a_u e_1[(n-u)T] \quad (7.1)$$

where the various a's and b's are constants. This equation is the same as that given in (4.53), leading to the pulse transfer function (4.55). The pulse transfer function which generates this relationship is given by

$$D(z) = \frac{a_0 + a_1 z^{-1} + a_2 z^{-2} + \cdots a_u z^{-u}}{1 + b_1 z^{-1} + b_2 z^{-2} + \cdots b_k z^{-k}} \quad (7.2)$$

where $D(z)$ is defined by

$$D(z) = \frac{E_2(z)}{E_1(z)} \quad (7.3)$$

If the digital controller is a pulsed network whose transfer function is $G(s)$, then the digital controller pulse transfer function is $G(z)$. If, on the other hand, the digital controller is an active element, then the various a's and b's can be set without restriction. The only restriction is the usual one of physical realizability, which requires that in the form of (7.2), the denominator must contain the term "1."

The basic concept of digital compensation is that the various constants in the pulse transfer function $D(z)$ are adjusted so that some desired over-all pulse transfer function $K(z)$ is realized. Depending on the structure of the sampled-data feedback system, that is, on the relative location of the various samplers, the $D(z)$ appears in various ways. For instance, in the system shown in Fig. 7.2, the over-all pulse transfer function $K(z)$ is

$$K(z) = \frac{D(z)G(z)}{1 + D(z)G(z)} \quad (7.4)$$

For a given $G(z)$, $D(z)$ must be so chosen as to produce a desired $K(z)$.

Supposing, for the moment, that the desired over-all pulse transfer function $K(z)$ has been chosen, then the $D(z)$ which is required is given by

$$D(z) = \frac{1}{G(z)} \frac{K(z)}{1 - K(z)} \quad (7.5)$$

In view of the fact that $D(z)$ is generally implemented by active elements, it is theoretically capable of producing any desired physically realizable $K(z)$.   For this reason, considerable attention must be given to the desired prototype forms of $K(z)$ which must be sought.   As will be seen later, there are some subtle limitations on $K(z)$ which must be examined before design procedures can be outlined.

7.3 "Minimal" Over-all Prototype Response Functions

In view of the flexibility possible with active digital controllers, there is a very large number of possible over-all prototype response functions which can be implemented.   As a starting point, however, the simplest,

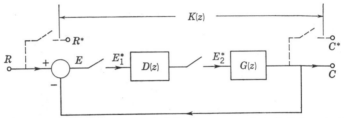

Fig. 7.3. Block diagram of sampled-data systems using digital controller.

or "minimal," prototype response functions[3] are convenient.   Minimal prototype systems are approached from the viewpoint that they must be able to respond satisfactorily to some convenient test input such as a step, ramp, or constant acceleration, or all three.   The requirements which are set for minimal response functions are:

1. The over-all response and the response of all elements of the system must be physically realizable.
2. The steady-state response to the test input must have zero systematic error.
3. The transient response should be as fast as possible and the settling time should be equal to a finite number of sampling intervals.

As an aid to applying these requirements, reference is made to the system in Fig. 7.3.   Here, both $D(z)$ and $G(z)$ must be physically realizable, as must the over-all pulse transfer function $K(z)$.   Taking $G(z)$ first, it can be assumed that it is a ratio of polynomials in z^{-1} of the form

$$G(z) = \frac{p_m z^{-m} + \cdots p_n z^{-n}}{q_0 + q_1 z^{-1} + \cdots q_b z^{-b}} \tag{7.6}$$

The presence of q_0 in this form is always assured if the system is physically realizable.   This is shown readily by expanding $G(z)$ into increasing powers of z^{-1} as follows:

$$G(z) = Az^{-m} + Bz^{-(m+1)} + \cdots \tag{7.7}$$

where A, B, etc., are constants which are functions of the various p's and q's. Since $G(z)$ defines the impulsive response of the plant, it follows that the presence of z^{-m} as the first term assures the fact that the output of the plant does not precede the input. In the limiting condition, the exponent m can be zero, although in practical plants it is never less than unity.

The digital controller whose pulse transfer function is $D(z)$ is also subject to this restriction, and its form must be as given in (7.2). Incidentally, in this form, the gain constant is a_0 since it can be factored out as a multiplicative term for the whole expression. The impulsive response of a digital controller of this form is seen to have a first output pulse whose amplitude is a_0. As a consequence of the restrictions placed on the forms of the pulse transfer functions $G(z)$ and $D(z)$, the over-all prototype response function $K(z)$ as given in (7.4) will likewise have restrictions. These are found by substituting the required forms of $G(z)$ and $D(z)$ in (7.4) as follows:

$$K(z) = \cfrac{\cfrac{(p_m z^{-m} + \cdots p_n z^{-n})(a_0 + a_1 z^{-1} + a_2 z^{-2} + \cdots a_u z^{-u})}{(q_0 + q_1 z^{-1} + \cdots q_b z^{-b})(1 + b_1 z^{-1} + b_2 z^{-2} + \cdots b_k z^{-k})}}{1 + \cfrac{(p_m z^{-m} + \cdots p_n z^{-n})(a_0 + a_1 z^{-1} + a_2 z^{-2} + \cdots a_u z^{-u})}{(q_0 + q_1 z^{-1} + \cdots q_b z^{-b})(1 + b_1 z^{-1} + b_2 z^{-2} + \cdots b_k z^{-k})}} \tag{7.8}$$

Simplifying this expression and collecting terms, the following results

$$K(z) = \frac{k_m z^{-m} + \cdots k_p z^{-p}}{l_0 + l_1 z^{-1} + \cdots l_q z^{-q}} \tag{7.9}$$

where the various k's and l's are combinations of the various p's, q's, a's, and b's.

It is concluded from this simple development that in order to accommodate physically realizable elements in the closed loop, the numerator of the over-all pulse transfer function $K(z)$ must contain z^{-1} to a power equal to and possibly greater than the lowest power m in the plant pulse transfer function $G(z)$. Also, it is necessary that the term l_0 appear in the denominator of $K(z)$, as shown in (7.9). By observing these simple rules it is assured that the specified prototype does not require physically unrealizable components in its implementation.

The second requirement for the minimal prototype response function is that it respond to a specified test function with zero systematic steady-state error. It is implied in stating the condition that this need only apply at sampling instants. From a practical viewpoint, however, it would be desirable that the system error be continuously zero in the steady-state, although to assure this condition requires special treatment, as will be shown later.   The discussions in this section will deal with the system error at sampling instants only.

In specifying the requirements on $K(z)$ to produce zero steady-state system error in response to a test function, a unity feedback system will be assumed.   Modifications of the results obtained in this manner will be necessary if the feedback is not unity.   From the system configuration given in Fig. 7.3, the system error sequence is equal to the control error sequence $E_1(z)$, given by

$$E_1(z) = R(z) - C(z) \qquad (7.10)$$

Since, by definition, $K(z)$ is given by

$$K(z) = \frac{C(z)}{R(z)} \qquad (7.11)$$

then (7.10) is expressed by

$$E_1(z) = R(z)[1 - K(z)] \qquad (7.12)$$

The second requirement on the form of $K(z)$ is that the inverse of $E_1(z)$ have a final value of zero when $R(z)$ is the z transform of the specified input function.   Applying the final-value theorem,

$$e_1(\infty) = \lim_{z \to 1} \{(1 - z^{-1})R(z)[1 - K(z)]\} \qquad (7.13)$$

If the class of input test functions includes only steps, ramps, or constant-acceleration inputs, then $R(z)$ takes the form

$$R(z) = \frac{A(z)}{(1 - z^{-1})^m} \qquad (7.14)$$

where $A(z)$ is a polynomial in z^{-1} which does not contain factors of the form $1 - z^{-1}$.   It is readily seen from (7.13) that for inputs of this type, the steady-state error $e_1(\infty)$ will be zero if $1 - K(z)$ satisfies the following relationship:

$$1 - K(z) = (1 - z^{-1})^m F(z) \qquad (7.15)$$

where $F(z)$ is an unspecified ratio of polynomials in z^{-1} and m is the order of the denominator of the input z transform $R(z)$.

The *minimal prototype* response function is defined such that $F(z)$ in (7.15) is *unity* and the resultant order of $K(z)$ in z^{-1} is minimum.   Thus, if the system is to follow a unit ramp input without steady-state error, $K(z)$ for a minimal prototype response is given by

$$1 - K(z) = (1 - z^{-1})^2 \qquad (7.16)$$

Solving for $K(z)$,

$$K(z) = 2z^{-1} - z^{-2} \qquad (7.17)$$

A table of minimal prototype response functions is given in Table 7.1. It is understood that, if a minimal prototype is used, the system will respond without error for any *lower*-order input function in the steady state.

The third stated requirement for a minimal prototype is that the system settle in a finite time after the application of an input.   As used in

TABLE 7.1. MINIMAL PROTOTYPE RESPONSE FUNCTIONS

Input	$r(t)$	$R(z)$	$K(z)$
Step	$u(t)$	$\dfrac{1}{1 - z^{-1}}$	z^{-1}
Ramp	$tu(t)$	$\dfrac{Tz^{-1}}{(1 - z^{-1})^2}$	$2z^{-1} - z^{-2}$
Acceleration	$t^2 u(t)$	$\dfrac{T^2 z^{-1}(1 + z^{-1})}{(1 - z^{-1})^3}$	$3z^{-1} - 3z^{-2} + z^{-3}$

this application, this means that the transient must disappear at sampling instants only.   There is the very likely possibility that, between sampling instants, a continuous output will differ from the desired output and that the system will *ripple* about the steady-state value.   However, in a minimal prototype, the output will be exact at sampling instants.   This effect is shown in Fig. 7.4, where it is seen that the output has settled after one sampling interval in so far as sampling instants are concerned, but that there is a substantial ripple component during the sampling intervals.   A system which is designed both to have finite settling time at sampling instants and to be *ripple-free* is one which can truly be called a finite-settling-time system.   This requires special treatment and will be considered later.   Minimal prototypes are concerned only with sampling instants.

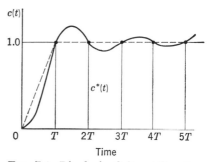

FIG. 7.4. Ripple in finite-settling-time systems.

In the expression for an over-all response function as given in (7.9) and (7.15), $K(z)$ may be the ratio of two polynomials in z^{-1}.   In (7.15) the unspecified function $F(z)$ may be the ratio of two polynomials.   In minimal prototypes, $F(z)$ is taken as unity, resulting in a minimal expression containing zeros anywhere in the z plane but having all its poles at the origin. It is this characteristic which produces a finite-settling-time response. The reason for this is found in the fact that the impulsive response of a system containing only a numerator polynomial in $K(z)$ is of finite duration. If properly designed, a system of this type will continue to generate the correct number after all the necessary past samples are weighted and added. Thus, minimal systems and, for that matter, all finite-settling-time systems are characterized by the fact that they have only a numerator polynomial in z^{-1} in their pulse transfer function.

EXAMPLE

A sampled-data system is to be designed with a minimal prototype response $K(z)$ such that it responds to a ramp input without error. From Table 7.1, the minimal prototype for this condition is

$$K(z) = 2z^{-1} - z^{-2}$$

The response to an input whose z transform is $R(z)$ is given by

$$C(z) = (2z^{-1} - z^{-2})R(z)$$

Taking three inputs, a unit step, a unit ramp (for which the system is specifically designed), and a unit acceleration, the following outputs result:

For a unit step,

$$C(z) = \frac{2z^{-1} - z^{-2}}{1 - z^{-1}}$$

For a unit ramp, t,

$$C(z) = \frac{Tz^{-1}(2z^{-1} - z^{-2})}{(1 - z^{-1})^2}$$

For a unit acceleration, $t^2/2$,

$$C(z) = \frac{T^2 z^{-1}(1 + z^{-1})(2z^{-1} - z^{-2})}{2(1 - z^{-1})^3}$$

The three transforms are inverted, resulting in the pulse sequences which are plotted in Fig. 7.5.

The response of the system to a ramp input for which the minimal prototype is designed is relatively docile. The system settles to zero error in two sampling intervals, with no overshoot. It is understood, of course, that the continuous output of the system probably does have overshoot between sampling instants but this component is referred to as ripple and is not considered in the minimal prototype. The response of the system to a step input is seen to have a severe overshoot of 100 per cent. The reason for this is that upon application of the first sample at $t = 0$, the system responds as though it were being subjected to a unit ramp since the sample at $t = -T$ is zero. Finally, the response to a unit acceleration is seen to have finite steady-state error, as expected. Analysis will show that the steady-state error should be equal to T^2, which it is on the diagram. Had a higher-order time function been applied, the system would fail to respond with a finite system error, and the error would gradually grow to infinity.

The example illustrates a typical characteristic of minimal prototypes when subjected to other than the test input for which they are designed. When subjected to inputs which are time functions of an order lower than the required one, the minimal prototype systems tend to have highly oscillatory performance. In the illustration, it was seen that 100 per cent overshoot resulted when a step instead of a ramp was applied. Minimal prototype systems are "tuned" to a particular form of input and not to a broad class of inputs.

In order to produce an average acceptable performance to a number of input test functions, modifications to the minimal prototype response function must be made. Typical of these is the use of the "staleness factor," to be discussed in a later section. When properly applied, the staleness factor can produce an adequate compromise performance for a whole class of input functions rather than highly "tuned" performance with a particular test function. The objec-

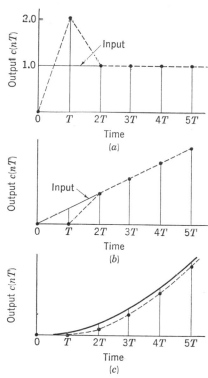

Fig. 7.5. Response of minimal prototype system to step, ramp, and acceleration.

tions arising from ripple oscillations caused by the use of minimal prototypes are overcome by using ripple-free over-all response functions, to be described later. While useful in many applications, the minimal prototypes serve more as a guide as to the minimum response which can be obtained, subject to the conditions outlined in this section.

7.4 Compensation of Open-loop Systems

While the main interest of the designer is to compensate closed-loop systems, several important points can be made by considering the compensation of open-loop systems first.   In Fig. 7.6, a plant whose pulse transfer function is $G(z)$ is to be compensated by a digital device whose pulse transfer function is $D(z)$ to implement an over-all pulse transfer function $K_d(z)$.   For purposes of discussion it may be assumed that a desired over-all response function $K_d(z)$ may be, though it does not necessarily have to be, a minimal prototype function described in the previous section.   In this case, the desired response would be related to the plant and compensator by the following relation:

$$K_d(z) = D(z)G(z) \tag{7.18}$$

where $D(z)$ is so chosen that it cancels the undesirable poles and zeros of $G(z)$ and replaces them by the poles and zeros of the desired over-all response function.

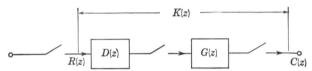

FIG. 7.6. Digital compensation of open-cycle system.

In implementing a technique like this one, certain limitations present themselves.   For instance, if the plant pulse transfer function $G(z)$ contains a pole b_g and a zero a_g which lie outside the unit circle, difficulties due to inaccurate cancellation are severe.   The presence of a pole in the plant outside the unit circle implies the instability of the plant, an unlikely circumstance.   On the other hand, the presence of a zero outside the unit circle is perfectly possible with stable plants found in practice. The digital compensator has a pulse transfer function $D(z)$ which cancels these poles and zeros and replaces them with desired poles and zeros. However, since the magnitudes of the actual plant poles and zeros are only approximately known and, furthermore, since the implementation of the digital compensator $D(z)$ cannot be perfectly implemented, it follows that poles and zeros of the plant can *never* be perfectly canceled.   This results in serious difficulties for those poles and zeros which lie outside the unit circle, as can be seen from the expression

$$K_a(z) = \frac{(z - a_g)(z - b_d)}{(z - b_g)(z - a_d)} K_d(z) \tag{7.19}$$

where $K_a(z)$ is the actual over-all pulse transfer function and $K_d(z)$ is the desired over-all pulse transfer function.   Ideally, the poles and zeros introduced by the plant, b_g and a_g, are canceled by the poles and zeros introduced by the digital compensator, b_d and a_d.   Actually, perfect cancellation is not achieved, and it is noted that the compensated over-all response function $K_a(z)$ then contains a pair of poles b_g and a_d which lie outside of the unit circle on the z plane. This means that the over-all sampled-data system is unstable.

It follows, therefore, that in the compensation of an open-loop system by a digital compensator, the poles and zeros of the plant pulse transfer function which lie outside of the unit circle cannot be canceled by the digital unit. This means that if a plant is unstable, that is, if it has poles outside the unit circle on the z plane, it is impossible to stabilize the system by means of a cascaded digital unit. Fortunately, this is not the case for a closed-loop implementation, as will be shown later. More serious than this limitation is the fact that if a stable open-loop plant has a pulse transfer function which has a zero outside the unit circle, it is not possible to cancel this zero by means of the digital compensator. To ensure this fact, (7.19) shows that the desired over-all pulse transfer function must contain as one of its zeros those zeros of the plant pulse transfer function which lie outside the unit circle. Thus, there is no complete freedom of choice in $K_d(z)$, and often the minimal prototype cannot be achieved.

7.5 Compensation of Closed-loop Systems

Less obvious but equally important are the limitations imposed on the designer in the compensation of closed-loop sampled-data systems.[3,4] In the error-sampled system shown in Fig. 7.7 the digital

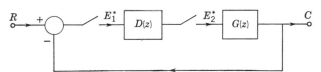

Fig. 7.7. Digital compensation of closed-loop system.

controller has a pulse transfer function $D(z)$ and the plant a pulse transfer function $G(z)$. The digital controller has a direct effect of canceling the undesired poles and zeros of the plant and replacing them with the poles and zeros required to implement some over-all response $K(z)$. To study the forbidden cancellations, let it be assumed that the plant pulse transfer function contains at least one pole and one zero which lie outside the unit circle in the z plane. For purposes of this development, it can be assumed that all the other singularities lie inside the unit circle. Thus, $G(z)$ can be expressed by

$$G(z) = \frac{z - a_g}{z - b_g} F_g(z) \qquad (7.20)$$

where a_g and b_g are the zero and pole, respectively, which lie outside the unit circle.

If the specified over-all pulse transfer function for this system is $K_s(z)$, then the required digital-controller pulse transfer function to produce this is given by

$$D(z) = \frac{1}{G(z)} \frac{K_s(z)}{1 - K_s(z)} \tag{7.21}$$

an expression equivalent to (7.5). Substituting $G(z)$ from (7.20) in this expression, there results

$$D(z) = \frac{z - b_d}{(z - a_d)F_d(z)} \frac{K_s(z)}{1 - K_s(z)} \tag{7.22}$$

where the constants b_d and a_d are made almost but not exactly equal to the plant constants b_g and a_g. Also, $F_d(z)$ and $F_g(z)$ are made almost identical, although, as will develop later, slight mismatches are of small consequence because it is assumed that all their poles and zeros lie inside the unit circle on the z plane.

To obtain the over-all pulse transfer function which actually results from inserting a digital-controller pulse transfer function given by (7.22) and a plant pulse transfer function given by (7.20), the actual over-all pulse transfer function $K_a(z)$ is obtained by substituting $G(z)$ and $D(z)$ from (7.20) and (7.22), respectively, into (7.4), resulting in

$$K_a(z) = \frac{(z - b_d)(z - a_g)F_g(z)K_s(z)}{(z - a_d)(z - b_g)[1 - K_s(z)]F_d(z) + (z - b_d)(z - a_g)K_s(z)F_g(z)} \tag{7.23}$$

In the ideal situation, the poles and the zeros of the digital controller match those of the plant *exactly*, so that

$$\begin{aligned} b_d &= b_g \\ a_d &= a_g \\ F_d(z) &= F_g(z) \end{aligned} \tag{7.24}$$

Then the complicated expression in (7.23) reduces simply to

$$K_a(z) = K_s(z) \tag{7.25}$$

For this condition, it is seen that the over-all pulse transfer function actually obtained matches exactly the desired function.

In the practical situation, however, exact cancellation of the plant poles and zeros by the controller poles and zeros cannot be realistically expected, so that b_d and b_g or a_d and a_g are not exactly equal. This means that expression (7.23) cannot be reduced, and its poles and zeros may lie outside the unit circle, as will be shown. For this development, it will be assumed that $F_d(z)$ and $F_g(z)$ are identical and that the imperfect cancellations are confined to poles and zeros which lie outside the unit circle.

To determine the effect of imperfect cancellation, it is assumed initially that the controller zero and pole, a_d and b_d, are identical to the plant zero and pole a_g and b_g, respectively. When this is so, perfect cancellations in the numerator and denominator of (7.23) take place, and the actual over-all response function is identical to the desired over-all response function. Now, if the plant zero and pole drift slightly by an amount Δa_g and Δb_g, these cancellations can no longer be made since the numerator of (7.23) differs from the denominator.

The denominator of (7.23) is a polynomial in z, and the locus of its roots as any parameter is varied is continuous. Starting then with Δa_g and Δb_g at zero, meaning that a_g and b_g are respectively equal to a_d and b_d, it is seen that the denominator polynomial has zeros at a_d and b_g (or a_g and b_d), which lie outside the unit circle. In this case, they are canceled by the numerator roots, which are equal. However, as the slight shifts Δa_g and Δb_g are introduced, the denominator roots shift slightly but are still outside of the unit circle in the z plane, and they are *not canceled* by equal roots in the numerator since its roots shift in a different manner.

The conclusion which is drawn from this discussion is that if a plant contained in a feedback sampled-data system has a pulse transfer function which contains zeros and poles which lie outside of the unit circle in the z plane, or in the limit, on the unit circle, no attempt should be made to cancel such poles with a digital-controller pulse transfer function since instability would inevitably result. This does not mean that a feedback system containing such a plant cannot be stabilized or compensated but rather that complete freedom of choice of over-all response functions is not possible.

By applying suitable restrictions on the form of the specified pulse transfer function $K_s(z)$, the cancellation of poles and zeros of the plant pulse transfer function by the digital-controller pulse transfer function can be prevented. These restrictions obtain by substituting the plant pulse transfer function from (7.20) in (7.21).

$$D(z) = \frac{z - b_g}{(z - a_g)F_g(z)} \frac{K_s(z)}{1 - K_s(z)} \tag{7.26}$$

If (7.26) is not to contain a pole a_g and a zero b_g in the pulse transfer function $D(z)$, these terms are to be contained in $K_s(z)$ and $1 - K_s(z)$, respectively. Thus, in specifying $K_s(z)$ which leads to a stable system, the following relations must be satisfied:

$$\begin{aligned} K_s(z) &= (1 - a_g z^{-1})M(z) \\ 1 - K_s(z) &= (1 - b_g z^{-1})N(z) \end{aligned} \tag{7.27}$$

where $M(z)$ and $N(z)$ are unspecified ratios of polynomials in z^{-1}. In words, *it is necessary that the specified over-all pulse transfer function $K_s(z)$ contain as its zeros all those zeros of the plant pulse transfer function which lie outside or on the unit circle in the z plane and that $1 - K_s(z)$ contain as* *its zeros all those poles of the plant pulse transfer function which lie outside or on the unit circle in the z plane.* In applying these restrictions it is not always possible to realize a minimal over-all prototype, although if $M(z)$ and $N(z)$ are made polynomials in z^{-1} with a finite number of terms and containing no denominator polynomial, finite settling time can always be obtained.

It is convenient to collect the various rules and restrictions which apply to the compensation of feedback sampled-data systems. They are:

1. In order to satisfy conditions of physical realizability, the specified over-all pulse transfer function must take the form

$$K_s(z) = \frac{k_m z^{-m} + \cdots k_p z^{-p}}{l_0 + l_1 z^{-1} + \cdots l_q z^{-q}}$$

where m is the lowest order in z^{-1} in the pulse transfer function

$$G(z) = \frac{p_m z^{-m} + \cdots p_n z^{-n}}{q_0 + q_1 z^{-1} - \cdots q_b z^{-b}}$$

2. For a minimal prototype, $K_s(z)$ contains only the numerator polynomial of lowest order in z^{-1}.

3. For the system to respond to an input of the form

$$R(z) = \frac{A(z)}{(1 - z^{-1})^k}$$

with zero steady-state error, it is necessary that $K_s(z)$ satisfy the relation

$$1 - K_s(z) = (1 - z^{-1})^k F(z)$$

where $F(z)$ is an arbitrary polynomial or ratio of polynomials in z^{-1}.

4. For those plants having pulse transfer functions containing poles or zeros which lie outside or on the unit circle of the z plane, the following must obtain

$$K_s(z) = \prod^{i} (1 - a_i z^{-1}) M(z)$$

$$1 - K_s(z) = \prod^{i} (1 - b_i z^{-1}) N(z)$$

where the a_i and b_i are all zeros and poles, respectively, of the plant pulse transfer function which lie outside or on the unit circle of the z plane.

The application of these rules of design is best understood by means of an illustrative example.

EXAMPLE[3]

The system which is to be compensated by means of a digital controller is shown in Fig. 7.8, where it is seen that the continuous plant consists of an integrator and a double simple time delay. The data hold is a simple zero-order hold. The problem is to design a linear program for the digital controller which will produce an over-all response of minimum finite settling time. If possible, this should be a minimal prototype. In addition, the over-all system is to respond to a ramp with zero steady-state error.

The continuous feedforward plant transfer function $G(s)$ is

$$G(s) = 10 \frac{1 - e^{-s}}{s^2(s + 1)^2}$$

The z transform corresponding to this transfer function is

$$G(z) = \frac{(1 + 2.34z^{-1})(1 + 0.16z^{-1})z^{-1}}{(1 - z^{-1})(1 - 0.368z^{-1})^2}$$

The pulse transfer function $G(z)$ contains zeros at -2.34, -0.16, and ∞, and poles at 1.0 and 0.368, the latter being a double pole. To obtain a finite settling time, the prototype response function $K(z)$ con-

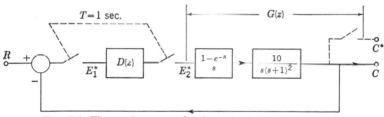

FIG. 7.8. Illustrative example of minimal prototype design.

tains only a numerator polynomial in z^{-1}. The lowest order in z^{-1} in the numerator of the function $G(z)$ is unity, so that $K(z)$ must contain z^{-1} as its lowest order also. It is seen that $G(z)$ contains a zero, 2.34, which lies outside of the unit circle in the z plane and for this reason must be contained in $K(z)$. The prototype response which satisfies these requirements is of the form

$$K(z) = (1 + 2.34z^{-1})(a_1z^{-1} + a_2z^{-2} + a_3z^{-3} + \cdots)$$

where the various a's are to be determined. To obtain the minimum settling time, only a minimum number of a's required to satisfy the other requirements will be used.

In order to respond with zero error to an input ramp function, the additional requirement is placed on $K(z)$ as follows:

$$1 - K(z) = (1 - z^{-1})^2(1 + b_1z^{-1} + b_2z^{-2} + \cdots)$$

It is seen that this requirement automatically satisfies the condition that $1 - K(z)$ contain the poles of $G(z)$ which lie outside or on the unit circle.

The constants in the above expressions are obtained by substituting $K(z)$ into the expression for $1 - K(z)$ and equating the coefficients of terms of the same power in z^{-1}. This results in the following simultaneous equations relating the coefficients:

$$-a_1 = b_1 - 2$$
$$-2.34a_1 - a_2 = 1 - 2b_1$$
$$-2.34a_2 = b_1$$

Three simultaneous equations define the values for three unknowns. Had more terms been included in $K(z)$, there would have been more unknowns than equations, and arbitrary values could be assigned to the excess coefficients. This would not result in a minimum finite settling time, however, as specified in the problem.

Solving the equations, the coefficients are

$$a_1 = 0.81$$
$$a_2 = -0.51$$
$$b_1 = 1.19$$

By substituting back in the expression for $K(z)$, the over-all prototype which results is

$$K(z) = 0.81z^{-1} + 1.38z^{-2} - 1.19z^{-3}$$

The response of this system to a unit ramp input is given by

$$C(z) = (0.81z^{-1} + 1.38z^{-2} - 1.19z^{-3}) \frac{z^{-1}}{(1 - z^{-1})^2}$$

which upon inversion yields the output sequence plotted in Fig. 7.9. The dashed lines are for guidance to indicate the location of the output samples. Plotted with a solid line is an estimate of the continuous output $c(t)$, which is seen to ripple about the final value after the system has settled at sampling instants.

To show the disadvantage of a minimum response prototype, the response to a unit step input is computed. The output sequence for this input is defined by

$$C(z) = (0.81z^{-1} + 1.38z^{-2} - 1.19z^{-3}) \frac{1}{1 - z^{-1}}$$

which upon inversion yields a pulse sequence plotted in Fig. 7.10. The overshoot is over 200 per cent and again, even though the system settles in three sample times, there will be a ripple in the output, as estimated by the solid-line curve. While disadvantages have been pointed out, it should also be emphasized that this system settles in the *minimum* number of sample times possible and that if the ripple and overshoot conditions are acceptable, it is the fastest system in the respect noted. It was not possible to realize the minimal prototypes of the form listed in Table 7.1 because of the presence of a zero in $G(z)$ outside of the unit

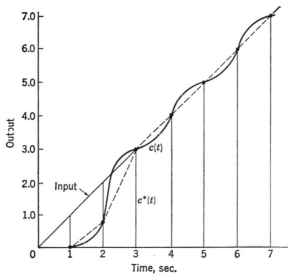

FIG. 7.9. Response of system in illustrative example to unit ramp input.

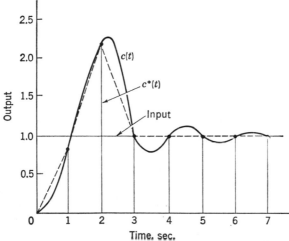

FIG. 7.10. Response of system in illustrative example to unit step input.

circle. The presence of this zero resulted in a settling time which was one sample time larger than the minimal system.

The digital controller which is required to produce the over-all performance in this example is described by its pulse transfer function $D(z)$, which is obtained by substitution in (7.5). This results in the following expression after simplification:

$$D(z) = \frac{0.81 - 1.106z^{-1} + 0.485z^{-2} - 0.069z^{-3}}{1 + 0.352z^{-1} - 1.159z^{-2} - 0.193z^{-3}}$$

This response can be physically implemented by using four number storages in the manner shown in Fig. 4.10. The number of storages required is a measure of the complexity of the digital controller. This factor will be referred to again when different over-all prototype response functions are used.

The foregoing example has served to illustrate many of the pertinent points applying to the design of "minimal" prototype systems. As shown there, minimal prototype systems cannot always be realized because of the presence of poles and zeros of the plant pulse transfer function which lie outside of the unit circle. In such a case, only a "minimum" response function can be obtained, which produces longer settling times than the minimal function, depending on how many uncancellable poles and zeros there are. A critical examination of the results of the previous example will show that the digital controller supplies the additional integration in the feedforward line of the system which is required to respond without error to a unit ramp input. The integration process implemented by the digital controller is a numerical integration, but the results on the over-all response are the same.

A precaution which must be observed relative to the design of digital controllers is that cognizance be taken as to their output under expected operating conditions. For instance, in the previous example, the digital controller implements a numerical integration process. In doing so it produces a system which responds to a unit ramp with zero system error. Physically, this means that the output of the digital controller in the steady state is a constant. On the other hand, if the plant contained no integration of its own, the digital-controller pulse transfer function would show a double integration process in order to produce a system which responds to a unit ramp input with zero system error. In this case, the output of the digital controller would have to rise without limit since it provides both integrations necessary to implement the condition. From the practical viewpoint, this is impossible, and the system would saturate very quickly upon application of a ramp input. The general rule which should be followed is that the output of the digital controller should never be expected to rise above some practical limit under operating conditions of the system.

Arbitrary response functions can be realized by taking the expression for $K(z)$ and including more than the minimum number of terms. For instance, in the illustrative example, only a_1 and a_2 were required in the expression for $K(z)$ in order to meet all the minimum requirements. If additional coefficients had been included, then a number of arbitrary samples in response to a test function could be realized. It is important to note that this is done at the expense of additional storage requirements in the digital controller. As a matter of fact, if the number of storage positions in the digital controller were increased without limit, a complete specification of the output at all sampling instants could be made.

7.6 Implementation of Systems with Staleness Factor

It has been demonstrated in the previous section that systems which are designed for minimum and finite settling time often do not give good performance when subjected to an input other than that for which they are designed. In this sense, minimal systems may be regarded as highly "tuned." In addition, in obtaining minimum finite settling time at sampling instants, the severe shocks which result in the plant cause substantial ripple in the continuous output, even though the output is correct at sampling instants. These effects were noted in the literature[1,2] and led to the introduction of a term in the over-all response function known as the "staleness factor." This factor led to a "softening" of the response, with the result that a system could be expected to respond adequately, though not perfectly, to a number of test inputs. The choice of staleness factor can be arrived at by optimizing procedures[4] or by observing the response to some most likely form of test input.

The staleness factor is introduced in the over-all prototype pulse transfer function in the following manner:

$$K(z) = \frac{K_m(z)}{(1 - cz^{-1})^N} \tag{7.28}$$

where c is a constant whose value for stable systems can range from -1.0 to $+1.0$, N is an exponent which may assume any positive value, and $K_m(z)$ is the minimal pulse transfer function. Investigations[4] have shown that not too much is to be gained by making the exponent N higher than unity, so that it generally is taken as unity in practical systems. The staleness factor is defined as the constant c. In some systems, a sequence of terms of the form $(1 - c_i z^{-1})$ may be used in the denominator of (7.28), in which case a number of different staleness factors are used.

To illustrate the effect of the staleness factor on the response of systems, the minimal prototype z^{-1} is used for $K_m(z)$.

$$K(z) = \frac{az^{-1}}{1 - cz^{-1}} \tag{7.29}$$

If a unit step function is applied to this system, application of the final-value theorem will show that the steady-state output is $a/(1 - c)$, so that to obtain unit output for unit input, the constant a must be made equal to $(1 - c)$.   Thus, a unit steady-state response prototype function $K(z)$ becomes

$$K(z) = \frac{(1 - c)z^{-1}}{1 - cz^{-1}} \tag{7.30}$$

For a unit step input, three response functions are computed and plotted in Fig. 7.11, one for c set equal to zero (the minimal prototype), one with c set equal to 0.5, and the third with c set equal to -0.5.   It is seen that

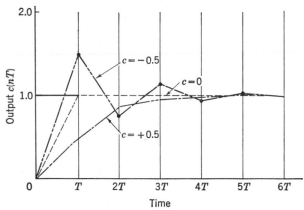

FIG. 7.11. Response of system with staleness factors of various amount to unit step input.

for the staleness factor c set equal to a positive number of damping effect very similar to that produced by a low-pass RC circuit in continuous systems is obtained.   A negative staleness factor brings about an oscillatory response, which is the usual result when a pulse transfer function has a pole which is negative real, in this case -0.5.   In practice, staleness factors are taken usually as positive in systems having the form of (7.28) and the exponent N is taken as unity or other small integer.

EXAMPLE

To illustrate the effect of a staleness factor on the performance of a system, the same problem which was considered in the example in the previous section will be considered here.   The block diagram of the system is given in Fig. 7.8.   The over-all pulse transfer function is the same as in the minimal prototype considered in this example, except for the addition of the staleness factor.   Thus

$$K(z) = \frac{(1 + 2.34z^{-1})(a_1 z^{-1} + a_2 z^{-2} + \cdots)}{1 - 0.5z^{-1}}$$

It is noted that $K(z)$ contains the zero, 2.34, of $G(z)$ which lies outside of the unit circle of the z plane.

DIGITAL COMPENSATION OF SAMPLED-DATA SYSTEMS

Since the system is to respond to a unit ramp with zero system error, the second condition must hold, namely,

$$1 - K(z) = \frac{(1 - z^{-1})^2(1 + b_1 z^{-1} + \cdots)}{1 - 0.5z^{-1}}$$

As in the example in the previous section, only a_1, a_2, and b_1 are required to satisfy the two preceding equations.   Solving for a_1 and a_2,

$$a_1 = 0.56$$
$$a_2 = -0.405$$
$$b_1 = 0.948$$

This yields an over-all pulse transfer function $K(z)$ given by

$$K(z) = \frac{0.56z^{-1} + 0.895z^{-2} - 0.948z^{-3}}{1 - 0.5z^{-1}} \qquad (7.31)$$

The response of this system to a ramp input and to a step input is found by multiplying $K(z)$ by the respective $R(z)$, resulting in an output pulse transform

$$C(z) = \frac{0.56z^{-2} + 0.895z^{-3} - 0.948z^{-4}}{1 - 2.5z^{-1} + 2z^{-2} - 0.5z^{-3}}$$

for the ramp input and

$$C(z) = \frac{0.56z^{-1} + 0.895z^{-2} - 0.948z^{-3}}{1 - 1.5z^{-1} + 0.5z^{-2}}$$

for the step input.

Inversion of these z transforms gives the pulse sequences, which are plotted in Figs. 7.12 and 7.13, respectively.   It is seen that the system no longer has a finite settling time at sampling instants as did the minimum finite-settling-time prototype.   On the other hand, the system approaches a tolerable error in a reasonable time, and the ripple component is not severe.   The response of the system to a step input shows that the peak overshoot is less than that for the finite-settling-time prototype, being approximately 175 per cent, as opposed to 225 per cent in the minimum prototype system.   The system is seen to approach steady state gradually, with some ripple component which is not as severe as that for the minimum prototype.

Substituting in (7.5) gives the pulse transfer function of the digital controller,

$$D(z) = \frac{0.56 - 0.818z^{-1} + 0.374z^{-2} - 0.05z^{-3}}{1 + 0.11z^{-1} - 0.94z^{-2} - 0.151z^{-3}} \qquad (7.32)$$

This pulse transfer function should be compared to that of the minimum prototype.   The comparison shows that the various coefficients and signs are different but that the required number of storages in the digital controller are the same.   This means that a system with staleness factor can be obtained merely by readjusting the linear program of the controller and not by increasing its complexity or design.

In the illustrative example a staleness factor of 0.5 was used arbitrarily.

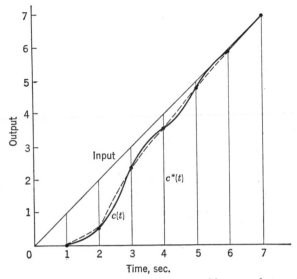

FIG. 7.12. Response of system with staleness factor used in example to unit ramp input.

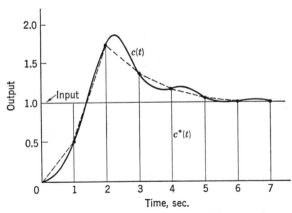

FIG. 7.13. Response of system with staleness factor used in example to unit step input.

By increasing the constant toward 1.0, increased damping effect in the system is produced. When the damping factor is to be reduced, the staleness factor is lowered toward zero, at which time the minimum prototype is reached. It has been shown[4] that a logical procedure can be used to select a desirable value of staleness factor. This procedure minimizes the system error in the integrated-square sense, that is,

$$S = \sum_{m=0}^{\infty} [E(mT)]^2 \rightarrow \min \tag{7.33}$$

Using this criterion, the value of c which minimizes S can be arrived at in logical fashion.

The sum S is obtained in the z domain by use of (4.67). To illustrate the technique, a minimal prototype with a single staleness factor as given in (7.30) is used. It is assumed that the feedback transfer function is unity, so that the error pulse transform is

$$E(z) = [1 - K(z)]R(z) \tag{7.34}$$

Substituting (7.30) in (7.34), there results the expression for the error pulse transform

$$E(z) = \frac{1 - z^{-1}}{1 - cz^{-1}} R(z) \tag{7.35}$$

Now, if $R(z)$ is a unit step function z transform, $E(z)$ is simply

$$E(z) = \frac{1}{1 - cz^{-1}} \tag{7.36}$$

Using the integral for the summation S as given in (4.67),

$$S = \frac{1}{2\pi j} \int_{\Gamma} \frac{1}{1 - cz^{-1}} \frac{1}{1 - cz} z^{-1} \, dz \tag{7.37}$$

where it is recalled that Γ is the unit circle. The residue is obtained resulting in a value for S given by

$$S = \frac{1}{1 - c^2} \tag{7.38}$$

It is seen that S is minimized for c set equal to zero, that is, the minimal prototype is best for this input using this criterion. Looking further, however, when a unit ramp is applied, the prototype given by (7.35) will produce a steady-state error $e(\infty)$ in response to a unit ramp with a unit sampling period, which is given by

$$e(\infty) = \frac{1}{1 - c} \tag{7.39}$$

In this instance, if c is made equal to -0.5, the integrated-square error given by (7.38) rises by one-third, but the steady-state error to a ramp is reduced by one-third. Thus, if the inputs to the system were mainly step functions and ramp functions, a compromise choice in staleness factor would be about -0.5. Considerations like these can be used to determine the optimum value of staleness factor in different situations.

To illustrate further how minimizing techniques can be used to obtain the staleness factor, a system similar to that of the preceding illustrative example is used.   Here

$$K(z) = \frac{(1 + z^{-1})(a_1 z^{-1} + a_2 z^{-2})}{1 - cz^{-1}} \tag{7.40}$$

and

$$1 - K(z) = \frac{(1 - z^{-1})^2 (1 + b_1 z^{-1})}{1 - cz^{-1}} \tag{7.41}$$

By substituting (7.40) into (7.41) and solving for b_1 in terms of c, it is found that

$$b_1 = \frac{3 - c}{4} \tag{7.42}$$

Thus, the z transform of the error sequence is given by (7.34), resulting in

$$E(z) = \left\{ \frac{(1 - z^{-1})^2 \left[1 + \left(\dfrac{3 - c}{4} \right) z^{-1} \right]}{1 - cz^{-1}} \right\} R(z) \tag{7.43}$$

The sum of the squared errors is found by evaluation of (4.67), which results in the following for a ramp input:

$$S = \frac{-7c + 25}{16(1 - c)} \tag{7.44}$$

and for a step input

$$S = \frac{-6c + 26}{16} \tag{7.45}$$

These functions are plotted in Fig. 7.14 over the permissible range of the staleness factor c.   In this situation it is seen that no minimum can be found which will result in optimum performance for both step and ramp inputs, and it depends on which type of response is to be favored as to where the staleness factor is set. For the illustrative problem in this section, the choice of 0.5 favored the step response at the expense of the ramp response.

Generally speaking, the use of the staleness factor is a means of obtaining a compromise performance of a system to more than one input. Its use does not require additional complexity in the digital controller

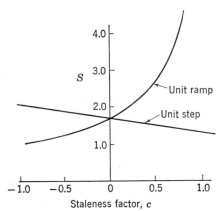

Fig. 7.14. Integrated-square error as function of staleness factor.

so long as the order of the denominator of $K(z)$ does not exceed that of the numerator. This can be readily ascertained from (7.5), where the ratio of $K(z)$ and $1 - K(z)$ produces a polynomial ratio in z which is of no higher order than the numerator of $K(z)$ if this condition obtains. Since most practical designs use a denominator in $K(z)$ which is of first order, no increase in complexity of the controller is expected.

7.7 The Design of Ripple-free Systems

In general, there is ripple in the output of systems which implement a minimal prototype or staleness factor. This ripple may be objectionable under certain circumstances. For instance, if mechanical elements are involved, excessive oscillatory stresses will be superimposed on those required to cause the system to respond smoothly to an input. A desirable objective is that the system contain no ripple after a suitably short transient period has elapsed. In this case, once the system has come to the steady state, no excess command input to the plant other than that required to maintain steady state is applied.

It is evident that, to obtain this type of performance, the feedforward components of the control system must be capable of generating a smooth output which is the same as the input. For instance, if the input is a ramp function, the output of the plant must also be a ramp function. To generate such a ramp, an integration must be present in the plant transfer function so that a constant command to the plant will, in the steady state produce the desired output. If the integration were not present in the plant, it would have to be supplied by some other cascaded element. It will be assumed in the discussions which follow that the feedforward element satisfies the condition that it contain the necessary integrations to produce ripple-free outputs as required. The problem then is to design the digital controller such that it will drive the system to this steady-state condition after some finite transient period.

The philosophy underlying such a design is to arrange the controller pulse transfer function in such a manner that the error-sequence response is of finite length, that is, the pulse transfer function $E_2(z)/R(z)$ contains a finite number of terms in z^{-1}. Referring to Fig. 7.3, the pulse sequence $E_2(z)$ which is applied to the plant and hold system typified by the pulse transfer function $G(z)$ is given by

$$E_2(z) = \frac{C(z)}{G(z)} \tag{7.46}$$

and
$$C(z) = K(z) R(z) \tag{7.47}$$

Substituting $C(z)$ from (7.47) in (7.46), there results

$$\frac{E_2(z)}{R(z)} = \frac{K(z)}{G(z)} \tag{7.48}$$

The over-all response function $K(z)$ must be so chosen that $E_2(z)/R(z)$ contain only a numerator polynomial in z^{-1}. Recalling that $G(z)$ is usually the ratio of polynomials in z^{-1}, it is immediately evident that $K(z)$ must contain *all* the zeros of $G(z)$, regardless of their location on the z plane. It is noted that this condition automatically includes the lesser condition applying to all error-sampled stabilized systems that $K(z)$ contain zeros of $G(z)$ which lie *outside* the unit circle in the z plane. In general, because $K(z)$ must contain as its zeros the additional zeros, the settling time of ripple-free systems exceeds that of minimal systems in so far as sample times are concerned.

The rules which apply to ripple-free design will be summarized:

1. All the rules for minimal prototype response systems apply to ripple-free systems.

2. To produce a ripple-free system response, it is necessary that the feedforward transfer function be capable of generating a continuous output function which is the same as the input function.

3. The over-all pulse transfer function $K(z)$ must contain as its zeros *all* the zeros of the plant pulse transfer function $G(z)$ and not just the zeros of $G(z)$ which lie outside the unit circle in the z plane.

The application of these rules can best be illustrated by means of an example. The system used to illustrate the minimal prototype and staleness factor in Secs. 7.5 and 7.6 will be used.

EXAMPLE

It is desired to design the digital-controller program $D(z)$ for the system of Fig. 7.8. The criterion is that the system respond to a step and ramp input with no ripple in the steady state and that the transient be of the shortest possible finite duration. First it is noted that the feedforward transfer function, including the zero-order hold, is capable of generating a continuous step or ramp function since a constant input E_2^* into the hold system will cause a continuous ramp at the output. This being the case, the system design can be carried out in the manner outlined in this section.

The feedforward pulse transfer function $G(z)$ was found in the illustrative example in Sec. 7.5 to be

$$G(z) = \frac{(1 + 2.34z^{-1})(1 + 0.16z^{-1})z^{-1}}{(1 - z^{-1})(1 - 0.368z^{-1})^2}$$

It is seen that there are zeros of $G(z)$ located at -2.34, -0.16, and ∞. To implement a ripple-free system, it is necessary that the over-all pulse transfer function $K(z)$ contain *all* these zeros and not just those which lie outside the unit circle in the z plane. Thus,

$$K(z) = z^{-1}(1 + 2.34z^{-1})(1 + 0.16z^{-1})(a_0 + a_1z^{-1})$$

By containing no denominator polynomial in z^{-1}, this form of $K(z)$ assures finite settling time, as well as ripple-free operation.

The second specification on $K(z)$ is that the system be capable of following a ramp input with zero steady-state error, in accordance with the requirement given by (7.15). This results in the equation for $1 - K(z)$, given by

$$1 - K(z) = (1 - z^{-1})^2(1 + b_1z^{-1} + b_2z^{-2})$$

Solving for $K(z)$ from the two relationships which contain it, there result the following numerical values for the constants:

$$a_0 = 0.73$$
$$a_1 = -0.47$$

which produce an over-all prototype response $K(z)$ given by

$$K(z) = 0.73z^{-1} + 1.35z^{-2} - 0.90z^{-3} - 0.18z^{-4}$$

This solution should be compared to that of the minimal prototype design given in Sec. 7.5, where it is seen that $K(z)$ contains terms in z^{-1} only up to the third power, while the ripple-free design contains terms up to the fourth power. This means that in so far as sampling instants are concerned, this design has a longer settling time by one sampling interval.

The response of the system to a unit ramp and a unit step are obtained by substitution of $K(z)$ in

$$C(z) = K(z)R(z)$$

where the appropriate expression for $R(z)$ is used. The resultant output sample sequences obtained from the inversion of $C(z)$ are plotted in Figs. 7.15 and 7.16, respectively. The intersample behavior of the system is sketched in solid lines, and it is seen that after the fourth sampling instant, the output ripple is reduced to zero. In the case of the step response plotted in Fig. 7.16, the overshoot is about 200 per cent, a figure which is comparable with that obtained in minimal prototype design and higher than that obtained with a system designed with a staleness factor.

The pulse transfer function of the digital compensator required to implement this over-all pulse transfer function is found by substitution in (7.5), resulting in

$$D(z) = \frac{0.73 - 1.007z^{-1} + 0.445z^{-2} - 0.0635z^{-3}}{1 + 0.27z^{-1} - 1.094z^{-2} - 0.176z^{-3}}$$

Again it is pointed out that the complexity of the digital controller is no greater with this approach than with the approach using minimal prototypes or staleness factor.

In applying the ripple-free design criterion, it is seen that $K(z)$ must contain as many zeros as does the plant pulse transfer function $G(z)$. This means that the settling time at sampling instants will generally be

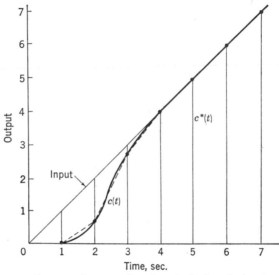

FIG. 7.15. Response of system in example using ripple-free design to unit ramp input.

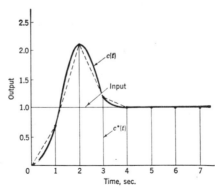

FIG. 7.16. Response of system in example using ripple-free design to a unit step input.

greater than that of minimal systems which have over-all pulse transfer functions containing only those zeros of the pulse transfer function which lie outside of the unit circle in the z plane.   Whether or not this is a disadvantage depends on the application.   If intersample ripple is considered a primary disadvantage, then the slight increase in settling time at sampling instants is a trivial factor.

7.8 Equivalent Digital-controller Systems

It is often possible to realize the over-all prototype pulse transfer functions described in previous sections without the use of an actual sampled-data processing unit or digital controller. Except for the sampler, all the elements in such systems are analogue or continuous and take the form of networks, tachometers, or active electronic elements. The general form

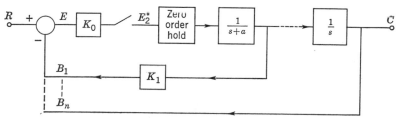

FIG. 7.17. Early feedback from system state variables.

of the system is shown in Fig. 7.17, where the error sampler is followed by a zero-order hold and a linear continuous plant. It is necessary that early feedback connections from each of the first-order cascaded elements of the plant transfer function $G(s)$ be tapped either directly or by simulation. The quantities being tapped are the "state variables" of the system. It is seen by a little reflection that the quantities $B_1, B_2, \ldots, B_n$ being fed back are linear combinations of the output and its n derivatives. As will be shown, it is possible to control the plant into ripple-free finite-settling-time operation, having these quantities available for feedback to the error line.

To facilitate the analysis of this system, a fictitious sampler will be inserted in each of the feedback lines, as shown in Fig. 7.18a. While these samplers do not exist in the actual system, their presence in the model used for analysis does not alter the system because they are seen to be redundant with the error sampler. If they operate synchronously with the error sampler, the additional sampling operations merely contribute a sequence of samples which are again sampled to form the error-sample sequence. Sampling twice synchronously is the same as sampling only once since any information between samples is not transmitted anyway.

The advantage of adopting this model is evident when it is realized that the feedback sequences at $B_1, B_2, \ldots, B_n$ can be related to the error sequence by a number of partial z transforms $G_1(z), G_2(z)$, etc., as shown in Fig. 7.18b. These partial z transforms need further explanation, but their product should yield the correct over-all pulse transfer function of the plant, $G_{12}(z)$. In the system shown in Fig. 7.18b, only two state variables C_1 and C are shown, indicating that the plant transfer function is second-order. The process to be described can readily be extended to higher-order systems.

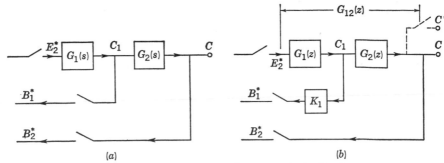

FIG. 7.18. Z-transform relationships for early feedback system.

The over-all pulse transfer function of the plant in Fig. 7.18b is chosen as $G_{12}(z)$, and it includes the hold system as well. If the continuous transfer function is separated as shown in Fig. 7.17, then the output of the first element, say $G_1(s)$, is the first state variable. The pulse transfer function corresponding to $G_1(s)$, namely, $G_1(z)$, is found. The second pulse transfer function $G_2(z)$ is then given by

$$G_2(z) = \frac{G_{12}(z)}{G_1(z)} \tag{7.49}$$

It is noted that $G_2(z)$ will not be exactly equal to the z transform corresponding to the element $G_2(s)$, as would have been the case if a sampler

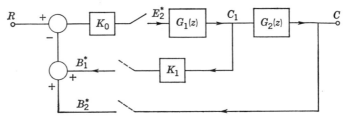

FIG. 7.19. Feedback system employing early feedback from system states.

had actually separated the two elements. The pulse transfer function $G_2(z)$ is fictitious and is introduced only the purposes of analysis. If there are more than two elements in the feedforward line, the process is repeated. The feedback pulse sequences $B_1(z)$ and $B_2(z)$ are given by the relation

$$B_1(z) = G_1(z)E_2(z)K_1 \tag{7.50}$$

and
$$B_2(z) = G_2(z)C_1(z) \tag{7.51}$$

Having these relations, and referring to Fig. 7.19, it is possible to derive

the over-all pulse transfer function by the usual methods, to give the
following:

$$K(z) = \frac{C(z)}{R(z)} = \frac{K_0 G_1(z) G_2(z)}{1 + K_0 G_1(z) G_2(z) + K_0 K_1 G_1(z)} \qquad (7.52)$$

The procedure in design is to adjust the gain constants K_0 and K_1 to
obtain the desired over-all pulse transfer function $K(z)$ which fulfills the
design specifications.

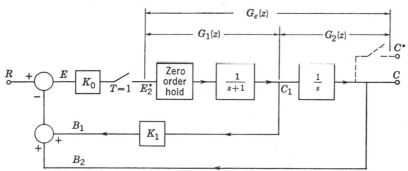

FIG. 7.20. System used to illustrate design of system with early feedback.

It is seen from (7.52) that in view of (7.49), the numerator contains all
the zeros of the plant pulse transfer function, thus fulfilling the requirement for ripple-free operation.   The other requirements on $K(z)$ to cause
the system to respond with zero error to a test input are fulfilled by adjustment of the gain constants, of which there are as many as the order of the
system.   It should be emphasized that ripple-free operation cannot be
obtained unless there are a sufficient number of integrations in the feedforward line to make this possible.   For instance, to respond to input
steps or ramps, at least one integration is required to make the design
practical.   Another point is that in order to implement such a system it
is necessary that each state variable, as indicated in Fig. 7.17, be available for instrumentation.   If this is not the case, these variables must be
generated by an auxiliary means.   In the extreme, if only the final output
of the plant is available, a complete analogue-computer simulation of the
plant would have to be placed in parallel with the actual plant and syn-
thetic state variables extracted from it.   Such a system might be as
complex as a full digitally controlled system.   On the other hand, where
most or some of the state variables are available, the system has many
desirable features.   This is illustrated most graphically by an example of
a simple instrument servomechanism.

EXAMPLE

To illustrate the design procedure, a servomechanism whose basic
block diagram is shown in Fig. 7.20 will be used.   The system consists
of a sampler in the error line, a zero-order data hold, and a transducer

consisting of an integrator and simple time delay. The latter is a typical transfer function found in small servomotors. It is assumed that the intermediate output C_1 is available for instrumentation, although in fact the equivalent effect could be obtained by using a tachometer at the output shaft of the servomechanism.

The design objective is to produce a system which is ripple-free, which has a finite settling time, and which is capable of responding to a step input without steady-state error. The desired over-all pulse transfer function $K(z)$ is specified by these requirements. As outlined in the preceding section, $K(z)$ must contain all the zeros of the plant pulse transfer function, which is given by

$$G_{12}(z) = \mathcal{Z} \frac{1 - e^{-Ts}}{s^2(s + 1)}$$

If it is assumed that the sampling interval T is unity, then $G_{12}(z)$ becomes

$$G_{12}(z) = \frac{0.368z^{-1}(1 + 0.718z^{-1})}{(1 - z^{-1})(1 - 0.368z^{-1})}$$

The zeros of $G_{12}(z)$ must be contained in the desired over-all pulse prototype function $K(z)$, thus,

$$K(z) = z^{-1}(1 + 0.718z^{-1})a_0$$

Only a_0 is included in this function since a minimum settling time is sought.

In order to respond without error to a unit step input without steady-state error, the following relation holds:

$$1 - K(z) = (1 - z^{-1})(1 + b_1z^{-1})$$

Solving these two relations containing $K(z)$ for the constants a_0 and b_1, there result the numerical values

$$a_0 = 0.581$$
$$b_1 = 0.418$$

Substituting these values back in the expressions for $K(z)$ and $1 - K(z)$,

$$K(z) = 0.581z^{-1}(1 + 0.718z^{-1})$$
$$1 - K(z) = (1 - z^{-1})(1 + 0.418z^{-1})$$

In order to achieve an over-all pulse transfer function $K(z)$ as specified, it is necessary that the equivalent feedforward pulse transfer function $G_e(z)$ be given by the usual expression

$$G_e(z) = \frac{K(z)}{1 - K(z)}$$

which, upon substitution of the expressions for $K(z)$ and $1 - K(z)$, becomes

$$G_e(z) = \frac{0.581^{-1}(1 + 0.718z^{-1})}{(1 - z^{-1})(1 + 0.418z^{-1})}$$

The selection of the gain constants K_0 and K_1 is made by causing the actual feedforward pulse transfer function of the system $G_a(z)$ to be equal to the required equivalent function $G_e(z)$. To obtain the expression for the actual feedforward pulse transfer function, Fig. 7.20 is seen to consist of two elements $G_1(z)$ and $G_2(z)$ such that their product is $G_{12}(z)$, which is to be altered by means of the early feedback to $G_a(z)$. The first step is to note that $G_1(z)$ is given by

$$G_1(z) = (1 - z^{-1})Z \frac{1}{s(s+1)}$$

which is, after simplification,

$$G_1(z) = \frac{0.632z^{-1}}{1 - 0.368z^{-1}}$$

The second pulse transfer function $G_2(z)$ is given by

$$G_2(z) = \frac{G_{12}(z)}{G_1(z)}$$

Substituting the expressions for $G_{12}(z)$ and $G_1(z)$, there results

$$G_2(z) = \frac{0.582(1 + 0.718z^{-1})}{1 - z^{-1}}$$

Now from Fig. 7.20, the actual feedforward pulse transfer function $G_a(z)$ which relates the output $C(z)$ and the command $E_2(z)$ is seen to be

$$G_a(z) = \frac{K_0 G_1(z)}{1 + K_0 K_1 G_1(z)} G_2(z)$$

Substituting $G_1(z)$ and $G_2(z)$ previously obtained, $G_a(z)$ becomes

$$G_a(z) = \frac{K_0(0.632)(0.582)(1 + 0.718z^{-1})z^{-1}}{[1 + (0.632K_0K_1 - 0.368)z^{-1}](1 - z^{-1})}$$

If the system being designed is to be identical with the required feedforward pulse transfer function, then

$$G_a(z) = G_e(z)$$

Equating these two functions and evaluating the constants K_0 and K_1 by identity, the following relations are obtained:

$$0.581 = (0.632)(K_0)(0.582)$$

and $\qquad 0.418 = 0.632K_0K_1 - 0.368$

Solving these equations for the gain constants,

$$K_0 = 1.58$$
$$K_1 = 0.786$$

By adjusting the gains to these values, the servomechanism which is designed will have the ripple-free finite settling time indicated by $K(z)$, which is

$$K(z) = 0.581z^{-1} + 0.418z^{-2}$$

The gain constant K_1 is seen to be a tachometer gain constant relating the signal which is fed back to the servoamplifier from the output shaft.

The foregoing example illustrates how "early" feedback connections can implement the equivalent of a digital controller, *provided* that all the early outputs are available and can be instrumented. These "early" feedback connections are identified with the "states" of the system in that their specification fully describes the performance of the linear system. If all the "states" of the system are not available for instrumentation, it is found that the full equivalence between the actual and desired feedforward pulse transfer function cannot be achieved and only partial compensation can be realized. In this case, a compromise in performance is sought rather than the full realization, as was the case in the illustrative example.

7.9 Finite-settling-time Systems Which Are Nonminimal

Except for those systems employing a staleness factor, finite settling time has characterized the systems considered in previous sections. Even with the staleness factor, a minimum prototype is used in the basic over-all pulse transfer function. These systems contained only the minimum number of terms consistent with the requirement that they be stable and that they respond to a prescribed test input without steady-state error. If additional constants are used in the over-all pulse transfer function, it was stated that these constants could be arbitrarily assigned. This opens up the possibility of selecting the extra system constants with a view of optimizing the system under some criterion. An approach[4] to this problem is to minimize the integrated-square error sequence in response to a test input.

In general, the over-all pulse transfer function for a system having finite settling time is given by

$$K(z) = a_1 z^{-1} + a_2 z^{-2} + \cdots + a_m z^{-m} \tag{7.53}$$

and to respond to a test input polynomial of order $n + 1$ without steady-state error,

$$1 - K(z) = (1 - z^{-1})^n[1 + b_1z^{-1} + \cdots + b_{m-n}z^{-(m-n)}] \quad (7.54)$$

Since (7.53) and (7.54) must be satisfied simultaneously, the order of the polynomials obtained by multiplying out must be the same; hence the final term in (7.54) must be of order $m - n$, as shown. The minimal prototype is the one which uses the minimum number of terms required to satisfy both (7.53) and (7.54). Any additional coefficients can be assigned values on the basis of optimization of the system, using the integrated-square error criterion. For a unity-feedback error-sampled system, the error to be minimized has a pulse transfer function given by

$$E(z) = [1 - K(z)]R(z) \quad (7.55)$$

To demonstrate the technique, a system which has been designed to respond to a unit ramp input without steady-state error will be used. For this case, the error z transform becomes

$$E(z) = [(1 - z^{-1})^2(1 + b_1z^{-1})]R(z) \quad (7.56)$$

The constant b_1 is to be assigned a value which optimizes the response of the system to a unit step input. It is recalled that finite-settling-time systems of the minimal type have considerable overshoot with step inputs, and the reduction of this effect is sought by choice of b_1. The integrated-square error is

$$\sum_{m=0}^{\infty} [e(mT)]^2 = \frac{1}{2\pi j}\int_{\Gamma} E(z)E(z^{-1})z^{-1}\,dz \quad (7.57)$$

For a unit step input, $E(z)$ is

$$E(z) = \frac{1}{1 - z^{-1}}[(1 - z^{-1})^2(1 + b_1z^{-1})] \quad (7.58)$$

which simplifies to

$$E(z) = 1 - (1 - b_1)z^{-1} - b_1z^{-2} \quad (7.59)$$

Substituting (7.59) back in (7.57) and evaluating the contour integral by the method of residues, there results for the integrated-square error the following:

$$\sum_{m=0}^{\infty} [e(mT)]^2 = 1 + (1 - b_1)^2 + b_1^2 \quad (7.60)$$

Simplifying this expression,

$$\sum_{m=0}^{\infty} [e(mT)]^2 = 2(1 - b_1 + b_1^2) \quad (7.61)$$

It is seen that the sum of the squared errors is a function of the constant b_1, which can, by ordinary methods, be evaluated to minimize (7.61). Differentiating and setting the derivative equal to zero, the value of b_1 is found to be 0.5.

With this value of b_1, the integrated-square error as obtained by substitution in (7.61) is 1.5. Had the minimal prototype been used instead, the integrated-square error sequence would have been 2.0, showing how a judicious choice of constant lowered the error in the sense shown. An important corollary is that by increasing the number of terms in $K(z)$ beyond the absolute minimum, the digital controller is complicated by the fact that it must have additional storage. The controller pulse transfer function $D(z)$ is of higher order the greater the number of terms included in $K(z)$.

To illustrate what can be done by these minimization procedures, a number of systems having the capability of responding to a ramp input with zero steady-state error will be considered. In general such systems have the error z transform given by

$$E(z) = (1 - z^{-1})^2(1 + b_1 z^{-1} + b_2 z^{-2} + \cdots b_n z^{-n}) \qquad (7.62)$$

If the minimal prototype is assumed, then all b's will be zero. On the other hand, increasing numbers of arbitrary constants are available for evaluation as more terms of (7.62) are used. A tabulation of the performance of this type of system is given in Table 7.2 for increasingly complex systems. The integrated-square error sequence is given for a unit impulse, a unit step, and a unit ramp input to the system.

TABLE 7.2. INTEGRATED-SQUARE ERROR SEQUENCES FOR OPTIMIZED RESPONSE TO UNIT STEP INPUT WITH UNIT IMPULSE, STEP, AND RAMP INPUTS

Type	$\sum_{m=0}^{\infty} [e(mT)]^2$			
	Coefficients	Impulse input	Step input (optimum)	Ramp input
Minimal	$b_n = 0$	6.0	2.0	1.0
	$b_1 = 0.5$	3.5	1.5	1.25
	$b_1 = 0.667$ $b_2 = 0.133$	2.889	1.33	1.556
	$b_1 = 0.75$ $b_2 = 0.50$ $b_3 = 0.25$	2.625	1.25	1.875

The first system for which all b's are zero is the minimal prototype.   It shows that the unit step for which optimization was implemented has an integrated-square error of 2.0.   The impulse-response and the ramp-response errors are 6.0 and 1.0, respectively.   As the system becomes more complex, the integrated-square error sequences for the unit step input become smaller and smaller since this is the input for which minimization is implemented.   The impulse input response likewise becomes better as more arbitrary constants are used.   On the other hand, this is done at the expense of the ramp input, as the figures show.   Such a state of affairs is typical since minimization with one form of input is generally achieved at the expense of the other form of input.   Had the system been optimized for a ramp input, this performance would have been increasingly improved as the complexity of the system increased.

The procedure outlined in this section is merely one way in which the arbitrary constants in the over-all response function can be evaluated. It is realized that the forms given here are for those systems where no complications such as those due to uncancellable poles and zeros arise. In these cases, the minimum number of constants is higher than for the class of systems described here, but the additional arbitrary constants over and above this minimum can be evaluated in much the same manner as for the uncomplicated case discussed here.   It should be noted also that a compromise can be reached where the integrated-square error sequence is minimized not for just one input, such as the step chosen in this discussion, but that the response to a number of inputs can be reduced, though not to their respective minima.   In all cases, the increased complication means that the digital-controller pulse transfer function $D(z)$ will contain more terms in both numerator and denominator than with minimum systems.   In the limit, if an infinite number of arbitrary constants were permitted, the response to any input could be fully programmed, but, of course, this would require an infinite storage in the digital controller.

7.10 Systems with Plant Saturation

Systems in which a gain factor saturates are, of course, nonlinear and cannot be designed or analyzed by the procedures described in this chapter.   Another view of such systems,[3] however, is that a controller be designed in such a manner that the system does not saturate when subjected to the most severe input expected.   For smaller inputs than this one, the system certainly will not saturate.   By adopting this approach, the design of the digital controller can be carried out as in the linear case. The requirement placed on the digital controller is that its output, which is the input to the plant, never exceed some upper limit under the worst input condition. Referring to Fig. 7.21, this means that with the largest test input at R, the pulse sequence E_2 should be limited to some upper bound E_m, the maximum command signal which the plant is capable of taking without saturating. The first condition required to bring this about is that the output of the digital controller be zero or a finite con-

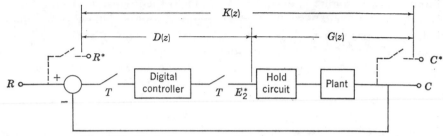

FIG. 7.21. Typical system having plant with saturation.

stant in the steady state. Assuming that this condition is met, there is a procedure[3] for preventing the pulse sequence applied to the plant from exceeding its specified upper bound.

This is done by noting that, by definition,

$$K(z) = \frac{C(z)}{R(z)} \tag{7.63}$$

and that

$$C(z) = E_2(z)G(z) \tag{7.64}$$

from which there results the equality

$$K(z)R(z) = E_2(z)G(z) \tag{7.65}$$

The test input function pulse transform $R(z)$ is specified, as is the plant pulse transfer function $G(z)$. It remains to find the over-all pulse transfer function $K(z)$ such that no pulse in $E_2(z)$ has a magnitude exceeding the upper bound.

Recalling the series form of the pulse transfer functions, (7.65) may be rewritten in the form

$$[r_0 + r_1 z^{-1} + \cdots][k_m z^{-m} + k_{m+1} z^{-(m+1)} + \cdots k_p z^{-p}]$$
$$= [e_0 + e_1 z^{-1} + \cdots e_b z^{-b}][g_m z^{-m} + g_{m+1} z^{-(m+1)} \cdots] \tag{7.66}$$

Multiplying this sequence through and collecting the coefficient of like orders of z^{-1}, there result a number of equalities obtained by equating the coefficients of like powers of z^{-1}. These equalities are

$$r_0 k_m = e_0 g_m$$
$$r_0 k_{m+1} + r_1 k_m = e_0 g_{m+1} + e_1 g_m$$
$$r_0 k_{m+2} + r_1 k_{m+1} + r_2 k_m = e_0 g_{m+2} + e_1 g_{m+1} + e_2 g_m$$
$$\text{etc.} \tag{7.67}$$

Expressed in this form it is possible to obtain the various coefficients of the pulse sequence whose pulse transfer function is $K(z)$.

The step-by-step procedure which is applied is to consider the first relation of (7.67). Here r_0 is the first pulse of the specified input pulse sequence, k_m is the first coefficient of the plant sequence, and e_0 is the first pulse in the command sequence whose pulse transfer function is $E_2(z)$. From this relation, k_m is obtained arbitrarily, *so long as it is not required for e_0 to be greater than its upper bound.* If the fastest possible rise time is desired, e_0 is set at this limit and k_m computed. The second coefficient of $K(z)$, k_{m+1}, is obtained in a similar manner from the second equation in (7.67) by attempting to set k_{m+1} at the value which satisfies the requirements for responding to a unit step or ramp without error. If so setting the value of k_{m+1} causes the error coefficient e_1 to exceed the limit, e_1 is set at this limit and the coefficient k_{m+1} computed from this relation. The procedure is repeated until such time as the limitation on the coefficient e_k is no longer set by the equations of (7.67), after which time the other necessary conditions on $K(z)$ can be imposed. The simultaneous satisfying of the relations of (7.67) and those ordinarily imposed on $K(z)$ will complete the design.

It is recognized that while $K(z)$ will represent a finite settling time using this procedure, this finite settling time will not be minimal or even minimum. Additional k's are required to simultaneously satisfy the requirements of (7.67) with regard to the upper limit of the e's. In effect, this procedure takes the controller design step by step during the transient period and limits the command magnitudes which the controller produces. At the same time, the general conditions on $K(z)$ concerning its structure to follow input test functions and the requirement of non-cancellation of poles and zeros on or outside the unit circle in the z plane must be observed also.

EXAMPLE

An error-sampled system has unity feedback and a feedforward pulse transfer function $G(z)$, including the data-hold circuit, given by the following:

$$G(z) = \frac{(0.368 + 0.264z^{-1})z^{-1}}{(1 - 0.368z^{-1})(1 - z^{-1})}$$

This pulse transfer function can be expanded into a power series in z^{-1} by the simple process of long division, yielding the following series:

$$G(z) = 0.368z^{-1} + 0.767z^{-2} + 0.915z^{-3} + 0.968z^{-4} + \cdots$$

The coefficients of the series in z^{-1} are the various values of g_k given in (7.67). The input is assumed to be a unit step function whose pulse transfer function is, in series form, the following:

$$R(z) = 1 + z^{-1} + z^{-2} + z^{-3} + \cdots$$

The system is to respond to a step function with zero steady-state error, so that a requirement on the over-all pulse transfer function is that

$$1 - K(z) = (1 - z^{-1})(1 + b_1 z^{-1} + b_2 z^{-2} + \cdots)$$

where the various b's are arbitrary or dependent on conditions brought about by saturation limitations. It is assumed that the maximum command signal applied to the plant not exceed 1.5 units. This limit is the saturation limit of the plant, and any higher signal at the input would produce no additional output.

Starting with the first equation of (7.67), substitution of r_0 and g_1 produces the relationship

$$k_1 = (e_0)(0.368)$$

If there were no other terms in the over-all pulse transfer function $K(z)$, all b's in the expression $1 - K(z)$ would be zero and $K(z)$ would be z^{-1}. Thus, if k_1 were taken at the minimal prototype value of unity, e_0 would be given by

$$e_0 = \frac{1}{0.368}$$
$$= 2.72$$

If the minimal prototype were desired, the first pulse applied to the plant is 2.72, which is higher than allowable. The maximum value of e_0 can be only 1.5, and hence the first term of the over-all pulse transfer function must be, from (7.67),

$$k_1 = (1.5)(0.368)$$

from which

$$k_1 = 0.552$$

Thus, the first term of the series representation of the over-all pulse transfer function $K(z)$ has been ascertained.

To find the second term of $K(z)$, the next higher-order prototype for $K(z)$ is used. To respond to a unit step input without error, it is necessary that

$$1 - K(z) = (1 - z^{-1})(1 + b_1 z^{-1})$$

which, upon multiplying out, becomes

$$1 - K(z) = 1 + (b_1 - 1)z^{-1} - b_1 z^{-2}$$

from which $K(z)$ is

$$K(z) = -(b_1 - 1)z^{-1} + b_1 z^{-2}$$

Returning now to the second expression in (7.67) and substituting r_0, r_1, k_1, e_0, g_1, and g_2, there results a relation between the second command pulse and the second over-all transfer function coefficient, k_2. Substituting numerical values,

$$k_2 + 0.552 = (1.5)(0.767) + (e_1)(0.368)$$

Simplifying,

$$k_2 = 0.598 + 0.368e_1$$

Also, from the expression for $K(z)$, k_1 is $(b_1 - 1)$, which has already been found to be equal to 0.552. From this same relationship, k_2 is seen to be equal to b_1, which means that

$$-(b_1 - 1) = 0.552$$

and

$$b_1 = k_2$$

Solving,

$$k_2 = 0.448$$

This value of k_2 is required, where the first term of $K(z)$ is equal to $0.552z^{-1}$, if the system is to respond to a unit step input without error. Thus, from the expression relating k_2 and e_1,

$$e_1 = -0.407$$

Since this value is less than the maximum allowable value of 1.5, it is a feasible term and the value of k_2 is acceptable. Thus, $K(z)$ is given by

$$K(z) = 0.552z^{-1} + 0.448z^{-2}$$

With this value of $K(z)$, the first command input to the plant is a pulse whose magnitude is 1.5 and the second a pulse of magnitude 0.407. This assumes, of course, that the input is a unit step function. If the input step is higher, the command signal to the plant will be higher in proportion and the design is not valid. In other words, the design is based on the largest input expected.

The command sequence applied to the plant when a unit step is applied to the input can be found by applying (7.65), using the $K(z)$ found in the example. Thus,

$$E_2(z) = \frac{K(z)}{G(z)} R(z)$$

which becomes

$$E_2(z) = \frac{(0.552 + 0.448z^{-1})(1 - 0.368z^{-1})}{0.368 + 0.264z^{-1}}$$

Simplifying this expression,

$$E_2(z) = 1.5 \frac{(1 + 0.81z^{-1})(1 - 0.368z^{-1})}{1 + 0.716z^{-1}}$$

Inverting this pulse transform by long division, the command sequence which is applied to the plant becomes

$$e_2^*(t) = 1.5\delta(0) - 0.41\delta(T) - 0.153\delta(2T) + 0.11\delta(3T) - 0.079\delta(4T)$$
$$+ \cdots$$

It is seen that the sequence applied to the plant never exceeds the specified limit of 1.5. The price for this limitation is that the settling time has been increased from the minimal value of one sample time to two sample times and the digital controller has been made more complicated by requiring an additional storage.

7.11 "Bypass" Digital Controllers

One of the important concerns of the designer of a control system is that a failure of a component or controller should not result in damaging failure of the entire system. In the language of the designer, systems should "fail safe" when one or more components fail. As an illustration, a chemical process being automatically regulated should be inherently stable so that failure of the controller would cause no violent behavior. Another good illustration is the piloted aircraft which employs an automatic pilot. For reasons of safety, the aircraft being controlled is designed to be inherently stable so that its open-cycle behavior is acceptable. In such a situation, failure of the automatic pilot would merely cause a drift off course or a change of altitude, but no major instability. In this circumstance, where the automatic pilot has failed, the human pilot takes over control of the aircraft. In the other extreme is the guided missile, which is entirely automatic and which relies on automatic equipment to pilot and guide it to its target. In this case, any sacrifices that are made to produce an inherently stable missile are misdirected since a failure of the automatic equipment would result in a failure to complete its mission. In this case, no direct problem of safety exists and a failure resulting in destruction of the missile would be acceptable.

For that class of systems which lie somewhere between the two extremes described, a compromise structure can be devised. If it is assumed that a digital controller is not as reliable as straight-through continuous instrumentation and data-transfer equipment, a compromise can be achieved in which the reliability of the continuous system and the improved performance of the digitally controlled system are attained.[43] The basic block diagram for such a system is shown in Fig. 7.22, where it is seen that the digital controller bypasses or is in parallel with a continuous connection from the error signal and the plant. The command signal to the plant $E_3(z)$ is the sum of the continuous and digital controller signals. Thus, if the digital controller becomes inoperative and is taken out of service, a continuous closed-loop system remains operative.

If this remaining system is designed to be stable, the system will not fail completely, though its performance will deteriorate.

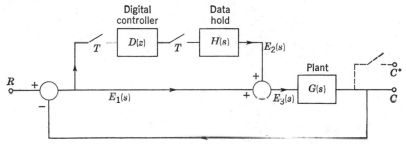

FIG. 7.22. System employing bypass digital controller.

The relations which hold for a system like this one are more complicated because the continuous and reconstructed sampled signals are mixed. Referring to Fig. 7.22, it is seen that

$$C(s) = G(s)E_3(s) \tag{7.68}$$

Also, the command signal transform $E_3(s)$ is given by

$$E_3(s) = E_1(s) + E_1^*(s)D^*(s)H(s) \tag{7.69}$$

Substituting (7.69) into (7.68),

$$C(s) = G(s)E_1(s) + G(s)H(s)D^*(s)E_1^*(s) \tag{7.70}$$

Now it is readily seen that

$$E_1(s) = R(s) - C(s) \tag{7.71}$$
$$\text{and} \qquad E_1^*(s) = R^*(s) - C^*(s) \tag{7.72}$$

Substituting (7.71) and (7.72) into (7.70), there results

$$C(s) = G(s)R(s) - G(s)C(s) + G(s)H(s)D^*(s)R^*(s)$$
$$- G(s)H(s)D^*(s)C^*(s) \tag{7.73}$$

Collecting terms and solving for $C(s)$,

$$C(s) = \frac{G(s)}{1 + G(s)} R(s) + \frac{G(s)}{1 + G(s)} H(s)D^*(s)R^*(s)$$
$$- \frac{G(s)}{1 + G(s)} H(s)D^*(s)C^*(s) \tag{7.74}$$

Defining $A(s)$ as

$$A(s) = \frac{G(s)}{1 + G(s)} \tag{7.75}$$

where it is recognized that $A(s)$ is the over-all transfer function of the continuous system with the digital controller omitted, (7.74) can be rewritten as

$$C(s) = A(s)R(s) + A(s)H(s)D^*(s)R^*(s) - A(s)H(s)D^*(s)C^*(s) \quad (7.76)$$

Taking the z transform of both sides and recalling that the z transform of a pulse transfer function such as $D^*(s)$ is the pulse transfer function itself and replacing $D^*(s)$ by $D(z)$, (7.76) becomes

$$C(z) = AR(z) + AH(z)D(z)R(z) - AH(z)D(z)C(z) \quad (7.77)$$

Solving for $C(z)$,

$$C(z) = \frac{AR(z) + AH(z)D(z)R(z)}{1 + AH(z)D(z)} \quad (7.78)$$

It is seen from (7.78) that an over-all pulse transfer function for the system is not readily obtained since $R(z)$ is not separable from the expression. It is possible, however, to define a quasi-over-all pulse transfer function as follows

$$K_R(z) = \frac{C(z)}{R(z)} = \frac{[AR(z)/R(z)] + AH(z)D(z)}{1 + AH(z)D(z)} \quad (7.79)$$

It is seen that $K_R(z)$ is dependent on the input $R(z)$. On the other hand, if a design procedure is adopted where a desired response is sought for a given test input, it is acceptable to consider $K_R(z)$ as an over-all pulse transfer function and to design a digital-controller pulse transfer function which will implement this desired result. Solving (7.79) for $D(z)$, there results

$$D(z) = \frac{1}{AH(z)} \frac{K_R(z) - [AR(z)/R(z)]}{1 - K_R(z)} \quad (7.80)$$

As in the case of the other digital-controller designs studied in this chapter, there will be certain restrictions placed on the selection of $K_R(z)$. The conditions of physical realizability are the same as those given in (7.9), where $K(z)$ must have a term of zero order in the denominator. Secondly, if the system is to respond to a test input which is a power of time such as a step, ramp, or constant acceleration, the restriction on $1 - K(z)$ given in (7.15) must be satisfied. Less obvious are the restrictions placed on $K_R(z)$ required to maintain a stable system.

In order to maintain a stable system, the digital-controller pulse transfer function $D(z)$ cannot be allowed to cancel poles or zeros of the system indiscriminately. It is seen from (7.80) that a situation similar to that discussed in Sec. 7.5 exists. The only difference is seen by contrasting (7.80) and (7.21). The numerator of (7.80), which must contain as its zeros all those zeros of $AH(z)$ whose magnitudes are equal to or greater than unity, is $K_R(z) - [AR(z)/R(z)]$, rather than the simpler form that would be found in (7.21), namely, $K_s(z)$.

The condition relative to the form of $1 - K_R(z)$ is less obvious and is found by manipulating (7.79) to yield the equality

$$1 - K_R(z) = \frac{1 - [AR(z)/R(z)]}{1 + AH(z)D(z)} \tag{7.81}$$

Solving for the characteristic equation,

$$1 + AH(z)D(z) = \frac{1 - [AR(z)/R(z)]}{1 - K_R(z)} = 0 \tag{7.82}$$

It is readily seen that in order that the characteristic equation not contain zeros stemming from $1 - [AR(z)/R(z)]$ whose magnitudes are greater than unity, it is necessary that $K_R(z)$ be so specified that $1 - K_R(z)$ contains such zeros.

These rules of design may be summarized as follows:

1. The specified over-all pulse transfer function $K_R(z)$ must satisfy the conditions of physical realizability as expressed in (7.9).

2. In order that the system respond to specified test inputs which are time functions of the form t^m with no steady-state error, it is necessary that $1 - K_R(z)$ contain a factor $(1 - z)^{m+1}$.

3. The digital-controller pulse transfer function $D(z)$ should not cancel those zeros of $AH(z)$ which have magnitudes equal to or greater than unity. This condition is met by selecting $K_R(z)$ such that the function $K_R(z) - [AR(z)/R(z)]$ contains all those zeros as its own.

4. The zeros of the function $1 - [AR(z)/R(z)]$ whose magnitudes are equal to or greater than unity must be contained in $1 - K_R(z)$.

By meeting all of these conditions, a stable system using a bypass controller is assured.

EXAMPLE

To illustrate the design procedure, the system given in Fig. 7.22 is assumed that

$$G(s) = \frac{1}{s(s + 0.5)}$$

The hold system is to be of zero order, and $H(s)$ is then

$$H(s) = \frac{1 - e^{-sT}}{s}$$

where T is taken as 1.5 sec. It is desired that this system respond without steady-state error to a unit step input so that

$$R(s) = \frac{1}{s}$$

From the definition given in (7.75), $A(s)$ is

$$A(s) = \frac{1}{s^2 + 0.5s + 1}$$

It is recalled that $A(s)$ is the over-all continuous response transfer function with the digital controller not connected. In this respect, the system is stable in the absence of the controller, but it is underdamped and has an undamped resonant period of some 6.6 sec.

The transfer function $A(s)H(s)$ is given by

$$A(s)H(s) = (1 - e^{-1.5s}) \frac{1}{s(s^2 + 0.5s + 1)}$$

Taking the z transform of this expression,

$$AH(z) = \frac{0.74z^{-1} + 0.57z^{-2}}{1 - 0.16z^{-1} + 0.47z^{-2}}$$

It is seen that $AH(z)$ has no zeros of magnitude greater than unity. This means that the restriction set forth in rule 3 above does not apply. Thus, $K_R(z)$ can be chosen arbitrarily and is taken as

$$K_R(z) = a_1 z^{-1} + a_2 z^{-2}$$

where the a's are constants to be determined.

To satisfy the condition that the steady-state error in response to a unit step input be zero, the condition on $K_R(z)$ is that

$$1 - K_R(z) = (1 - z^{-1})(1 + b_1 z^{-1})$$

The final condition is that given in rule 4. The required expression is

$$\frac{AR(z)}{R(z)} = \frac{Z\{1/[s(s^2 + 0.5s + 1)]\}}{Z 1/s}$$

which is

$$\frac{AR(z)}{R(z)} = (1 - z^{-1})Z \frac{1}{s(s^2 + 0.5s + 1)}$$

It is seen that this expression is identical to $AH(z)$ in this problem so that the previously derived numerical expression can be used. Substituting this expression in the following,

$$1 - \frac{AR(z)}{R(z)} = \frac{1 - 0.90z^{-1} - 0.10z^{-2}}{1 - 0.16z^{-1} + 0.47z^{-2}}$$

The zeros of this expression are at 1.0 and −0.10, which means that $1 - K_R(z)$ must also contain a zero at 1.0 to produce a stable system. It so happens that this requirement is also that for having the system respond to a step input without steady-state error. Thus,

$$K_R(z) = a_1 z^{-1} + a_2 z^{-2}$$

and $$1 - K_R(z) = (1 - z^{-1})(1 + b_1 z^{-1})$$

It is seen that these two conditions on $K_R(z)$ are satisfied by taking a_2 and b_1 equal to zero and a_1 equal to unity. This would produce a system having a finite settling time of one sampling interval. The extra terms permit the arbitrary assignment of one coefficient. Taking a value of 0.567 for a_1, it follows that a_2 and b_1 must be 0.433 and 0.433, respectively. Thus,

$$K_R(z) = 0.567z^{-1} + 0.433z^{-2}$$

This expression holds only for a unit step input since the form of $K_R(z)$ depends on the input.

The output pulse sequence resulting from the application of a unit step input is obtained by inverting $C(z)$,

$$C(z) = \frac{0.567z^{-1} + 0.433z^{-2}}{1 - z^{-1}}$$

which upon inversion yields the output sequence $c^*(t)$,

$$c^*(t) = 0.567\delta(t) + 1.0\delta(t - T) + 1.0\delta(t - 2T) + \cdots$$

The system settles at sampling instants in two sample times. In contrast, the system without the digital controller would have a sequence of values measured at sampling instants given by

$$c_1^*(t) = 0.742\delta(t) + 1.430\delta(t - T) + 1.193\delta(t - 2T)$$
$$+ 0.830\delta(t - 3T) + \cdots$$

The digitally compensated system settles in a shorter time and, as expected, can respond to a step input with zero steady-state error. It should be pointed out that there will be intersample ripple in the digitally compensated system which does not appear in the sequence representation. It should also be pointed out that the assumption is made that the input step function appears at the instant of the first sample. If this does not occur, there will be more overshoot since the digital compensator does not produce a command output until a sample time is reached.

The illustrative example shows how the design procedure is applied to a simple problem. By properly designing the bypass digital controller, improved performance can be achieved. Naturally, the sampling period must be high enough to generate command outputs frequently. This is particularly important for those cases where the input occurs at instants of time not corresponding to sampling instants. During the period preceding the first sample time, the system is controlled by the continuous elements and the desired response is not achieved. Experimental results obtained on a system like that of the illustrative example[43] show that systems may have overshoots which are many times greater than those obtained with a step function applied at or near a sampling instant. To prevent this form of overshoot, the sampling frequency is increased and the effect is reduced.

7.12 Effect of Disturbances on Digitally Controlled Systems

In the previous discussions, it was assumed that the only excitation of the control system was at the input, where it was subtracted from the output to form an error signal. Such systems are classed as servo-mechanisms or duplicator feedback control systems. In practical systems, inputs may be experienced elsewhere in the system and are usually

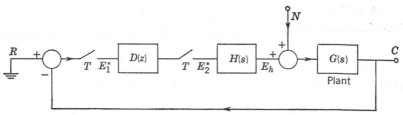

FIG. 7.23. Digitally stabilized system with disturbances.

in the form of disturbances to which the system should not respond. A pure regulator system has a fixed reference or set point, and the only dynamic effects are the result of disturbances which the controller attempts to neutralize. In regulator-system design, these inputs are the important ones, and the controller design is dictated by them rather than response to set-point changes.

A general discussion of regulator-system design is not entirely possible, because the disturbances may enter almost anywhere in a system. For purposes of discussion, however, the system shown in Fig. 7.23 will be used. In this system a disturbance input is assumed to enter the system just before the plant and after the data hold of the digital controller. This input N is assumed to be systematic, that is, it is a definable function, such as a step. The reference input R is assumed to be a constant and, since the system is linear, only that component of the output caused by the disturbance need be considered since it can be superimposed on any other outputs produced by other sources of excitation. The relations which hold in this system are

$$C(s) = N(s)G(s) + E_h(s)G(s) \qquad (7.83)$$

and
$$E_h(s) = E_1^*(s)D^*(s)H(s) \qquad (7.84)$$

Also, since the input R is assumed to be zero for this development,

$$E_1^*(s) = -C^*(s) \qquad (7.85)$$

Combining (7.83), (7.84), and (7.85),

$$C(s) = N(s)G(s) - C^*(s)D^*(s)H(s)G(s) \qquad (7.86)$$

Taking the z transform of both sides of the equation,

$$C(z) = NG(z) - C(z)D(z)GH(z) \tag{7.87}$$

Solving for $C(z)$,

$$C(z) = \frac{NG(z)}{1 + D(z)GH(z)} \tag{7.88}$$

It is seen that an over-all pulse transfer function relating the output to the disturbance cannot be obtained because it is not possible to separate $N(z)$ from $NG(z)$.

Using an approach similar to that of the previous section, a quasi-over-all pulse transfer function is obtained as follows:

$$K_N(z) = \frac{NG(z)/N(z)}{1 + D(z)GH(z)} \tag{7.89}$$

This pulse transfer function is meaningful only for a particular $N(z)$ and must be used in that manner.

Recalling that the over-all pulse transfer function for excitation at the input R is given by

$$K(z) = \frac{D(z)GH(z)}{1 + D(z)GH(z)} \tag{7.90}$$

It is readily ascertained that

$$K_N(z) = \frac{NG(z)}{N(z)} [1 - K(z)] \tag{7.91}$$

If the system is to regulate to cancel out a disturbance $N(z)$, it is necessary that $K_N(z)$ have a form which produces zero steady-state error for the particular $N(z)$ for which it is designed.

As an example, if $N(z)$ is a step-function disturbance such as that produced by the sudden closure of a valve in a process control system, then to cancel out this effect in the steady state it is necessary that

$$K_N(z) = (1 - z^{-1})F(z) \tag{7.92}$$

where $F(z)$ is an unspecified polynomial ratio in z. In many cases it is seen from (7.91) that this is automatically satisfied since the same requirement may have been put on $1 - K(z)$. There is the possibility, however, that the term $NG(z)/N(z)$ may affect the result.

EXAMPLE

The example relates to the system whose block diagram is shown in Fig. 7.23. The plant transfer function $G(s)$ is

$$G(s) = \frac{1}{s(s + 1)}$$

The data hold is of the zero-order type, and its transfer function is

$$H(s) = \frac{1 - e^{-s}}{s}$$

since the sampling interval T is taken as 1 sec.   The disturbance N is a unit step function so that

$$N(s) = \frac{1}{s}$$

The various pulse transfer functions required for substitution in (7.91) are

$$NG(z) = \frac{0.368z^{-1}(1 + 0.718z^{-1})}{(1 - z^{-1})^2(1 - 0.368z^{-1})}$$

and

$$N(z) = \frac{1}{1 - z^{-1}}$$

The system has been designed to respond to a unit step input with zero steady-state error, and the design for this condition leads to the result

$$1 - K(z) = (1 - z^{-1})(1 + 0.418z^{-1})$$

Substituting these pulse transforms in (7.91), the disturbance pulse transfer function becomes

$$K_N(z) = \frac{0.368z^{-1}(1 + 0.718z^{-1})(1 + 0.418z^{-1})}{1 - 0.368z^{-1}}$$

It is seen that $K_N(z)$ does not contain $1 - z^{-1}$ as a factor so that it will not reduce the disturbance to zero.   As a matter of fact if a unit step function is applied, the steady-state output (or error) is obtained by the usual final-value theorem and turns out to be 1.43.   This is not good performance in reducing the effect of a disturbance; as a matter of fact, the output amplifies the disturbance.   This result is not too surprising when it is recalled that regulating effect is produced by a high or infinite gain in the feedback line between the output of the plant and the point of application of the disturbance.   The system design results in no integration in the digital controller since none is needed to respond to a step at the input.

To reduce the effect of the disturbance to zero in the steady state, it is necessary that $1 - K(z)$ contain an additional factor $1 - z^{-1}$.   Thus, for steady-state error suppression, it is necessary that the following be true:

$$1 - K(z) = (1 - z^{-1})^2 F(z)$$

if the error is caused by a step disturbance applied at N.   This result causes the digital controller to supply an additional integration in the feedforward loop so that the system will not only reduce the effect of a step disturbance applied at N to zero in the steady state but will also make the system capable of responding to a ramp at the input.

7.13 Implementation of Digital Controllers

A linear digital controller is characterized by a pulse transfer function, which was shown in Sec. 4.6 to represent a linear recursion formula in the time domain. The output sample of the controller is the weighted sum of a number of past input and output samples. This process requires a storage function which holds the past samples and an arithmetic operation which carries out the weighting and summing. Such a program can be implemented by a digital computer which is programmed to carry out the necessary operation. Schematically, the operation of the computer is shown in Fig. 4.10, where the sequence of operations is shown. From a practical viewpoint, however, digital controllers need not be in the form of digital computers. For instance, it is possible to implement the controller using completely analogue techniques.

A typical analogue implementation* is shown in Fig. 7.24a, where the two groups of eight dials operate potentiometers which adjust the weighting coefficients applied to eight input and eight output samples. Lower-order pulse transfer functions are realized by setting some of these coefficients to zero. The sequence of operations is controlled by a set of stepping switches actuated by a central timer. The latter is a constant adjustable speed drive which operates a set of cams and microswitches. It is possible to obtain sampling intervals ranging from 1 to 20 sec with this system. This unit is strictly for experimental laboratory use and was not designed for field applications.

One of the disadvantages of a fully analogue unit is the drift which occurs in the storage units. The use of condensers, and the mechanical switching involved, leads to leakage problems. It is more advantageous to use drift-free storage elements, such as digital registers, for data storage. On the other hand, the simplicity of analogue methods to perform the arithmetic operations and the fact that the plant must be supplied with an analogue command signal suggests that a mixed system of this type is optimum from a practical point of view. Such a system shown in Fig. 7.24b has been designed and constructed.† If a digital computer is used for other functions in a complex system, it can be programmed to give real-time command signals to the plant at sampling intervals. Digital control, whether it be by the use of a complete analogue imple-

---

* This unit was constructed at the Department of Electrical Engineering, Columbia University, New York.

† Department of Electrical Engineering, Columbia University, New York.

mentation or by mixed implementation of a fully digital implementation, is practical.

One of the advantages of digital controllers is that they are particularly applicable to systems having large time constants, on the order of minutes or even hours.   If such systems were to be compensated by conventional continuous methods, inordinately large time constants would be required

(a)   (b)

FIG. 7.24. Laboratory implementation of digital controller.   (a) Early analogue model.   (b) Later model using digital number storage and analogue arithmetic operations.

in the compensating networks.   For instance, there are some chemical processes whose time constants are measured in hours or fractions thereof. Since the digital controller can store data for very long periods, provided that drift-free methods are used, it is relatively simple to implement a digital controller for such a plant.   The sampling interval would be chosen consistent with the plant characteristics and, regardless of its magnitude, a digital controller could be designed.   In those systems where a digital computer forms part of the data-processing system, a control program could be used which would compute commands to the plant at sampling instants. The exact form of the digital controller depends on the application.

7.14 Summary

Feedback control systems can be compensated by means of active devices known as digital controllers. These devices accept a sequence of input samples and process them linearly to generate a sequence of commands which are applied to the plant. The linear program is designed to compensate for deficiencies in the plant pulse transfer function and to produce a system which has an over-all pulse transfer function which is acceptable and desirable.

There are a number of possible over-all prototype response functions. The minimal prototype is one which produces the shortest finite settling time consistent with steady-state characteristics in response to some test function applied to the input. In this, as well as other prototypes, there are certain limitations imposed by the poles and zeros of the plant pulse transfer function which lie outside of the unit circle in the z plane. In such cases, the minimal prototype response cannot be realized, but, instead, a longer minimum finite settling time results. One of the disadvantages of minimal prototypes is that the system emerges from the transient in a nonneutral state and continues to ripple between sampling instants long after the system has settled at sampling instants. Another disadvantage is that the system response to inputs other than that for which it is designed is apt to be poor.

A compromise prototype response function is the one employing a staleness factor, which essentially smooths the response to various inputs and which produces acceptable but not minimum response. This system also has ripple at its output, and the settling time even at sampling instants is infinite. Ripple-free prototypes having finite settling time can be devised. In this prototype, the system emerges from the transient in a neutral state after the transient period at sampling instants has passed. The settling time at sampling instants is always longer than that of the minimal prototype but the improvement obtained in ripple-free operation is generally desired. In all cases, the desired over-all prototypes can be realized by programming a linear relationship between the input and output samples of the digital controller.

An equivalent effect can be achieved by the use of multiple early feedback from the feedforward system. In this form, continuous elements are used, and by adjusting a set of gain constants, an equivalent effect to that produced by a digital controller is achieved. Still another form of digitally controlled system is the one using the bypass digital controller, in which failure of the latter produces no serious effect other than degraded performance.

Digital controllers can be used with systems that are normally continuous. In such cases a sampling operation is deliberately introduced, and the sampled data so derived are applied to a digital controller. In this way, the advantages of this form of system can be applied to systems which are not sampled normally. On the other hand, where the data are normally in sampled form anyway, digital control is a natural means for processing the data and compensating the system in which they occur. Practical digital controllers need not be complex devices, and their use in the field is practical.

CHAPTER 8

BEHAVIOR OF SYSTEMS BETWEEN SAMPLING INSTANTS

The z transformation describes the behavior of the sampled-data system at sampling instants only, unless a modified or delayed form of the transformation is employed. Despite this apparent limitation, the simplicity, clarity, and ready manipulation of the standard z transformation makes it a most valuable tool. On the other hand, where critical evaluation of the performance of sampled-data filters or control systems is to be made, the behavior of the system between sampling instants is an important factor. For instance, some systems which are designed to have finite settling time at sampling instants do not necessarily settle to an equilibrium condition between sampling instants. There will be over- and undershoots in the output of such systems, even though the response at sampling instants is perfect after the finite settling time has passed. A comprehensive design procedure should include behavior during the sampling intervals, as well as at sampling instants.

The behavior of the system between sampling instants has been referred to as "ripple." Under certain conditions, this ripple may take the form of "hidden oscillations,"[1,2,24] whose amplitude might increase without limit with time despite the fact that the response at sampling instants is perfect. While this phenomenon is of academic interest, it can be readily avoided in practice and is therefore only of secondary importance. Various techniques are available for the study of the performance of sampled-data systems between sampling instants. These will be discussed in this chapter. While there are advantages and disadvantages in the application of the various methods, it is generally true that each method should be thoroughly understood in order that it can be applied to optimum advantage in each circumstance.

8.1 Approximation of Ripple Using Infinite Summation

If a linear continuous system is subjected to a sampled input, the output at sampling instants is fully described by the z transform. On the other hand, if the continuous output is desired, the Laplace transform of the continuous output must be obtained. Referring to Fig. 8.1, the transfer function of the continuous system is $G(s)$. The input to the system has a Laplace transform given by $R^*(s)$. The output of the continuous system is $C(s)$, whose inverse gives the time function which contains the ripple component being sought. If this output is sampled by a synchronous switch, the output pulse sequence is obtained from $C(z)$. An approach to obtaining $C(s)$ is to express the pulse sequence at the input of the system by the Laplace transform $R^*(s)$.

The Laplace transform of the continuous output $C(s)$ is given by

$$C(s) = R^*(s)G(s) \tag{8.1}$$

Recalling that $R^*(s)$ is given by the summation of displaced transforms as follows:

$$R^*(s) = \frac{1}{T} \sum_{n=-\infty}^{+\infty} R(s + nj\omega_0) \tag{8.2}$$

where ω_0 is $2\pi/T$, the output $C(s)$ is then given by

$$C(s) = \frac{1}{T} \sum_{n=-\infty}^{+\infty} R(s + nj\omega_0)G(s) \tag{8.3}$$

It is recognized that the central term of this series, $R(s)G(s)$, is the output that would be obtained had the system not been sampled or sampled at a very high rate. Thus, (8.3) can be written as follows:

$$C(s) = \frac{1}{T}G(s)R(s) + \frac{1}{T}G(s) \sum_{n=1}^{+\infty} R(s \pm nj\omega_0) \tag{8.4}$$

where the first term in (8.4) represents the "smooth" output and the summation represents the ripple component. The summation is the result of sampling and may be expressed as a percentage of the smooth output at the various sampling intervals. While the inversion of (8.4) is possible in principle, it is evident that consideration of an infinite number of terms is not practical. As a result, only the first few terms of the summation are employed in practical situations.

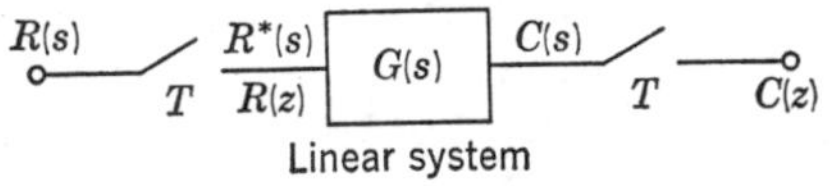

FIG. 8.1. System used for evaluation of ripple.

EXAMPLE

To illustrate the application of this representation of ripple effects, it is assumed that $G(s)$ in Fig. 8.1 is

$$G(s) = \frac{1}{s + a}$$

If the input is a unit step function, $R(s)$ is

$$R(s) = \frac{1}{s}$$

For these assumptions, the continuous output $C(s)$ is

$$C(s) = \frac{1}{s(s+a)} + \frac{1}{s+a} \sum_{n=1}^{+\infty} \frac{1}{s \pm nj\omega_0}$$

where it is assumed that the sampling interval T is unity.

The ripple component is given by the summation, and it will be approximated by considering only the first terms in which $n = 1$ and $n = -1$. The inverse of the ripple component so described is

$$p(t) = \mathcal{L}^{-1} \frac{1}{(s+a)(s+j\omega_0)} + \frac{1}{(s+a)(s-j\omega_0)}$$

which reduces to

$$p(t) = \frac{2a}{a^2 + \omega_0^2} \left(\cos \omega_0 t + \frac{\omega_0}{a} \sin \omega_0 t - e^{-at} \right)$$

The smooth component of the output is

$$c_s(t) = \mathcal{L}^{-1} \frac{1}{s(s+a)}$$

which reduces to

$$c_s(t) = \frac{1}{a} (1 - e^{-at})$$

The ripple component can be compared to the smooth output at each sampling interval and can be obtained as a percentage by dividing the ripple component $p(t)$ by the smooth component $c_s(t)$.

A useful result can be obtained by consideration of the steady-state condition which expresses the ripple as a percentage of the steady-state smooth output. The former is obtained by taking only the sinusoidal terms in $p(t)$, which can be combined to give

$$p_{ss}(t) = \frac{2}{\sqrt{a^2 + \omega_0^2}} \cos (\omega_0 t + \phi)$$

The steady-state smooth output obtained from $c_s(t)$ is

$$c_s(t)_{ss} = \frac{1}{a}$$

The per cent ripple is obtained by dividing the steady-state ripple by the steady-state smooth output; hence,

$$\% \text{ ripple} = \frac{2a}{\sqrt{a^2 + \omega_0^2}} \times 100$$

This steady-state ripple is constant and dependent on the sampling frequency and system time constant.

The procedure outlined in this section and illustrated in the example is not readily applicable to the problem of obtaining an exact expression for the ripple. Other procedures to be described in later sections can be used to better advantage for this problem. However, for steady-state conditions where ripple is present, the approach outlined in this section has considerable usefulness.

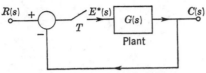

FIG. 8.2. Feedback sampled-data system used for evaluation of ripple.

The method outlined here has more limited application in the case of feedback systems, such as those shown in Fig. 8.2. Here the Laplace transform of the continuous output $C(s)$ is related to the Laplace transform of the sampled error sequence $E^*(s)$ by the expression

$$C(s) = G(s)E^*(s) \qquad (8.5)$$

and it has been shown that $E^*(s)$ is given by

$$E^*(s) = \frac{\dfrac{1}{T} \displaystyle\sum_{n=-\infty}^{+\infty} R(s + nj\omega_0)}{1 + \dfrac{1}{T} \displaystyle\sum_{n=-\infty}^{+\infty} G(s + nj\omega_0)} \qquad (8.6)$$

Then $C(s)$ is given by

$$C(s) = \frac{\dfrac{1}{T} \displaystyle\sum_{n=-\infty}^{+\infty} R(s + nj\omega_0)}{1 + \dfrac{1}{T} \displaystyle\sum_{n=-\infty}^{+\infty} G(s + nj\omega_0)} \, G(s) \qquad (8.7)$$

The inversion of (8.7) is a difficult, if not impossible, procedure. It is possible, however, to obtain approximations by taking only a few of the terms of the infinite summations in both numerator and denominator. If the system is low-pass relative to the sampling frequency, only the first term or two is significant. In view of the fact that other methods are available to obtain exact expressions for the ripple in any given sampling interval, the approximation techniques described here are of limited value.

8.2 The Multiple-rate Sampling Technique

An approach to the evaluation of the ripple involves the use of a fictitious sampler at the output of the system whose period is a fraction of that of the input sequence.[40] As originally proposed, this method places a sampler whose period is one-half that of the input sampler at the output of the sampled system, as shown in Fig. 8.3a, in which it is seen that the input sampling interval is T while the output sampling interval is $T/2$. Subsequent extensions of this theory[29] have considered the case where the output sampler is operated at a period T/n, where n is any integer. This more general theory will be treated in the next chapter, and this discussion will consider only the case where n is taken as 2.

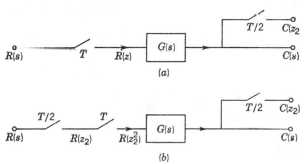

$$R(s) \quad T \quad R(z) \quad G(s) \quad T/2 \quad C(z_2) \quad C(s)$$
(a)

$$R(s) \quad T/2 \quad R(z_2) \quad T \quad R(z_2^2) \quad G(s) \quad T/2 \quad C(z_2) \quad C(s)$$
(b)

Fig. 8.3. (a) Sampled-data system with double-rate output sampling.   (b) Equivalent system.

By operating the fictitious output sampler at twice the frequency of the input sampler, a value of the continuous output at the mid-point of the basic sampling interval is obtained. While this does not define the entire ripple, it does give an additional piece of information which enables the designer to estimate the true value of the ripple over the entire interval. It is seen that the input sampler closes at every other sampling instant of the output sampler. This suggests the use of a modified auxiliary variable z_2, which is defined by

$$z_2 = e^{Ts/2} \tag{8.8}$$

It is seen that z_2 is related to the variable z, as previously used, by

$$z = z_2{}^2 \tag{8.9}$$

To obtain relationships between the double-rate sampled output and the input pulse sequence, reference is made to Fig. 8.3b. In this figure, the sampler operating at the basic interval T is preceded by another sampler operating at the interval $T/2$. Since the second switch closes only at every other closure of the fictitious double-rate sampler, its introduction has not altered the input sequence to the continuous system in any way whatsoever. The z transform of the pulse sequence of the input applied to the continuous system is $R(z)$. On the other hand, in view of (8.9), it is readily seen that this input sequence is also given by

$$R(z) = R(z_2{}^2) \tag{8.10}$$

The input is now expressed in terms of the double-rate auxiliary variable z_2 by the simple process of squaring all z's and then replacing them with z_2's. Physically, this means that every other double-rate sample is zero, as expected.

The double-rate output pulse transform $C(z_2)$ is related to the input double-rate pulse transform $R(z_2^2)$ by the double-rate pulse transfer function $G(z_2)$,

$$C(z_2) = G(z_2) R(z_2^2) \tag{8.11}$$

The double-rate output pulse transform is inverted in the usual manner to obtain the double-rate pulse sequence. This inversion includes an extra sample midway between two sampling instants of the basic rate. This procedure is easy to apply but, at the same time, it produces information on the output ripple only midway between the basic sampling instants. If this is considered sufficient, the slightly increased complexity involved in determining the double-rate output pulse transform is well worthwhile.

EXAMPLE

To illustrate the technique, the same example given in the previous section will be used. In this system,

$$G(s) = \frac{1}{s + a}$$

and
$$R(s) = \frac{1}{s}$$

The z transform of the input at the basic rate is given by

$$R(z) = \frac{1}{1 - z^{-1}}$$

The double-rate z transform is obtained by replacing z by z_2^2.

$$R(z_2^2) = \frac{1}{1 - z_2^{-2}}$$

The double-rate pulse transfer function $G(z_2)$ is given by

$$G(z_2) = \frac{1}{1 - e^{-aT/2}z_2^{-1}}$$

The output double-rate z transform is given by (8.11) and becomes

$$C(z_2) = \frac{1}{(1 - z_2^{-2})(1 - e^{-aT/2}z_2^{-1})}$$

which, upon inversion by the normal procedure, gives

$$c_2^*(t) = 1 + e^{-aT/2}\delta(t - T/2) + (1 - e^{-aT})\delta(t - 2T/2)$$
$$+ e^{-aT/2}(1 - e^{-aT})\delta(t - 3T/2) + (1 - e^{-aT} + e^{-2aT})\delta(t - 4T/2) + \cdots$$

By contrast, if the normal z transform at the basic rate, $C(z)$, is taken, its inversion will yield

$$c^*(t) = 1 + (1 + e^{-aT})\delta(t - T) + (1 + e^{-aT} + e^{-2aT})\delta(t - 2T) + \cdots$$

It is seen that every second term of the double-rate sampling sequence corresponds to the terms of the basic rate sequence. The extra point obtained from $C(z_2)$ gives the mid-point value of the ripple.

By using higher than double-rate sampling at the output, more points describing the ripple can be obtained within a given sampling interval. The procedure is very much the same as that for double-rate sampling and will be discussed in the next chapter. Though the resulting expressions are more complex than those for double-rate sampling, the cost in labor is not prohibitive.

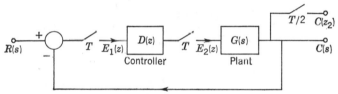

FIG. 8.4. Digitally compensated system with double-rate output sampling.

Feedback sampled-data systems are analyzed for the ripple in very much the same manner as for open-cycle systems. For instance, a typical system is one given in Fig. 8.4, where a digitally compensated control system is shown. The double-rate sampled output of interest here is expressed by $C(z_2)$, which is the double-rate z transform of the output obtained by means of a fictitious sampler. The continuous plant transfer function, including the data hold, is $G(s)$, and it is the output from this component, when subjected to the pulse sequence $E_2(z)$, that describes the ripple. It has been shown that the z transform $E_1(z)$ of the control error is given by

$$E_1(z) = [1 - K(z)]R(z) \tag{8.12}$$

where $K(z)$ is the over-all pulse transfer function. The output of the digital controller, which is the input to the plant including the data hold, is then given by

$$E_2(z) = D(z)[1 - K(z)]R(z) \tag{8.13}$$

As shown previously, the double-rate z transform corresponding to $E_2(z)$ is simply $E_2(z_2^2)$, where z_2^2 replaces z. Thus, from (8.13),

$$E_2(z_2^2) = D(z_2^2)[1 - K(z_2^2)]R(z_2^2) \tag{8.14}$$

The double-rate z transform of the output $C(z_2)$ is given by

$$C(z_2) = E(z_2^2)G(z_2) \tag{8.15}$$

which, upon substitution of $E(z_2{}^2)$ from (8.14), becomes

$$C(z_2) = D(z_2{}^2)[1 - K(z_2{}^2)]R(z_2{}^2)G(z_2) \qquad (8.16)$$

Inversion of $C(z_2)$ will give the mid-points of the output ripple of the system. It should be noted that if $K(z)$ has been chosen to produce a finite-settling-time response, it does not necessarily follow that $C(z_2)$ will invert into a finite-settling-time sequence. Only every second sample will definitely exhibit this property since the mid-point samples are sensitive to ripple. On the other hand, if the over-all prototype response function has been designed to be ripple-free, inversion of $C(z_2)$ will produce a ripple-free response at all sample times after the transient period has passed.

8.3 Partial-fraction Expansion Technique

A useful technique for obtaining the ripple in any chosen sampling interval involves the expansion of the plant continuous transfer function

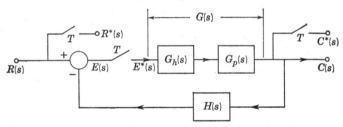

FIG. 8.5. Typical sampled-data system for which ripple is to be determined.

into partial fractions.[60] This technique takes advantage of the simple relationships obtainable with ordinary z transforms and combines them with the Laplace transform describing the plant. To illustrate the method, reference is made to Fig. 8.5, where it is seen that the continuous output of the plant is given by the inversion of $C(s)$ in response to an input $R(s)$. The continuous plant transfer function includes the data hold, although, as shown later, part of the data-hold transfer function is separated out and included in the relation describing the z transform of the error sequence. While the discussion which follows centers around the system illustrated in Fig. 8.5, it will be readily seen that only minor modifications of the method will be required to handle other configurations.

Referring to Fig. 8.5, it is seen that the Laplace transform of the continuous output is $C(s)$ and is related to the error transform $E^*(s)$ by

$$C(s) = G(s)E^*(s) \qquad (8.17)$$

where $G(s)$ is $G_h(s)G_p(s)$. It has been shown that the Laplace transform of the error pulse sequence is

$$E^*(s) = \frac{R^*(s)}{1 + GH^*(s)} \qquad (8.18)$$

from which it follows that

$$C(s) = \frac{G(s)R^*(s)}{1 + GH^*(s)} \qquad (8.19)$$

The problem is to reduce (8.19) to a form which will be amenable to ready inversion into the time domain. The exact procedure for doing this depends somewhat on the form of the data hold.

If it is assumed that the data hold is a simple clamp, or zero-order hold, the transfer function $G_h(s)$ is given by

$$G_h(s) = \frac{1 - e^{-Ts}}{s} \qquad (8.20)$$

and the approach is to include all factors containing rational powers of s in the plant transfer function $G_p(s)$. For the situation assumed, the

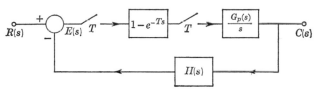

FIG. 8.6. Model of system used for determination of ripple at output.

model used to develop the desired relationships is given by Fig. 8.6, where it is seen that the numerator of (8.20) is a pulse-to-pulse relationship and is contained in a separate box. The addition of the extra sampler in the error line is redundant since the operation $1 - e^{-Ts}$ represents the difference of two samples. The modified plant pulse transfer function is now $G_p(s)/s$ and is assumed to be the ratio of rational polynomials in s.

If $G(s)/s$ is the ratio of rational polynomials in s, it may be expanded into partial fractions as follows:

$$\frac{G_p(s)}{s} = \frac{A_1}{s^{n+1}} + \frac{A_2}{s^n} + \frac{A_3}{s^{n-1}} + \cdots + \frac{A_a}{s+a} + \frac{A_b}{s+b} + \cdots \qquad (8.21)$$

where n is the order of the pole of $G_p(s)$ at the origin. For purposes of discussion it is assumed that all other poles are simple. This decomposition into partial fractions makes possible the rearrangement of the model into the form shown in Fig. 8.7. The output of each elementary path contributes to the continuous output. At the same time, it is possible to connect fictitious samplers at the output of each elementary path to obtain expressions describing the pulse sequences of these paths. For instance, the output pulse sequence of the qth path, $c_q^*(t)$, is described by its z transform, $C_q(z)$, given by

$$C_q(z) = \frac{(1 - z^{-1}) R(z)}{1 + GH(z)} G_q(z) \qquad (8.22)$$

where $G_q(z)$ is the pulse transfer function of the qth path and the term $(1 - z^{-1})$ enters in consequence of the difference operation between $E_1(z)$ and $E(z)$.

Having the expression for $C_q(z)$ makes it possible to obtain the contribution to the ripple by this elementary path during any desired sampling interval. The reason for this is that by having expanded the plant trans-

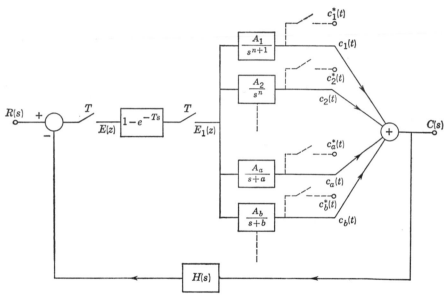

FIG. 8.7. Expanded feedforward transfer function.

fer function into partial fractions of the first order, the time function in any interval is fully specified by the initial value of the time function at the beginning of that interval. The latter is obtainable directly by inversion of (8.22) for the sampling instant in question. For instance, the time function $c_a(t)$ in the ath path is given by

$$c_a(t) = c_a(mT)e^{-a(t-mT)} \qquad (m + 1)T \geq t \geq mT \qquad (8.23)$$

for the time interval specified. It is seen that the time function depends on a knowledge of $c_a(mT)$, which is the mth sample obtained from the inversion of $C_a(z)$ in Fig. 8.7.

For those elementary paths which are dependent on simple and multiple poles at the origin of the s plane, the contributions to the continuous output during the interval extending from mT to $(m + 1)T$ are given by

$$c_s(t) = L + M(t - mT) + N(t - mT)^2 + \cdots \qquad (8.24)$$

where the order of the polynomial depends on the highest order of pole at the origin contained in $G_p(s)/s$. The evaluation of the various constants, L, M, N, etc., in (8.24) can be handled by considering simultaneously all the channels in Fig. 8.7 containing terms of the form $1/s^q$. Their various contributions are contained in (8.24).

Assuming for the sake of illustration that the highest-order term in $1/s$ of $G_p(s)/s$ is the third, then (8.24) will contain terms of the second order in time. The constant L is the initial value of the polynomial at time mT and is the sum of the various terms of $c_s(t)$ at that instant. Thus, if $c_1(t)$, $c_2(t)$, and $c_3(t)$ are the continuous outputs from the elementary channels whose transfer functions are $1/s$, $1/s^2$, and $1/s^3$, respectively, L is given by

$$L = c_1(mT) + c_2(mT) + c_3(mT) \tag{8.25}$$

The second term of (8.24) has the constant M, which is the slope of the polynomial at the time mT. Since the slope of the term from $1/s$ is zero, only the contributions of the other two channels are considered. Thus, if the z transform corresponding to $sC_s(s)$ is formed for these two channels and is inverted at the time mT, the value of the initial derivative is obtained. Thus,

$$M = c_2'(mT) + c_3'(mT) \tag{8.26}$$

Finally, the third term in (8.24) has the constant N, which is one-half the second derivative of $c_s(t)$ at the beginning of the interval at time mT. Since the first and second channels containing $1/s$ and $1/s^2$ have zero initial second derivatives, the only contribution is given by the channel containing $1/s^3$. Thus, the z transform corresponding to $s^2C_s(s)$ is formed for the third channel and is inverted at the time mT and the value of the initial second derivative obtained. Thus,

$$N = \tfrac{1}{2}c_3''(mT) \tag{8.27}$$

In the manner outlined previously, it is seen possible to obtain the time function which describes the ripple in any chosen sampling interval. This is very valuable since ripple may be undesirable only at given intervals and trivial at others. For instance, when a step input is applied to a sampled system, it is only the first overshoot which may be excessive, and the procedure outlined above permits its calculation without the necessity of calculating all other intervals. Thus, by adding the contributions of all channels, an exact determination of the ripple is possible. In addition, by having divided the contributions to the ripple in terms of each of the poles of the plant transfer function, it is possible to localize the more significant effects, should that be necessary.

EXAMPLE

To illustrate the method, the system shown in Fig. 8.8 will be used. Here the plant is a simple integrator, and the data hold is an RC circuit

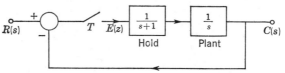

FIG. 8.8. Sampled-data control system used in example.

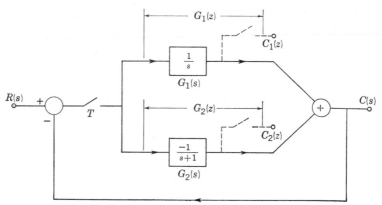

FIG. 8.9. System used in example expanded into partial fractions.

as shown. In this case, the over-all plant transfer function including the data hold is

$$G(s) = \frac{1}{s(s + 1)}$$

which can be expanded into the partial fractions

$$G(s) = \frac{1}{s} - \frac{1}{s + 1}$$

thus giving two elementary paths, as shown in Fig. 8.9. Referring to the corresponding z transforms $G_1(z)$ and $G_2(z)$ as follows:

$$G_1(z) = \mathcal{Z}\,\frac{1}{s}$$

$$= \frac{1}{1 - z^{-1}}$$

and

$$G_2(z) = \mathcal{Z}\,\frac{-1}{s + 1}$$

$$= -\frac{1}{1 - e^{-T}z^{-1}}$$

The significance of these transfer functions is better seen in Fig. 8.9.

The z transform of the first elementary output $C_1(z)$ is given by

$$C_1(z) = \frac{R(z)G_1(z)}{1 + G(z)}$$

and $C_2(z)$ is given by

$$C_2(z) = \frac{R(z)G_2(z)}{1 + G(z)}$$

where $G(z)$ is the loop pulse transfer function. $G(z)$ is given by

$$G(z) = Z\frac{1}{s(s + 1)}$$
$$= \frac{(1 - e^{-T})z^{-1}}{(1 - z^{-1})(1 - e^{-T}z^{-1})}$$

If, further, it is assumed that the input is a unit step function, so that $R(z)$ is

$$R(z) = \frac{1}{1 - z^{-1}}$$

then, substituting the various expressions, $C_1(z)$ and $C_2(z)$ become

$$C_1(z) = \frac{1}{1 - z^{-1}} + \frac{e^{-T}z^{-1}}{1 - 2e^{-T}z^{-1} + e^{-T}z^{-2}}$$

and $$C_2(z) = -\frac{1}{1 - 2e^{-T}z^{-1} + e^{-T}z^{-2}}$$

It will be assumed for purposes of illustration that the sampling interval T is such that e^{-T} is 0.5. Using this value and inverting $C_1(z)$ and $C_2(z)$,

$$c_1(mT) = 1 + 2^{-m/2} \sin m\pi/4$$
$$c_2(mT) = -2^{-m/2} (\cos m\pi/4 + \sin m\pi/4)$$

In view of the fact that there are no higher-order poles than the first, the continuous output during the interval from mT to $(m + 1)T$ is given by

$$c(t) = c_1(mT) + c_2(mT)e^{-(t-mT)}$$

The continuous output $c(t)$ can thus be obtained for any desired interval.

For instance, supposing that it were desired to obtain the continuous function for the interval between $2T$ and $3T$, then $c_1(2T)$ and $c_2(2T)$ are computed by substituting $m = 2$. Doing so results in the values

$$c_1(2T) = 1.5$$
$$c_2(2T) = -0.5$$

The continuous output function for the interval is

$$c(t) = 1.5 - 0.5e^{-(t-2T)}$$

This output is plotted in Fig. 8.10 in the interval in question. The output samples in this plot at other sampling instants are obtained by inversion of $C(z)$ in the normal manner.

It is seen that the application of this technique is relatively straight-forward, though it can be tedious in the case of more complex systems of

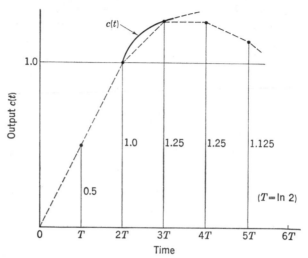

FIG. 8.10. Continuous response in third interval for unit step input in example.

higher order containing a data hold such as the zero-order type. On the other hand, it has the advantage of giving the continuous time function at any chosen sampling interval without requiring the computation of the function at other intervals.   Thus, if a peak overshoot is being investigated, its position to one sampling interval is readily estimated, and the continuous time function computed for that interval only.   The method is exact, so that no hidden effects will be unnoticed.   Finally, the expansion of the system into its partial-fraction form permits an evaluation as to which terms in the expression contribute most to the ripple.

8.4 Use of Advanced or Modified Z Transforms

Advanced or modified z transforms can be applied to the problem of determining the ripple at the output of a sampled-data system.[1,2,22,24] The application of the modified z transform is best shown by referring to the block diagram of Fig. 8.11.   A fictitious negative delay or advance ΔT is placed in cascade with the plant whose ripple output is to be studied. If the output of the system containing this fictitious time advance is sampled at synchronous rate, the output samples will be displaced in time from the input samples by a time ΔT.   If Δ is taken as a number ranging between zero and unity, it is seen that the value of the continuous output is explored at any and all sampling intervals.

If $G(z)$ is the pulse transfer function of the system shown in Fig. 8.11a,

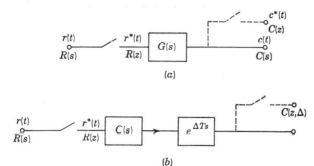

(a)

(b)

Fig. 8.11. Application of modified z transform to determine ripple.

then the output of the system at sampling instants is obtained by inversion of the output z transform $C(z)$, given by

$$C(z) = G(z) R(z) \qquad (8.28)$$

With the fictitious time advance inserted as shown in Fig. 8.11b, the z transform of the output is a function of Δ and is given by

$$C(z,\Delta) = G(z,\Delta) R(z) \qquad (8.29)$$

Inversion of $C(z,\Delta)$ gives the output as a function of the sampling instant and Δ. Hence,

$$c(mT,\Delta) = \mathcal{Z}^{-1} C(z,\Delta) \qquad (8.30)$$

By leaving Δ as a parametric variable, it is possible to determine the output anywhere within a sampling interval.

EXAMPLE

If the transfer function of the continuous element $G(s)$ in Fig. 8.11 is taken as

$$G(s) = \frac{1}{s + a}$$

From Appendix II, the advanced pulse transfer function $G(z,\Delta)$ is given by

$$G(z,\Delta) = \frac{e^{-a\Delta T}}{1 - e^{-aT}z^{-1}}$$

If the input to the system is a unit step function, then the advanced output $C(z,\Delta)$ is given by

$$C(z,\Delta) = \frac{e^{-a\Delta T}}{(1 - z^{-1})(1 - e^{-aT}z^{-1})}$$

Inverting $C(z,\Delta)$ and keeping Δ as a constant parameter, the output pulse $c(mT,\Delta)$ is, by evaluation of (4.20), the following:

$$c(mT,\Delta) = \left(\frac{1 - e^{-aT}e^{-maT}}{1 - e^{-aT}} \right) e^{-a\Delta T}$$

Thus, if the ripple in any sampling interval following the mth sampling instant is desired, the appropriate value of m is substituted in this expression and Δ is permitted to vary from zero to unity. It is seen that for this simple example, the ripple at any sampling instant is an exponentially decaying term whose initial value is that in the parenthesis.

While the example is a very simple one, it does illustrate the basic technique. Its application to more complex systems involves merely more labor but does not add to the theoretical complexity. The same technique can be applied directly to feedback systems with only minor modifications. Referring to Fig. 8.12, the block diagram shown is that

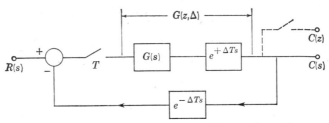

Fig. 8.12. Feedback system using modified z transform to determine output ripple.

of an error-sampled system having a feedforward transfer function $G(s)$. The technique is to insert a fictitious time advance, just as in the case of open-cycle systems. In so doing, however, the loop pulse transfer function is affected, thus resulting in an erroneous over-all response function. To restore the system so that it is the same as the actual system except for the time advance in the feedforward element, it is necessary to insert an equal time delay in the feedback line. In this manner, the over-all pulse transfer function is unaffected except for the advance in the output pulse transfer function. By varying the number Δ, it is possible to determine the variations of the output between chosen sampling instants.

Referring once again to Fig. 8.12, it is seen that the sampled output is given by

$$C(z,\Delta) = \frac{G(z,\Delta)}{1 + G(z)} R(z) \tag{8.31}$$

Inversion of $C(z,\Delta)$ gives the output samples as a function of Δ, which is varied as a parameter from zero to unity. The application of the method is best illustrated by means of an example.

EXAMPLE

To demonstrate the application of the method of modified pulse transforms, the same problem which was considered in the previous section will be used. The basic system is shown in block form in Fig. 8.8, where it is seen that the feedforward transfer function $G(s)$ is

$$G(s) = \frac{1}{s(s + 1)}$$

Inserting the time advance in this feedforward element,

$$G(s,\Delta) = \frac{e^{\Delta Ts}}{s(s + 1)}$$

From the tables of advanced z transforms in Appendix II, the advanced pulse transfer function $G(z,\Delta)$ is

$$G(z,\Delta) = \frac{1 - e^{-\Delta T} + z^{-1}(e^{-\Delta T} - e^{-T})}{(1 - z^{-1})(1 - e^{-T}z^{-1})}$$

If Δ is set equal to zero, the ordinary z transform for the feedforward element results.

Substituting $G(z,\Delta)$ in (8.31), the advanced output pulse transform becomes

$$C(z,\Delta) = \frac{(1 - e^{-\Delta T}) + z^{-1}(e^{-\Delta T} - e^{-T})}{(1 - z^{-1})(1 - e^{-T}z^{-1}) + z^{-1}(1 - e^{-T})} R(z)$$

If, for the sake of illustration, T is chosen as $\ln 2$ so that $e^{-T} = \frac{1}{2}$, $C(z,\Delta)$ becomes

$$C(z,\Delta) = \frac{1 - 0.5^\Delta + z^{-1}(0.5^\Delta - 0.5)}{(1 - z^{-1})(1 - 0.5z^{-1}) + 0.5z^{-1}} R(z)$$

If, for purposes of illustration, it is assumed that the input is a unit step function, then

$$R(z) = \frac{1}{1 - z^{-1}}$$

Substituting this expression in the delayed z transform of the output and simplifying, there results

$$C(z,\Delta) = \frac{1 - 0.5^\Delta + z^{-1}(0.5^\Delta - 0.5)}{1 - 2z^{-1} + 1.5z^{-2} - 0.5z^{-3}}$$

This transform can be inverted by long division by expanding $C(z,\Delta)$ into a power series in z^{-1} as follows:

$$C(z,\Delta) = A + (B + 2A)z^{-1} + (2B + 2.5A)z^{-2} + (2.5B + 2.5A)z^{-3} \\ + (2.5B + 2.25A)z^{-4} + \cdots$$

where the parameters A and B are defined as follows:

$$A = 1 - 0.5^\Delta$$
$$B = 0.5^\Delta - 0.5$$

This expression is inverted to yield the following impulse sequence:

$$c(t) = A\delta(t) + (B + 2A)\delta(t - T) + (2B + 2.5A)\delta(t - 2T)$$
$$+ (2.5B + 2.5A)\delta(t - 3T) + (2.5B + 2.25A)\delta(t - 4T) - \cdots$$

If the ripple in the sampling interval between $3T$ and $4T$ is desired, the fourth term in the expression for $c(t)$ is considered, so that

$$c_3(t) = 2.5(1 - 0.5^\Delta) + 2.5(0.5^\Delta - 0.5)$$

If Δ is taken as zero, the ordinary z-transform inversion is obtained, which gives the values of the pulse sequence at sampling instants. This sequence is

$$c^*(t) = 0.5\delta(t - T) + 1.0\delta(t - 2T) + 1.25\delta(t - 3T)$$
$$+ 1.25\delta(t - 4T) + \cdots$$

The pulse sequence represented by $c^*(t)$ is plotted in Fig. 8.13, where it is seen that the values of the output at sampling instants as given by $c^*(t)$ are marked. The intersample instant ripple as given by $c_3(t)$ is plotted in the third sampling interval by allowing the parameter Δ to vary between 0 and 1. The ripple at any other sampling interval could be obtained by a similar procedure, although the peak overshoot probably occurs in the interval shown.

As with the methods discussed in previous sections, the use of advanced or delayed z transforms is relatively straightforward theoretically, though somewhat complex to apply. This should be expected since the Laplace transform of the continuous output is itself very complicated. The use of the advanced or modified z transform has the advantage of being orderly in form and of requiring the development of no new techniques for its inversion. Tables of modified z transforms are used directly, just as in the case of ordinary z transforms. Because Δ appears usually as an exponent in the resultant modified z transform expressions, it is not readily evident how to synthesize systems having prescribed specifica-

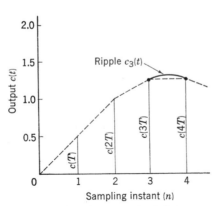

FIG. 8.13. Plot of output ripple between third and fourth sampling instants in example.

tions in regard to ripple component directly from the transform expressions. On the other hand, the partial-fraction-expansion method shows the major contributory terms producing output ripple somewhat more explicitly than does the modified z-transform method described in this section.

8.5 Hidden Oscillations in Sampled-data Systems

It has been mentioned previously that it is possible for sampled-data systems to have hidden oscillations[1,2,24] which are not detected by the inversion of the ordinary z transform of the output pulse sequence. This

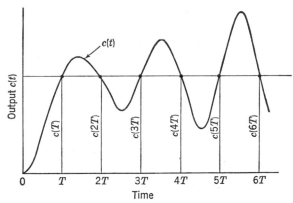

FIG. 8.14. Output of system containing "hidden oscillations."

comes about from the fact that the continuous output may contain oscillatory components whose frequency coincides exactly with the sampling frequency or integral multiples thereof. In this circumstance, the sampler takes values of the continuous hidden oscillation at the same relative phase each time, and the output of the sampler will be zero or a constant. For instance, if the sampler takes values of an output as shown in Fig. 8.14, no evidence of the presence of an increasing oscillation will be contained in the output $c(nT)$, even though the system is oscillating. As mentioned previously, this circumstance is hardly to be expected in practical situations and can readily be avoided in theoretical studies by making note of the continuous-system transfer function poles and determining if their imaginary parts are integral multiples of $2\pi/T$.

The condition for the presence of hidden oscillations is that the system have a continuous element in the control loop whose transfer function contains poles whose imaginary component is an integral multiple of the sampling frequency expressed in radians per second. This is seen by considering a continuous loop transfer function $G(s)H(s)$ which contains, among others, partial fractions of the form

$$G(s)H(s) = \frac{A_1}{s + jk\omega_0} + \frac{A_2}{s - jk\omega_0} + \cdots \qquad (8.31)$$

where ω_0 is $2\pi/T$ and k is an integer. If the z transform corresponding to $G(s)H(s)$ is taken, it results in the following expression for $GH(z)$:

$$GH(z) = \frac{A_1}{1 - e^{-jk\omega_0 T}z^{-1}} + \frac{A_2}{1 - e^{+jk\omega_0 T}z^{-1}} + \cdots \qquad (8.32)$$

From the definition of ω_0, it is seen that $k\omega_0 T$ is simply $2\pi k$ and that $e^{-jk\omega_0 T}$ is unity. Thus, the loop pulse transfer function $GH(z)$ becomes

$$GH(z) = \frac{A_1}{1 - z^{-1}} + \frac{A_2}{1 - z^{-1}} + \cdots \qquad (8.33)$$

It is seen from (8.33) that the oscillatory effects which are present in the impulsive response resulting from the inversion of $G(s)H(s)$ are totally hidden in the sampled sequence resulting from the inversion of $GH(z)$. This condition is the basic theoretical source of the hidden oscillation. However, unless the imaginary component of the pole of $G(s)H(s)$ is precisely a multiple of the sampling frequency this condition will not occur.

In the practical situation, if it is desired to observe the effect of hidden oscillations of this type by means of ordinary z transforms, all that need be done is to alter the loop transfer function slightly so that it is not "tuned" to the sampling frequency. This will ensure that the inversion of the z transform will contain such oscillatory terms. This simple procedure forms the basis of the statement that hidden oscillations can readily be coped with and that the subject tends to be of academic interest only.

8.6 Summary

The application of the ordinary z transform to the analysis and synthesis of sampled-data systems gives information which can be used to evaluate the variables at sampling instants only. In a complete study, however, the behavior of the system between sampling instants is of considerable importance. For instance, finite-settling-time-systems prototypes may have considerable overshoots between sampling instants during the transient period, even though the response at sampling instants has settled completely. The oscillatory behavior in the time domain between sampling instants is called "ripple."

Unfortunately, the direct inversion of the Laplace transform which gives the continuous output of sampled systems is very complex, and its use does not lead to results which are readily assessed or corrected should they be unacceptable.   Various techniques have been developed which will permit partial or selective evaluation of the time function between sampling instants.   The least accurate of these methods uses the infinite-summation form of the Laplace transform of the sampled signal combined with the continuous plant transfer function.   The resultant expression is inverted approximately by taking only the first few significant terms of the infinite summation.   This method is very difficult to apply to feed-back systems and has only limited value.

A more satisfactory method involves the use of multiple-rate sampling at the output of the system.   By obtaining exactly the values of the extra samples which lie between the unit rate samples of the variable a measure of the ripple is obtained.   The method gives only limited though accurate information describing the ripple, but because of its simplicity, it can be readily applied and interpreted.

The partial-fraction technique is an exact method which gives the Laplace transform of the continuous output in any chosen interval. Because the particular sampling interval can be chosen at will, this method can be applied directly to feedback control systems whose peak overshoot is being sought.   Furthermore, because the continuous-element transfer function is decomposed into partial fractions, the components which contribute most to the ripple output can be readily identified. Corrective compensation can then be applied, though even with this method it is not readily accomplished.

A closely related method is the one in which advanced or modified z transforms are used.   In this approach, an exact expression for the ripple is obtained by using methods which are entirely analogous to those for ordinary z transforms.   A disadvantage of the method as compared with the partial-fraction-expansion method is that it is not readily evident which parts of the plant transfer function contribute most significantly to the ripple.   On the other hand, the one-to-one relationship to the ordinary z-transform method makes the advanced z-transform technique attractive.

A phenomenon which is observed in sampled-data systems is that of "hidden oscillations."   These can occur as a result of the presence of poles in the continuous elements, which happen to produce oscillations whose periods are exactly equal to or multiples of the sampling period. From a practical viewpoint, these can be readily anticipated and avoided by the designer.   In conclusion, the behavior of sampled-data systems between sampling instants can be studied by one or more methods, each of which has advantages and disadvantages.   They should be applied with a view of obtaining the desired information with the least effort.

CHAPTER 9

MULTIRATE SAMPLED SYSTEMS

The sampled-data feedback systems which have been discussed so far have sampling switches, all of which operate with the same period or sampling rate. These systems are single-rate systems. It is the purpose of this chapter to extend the treatment of sampled-data control to a study of multirate systems. A multirate sampled-data system is defined as a system which has at least two samplers which operate at different rates. An open-loop example of multirate operation was given in the last chapter, where a double-rate switch was used to read the intersample ripple. In Chap. 6 a method was described for the design of continuous shaping networks for single-rate systems by an approximation which resulted in the introduction of double- or higher-rate sampling. The practical value of multirate sampling, however, goes beyond the mere convenience of such systems used as an analytical tool. It will be shown, for example, how multirate digital controllers can be designed to improve the response of systems which are receiving data sampled at a lower rate. Another practical possibility exists in that large-scale control systems may have a number of links which are, for reasons beyond those pertaining to the control function, sampled at different rates. In particular, systems which include remote data-transmission links are most likely to involve several different data rates in the same control loop. For all these reasons, it is important to understand the analysis methods and the synthesis possibilities inherent in multirate feedback systems.

The introduction of different sampling rates in the control loop requires a redevelopment of the basic system analysis techniques which were described in the early chapters for single-rate systems. At the present time the theory of multirate systems, which is largely due to Kranc,[28,29,30] is able to handle, in a practical pencil-and-paper manner, only those systems containing sampling rates whose ratios are the ratios of small numbers. While more complicated cases, including sampling at widely different rates, can, in theory, always be analyzed, the complicated nature of the resulting equations forces one to think in terms of simulation or automatic computation as aids in their analysis and design. As in the previous chapters, the emphasis in this chapter will be on the single-loop error-sampled configuration, which displays the essential characteristics of the problem in the simplest possible way.

9.1 Analysis of Open-loop Multirate Systems

As in the case of single-rate sampled systems, the important concept in dealing with linear multirate systems is the pulse transfer function.   As a first example, consider the system shown in Fig. 9.1, where an input R is sampled with the uniform period T and applied to the continuous system G.   The output of G is sampled at an increased rate with period T/n to form a sequence of output samples

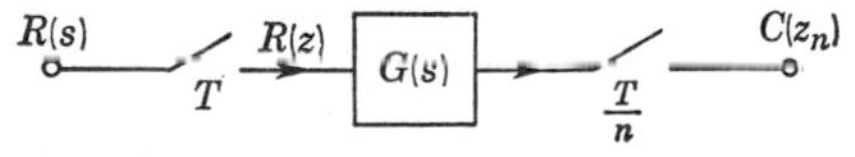

FIG. 9.1. Multirate system with slow input and fast output sampling.

whose transform (which will be defined shortly) is designated $C(z_n)$.   The analysis problem requires that the input transform $R(z)$ be related to this output transform.   The necessary relation can be established directly from the convolution summation developed earlier for single-rate systems.   By adding up the impulse responses of the linear system G, the continuous output $c(t)$ is calculated to be

$$c(t) = \sum_{k=0}^{\infty} r(kT)g(t - kT) \tag{9.1}$$

The samples which appear at the output of the "fast" switch are the values of (9.1) at the times $t = lT/n$, or

$$c(lT/n) = \sum_{k=0}^{\infty} r(kT)g\left(\frac{lT}{n} - kT\right) \tag{9.2}$$

If the transform of this output is to be of use in later calculations, it must obviously include *all* the samples in (9.2); that is, the output transform must be defined on samples separated by T/n sec rather than the T sec which separate samples of the input $r^*(t)$.   To distinguish the transform variables according to the separation between successive samples which they represent, the variable z_n will be used in the pulse transform of samples separated by T/n sec and the variable z retained for sequences separated by T sec.   In all cases, the definitions will be made clear by the example problem.   For the case illustrated in Fig. 9.1 and described by Eq. (9.2), the z_n transform of the output is defined as

$$C(z_n) = \sum_{l=0}^{\infty} c(lT/n)z_n^{-l}$$

$$= \sum_{l=0}^{\infty} \sum_{k=0}^{\infty} r(kT)g\left(\frac{lT}{n} - kT\right)z_n^{-l} \tag{9.3}$$

For large values of z_n, where the series of (9.3) converges uniformly, summation with respect to l and k may be interchanged, with the result

$$C(z_n) = \sum_{k=0}^{\infty} r(kT) \sum_{l=0}^{\infty} g\left(\frac{lT}{n} - kT\right) z_n^{-l} \tag{9.4}$$

In the second sum, it is always possible to find an integer j such that $(l - nk) = j$, and the transform may then be written in terms of j as follows:

$$C(z_n) = \sum_{k=0}^{\infty} r(kT) \sum_{j=0}^{\infty} g\left(j\frac{T}{n}\right) z_n^{-(j+nk)} \tag{9.5}$$

The second sum in (9.5) is written from $j = 0$ rather than from $j = -nk$ because the realizable impulse response $g(t)$ is zero for negative values of the argument. The powers of z_n can be separated out so that

$$C(z_n) = \sum_{k=0}^{\infty} r(kT)(z_n{}^n)^{-k} \sum_{j=0}^{\infty} g\left(j\frac{T}{n}\right) z_n^{-j} \tag{9.6}$$

$$= R(z_n{}^n)G(z_n) \tag{9.7}$$

A word must be said about the notation in (9.7). As is evident from (9.6), the function $R(z_n{}^n)$ is the z transform of the input $R(s)$ (based on samples separated by T sec) with the variable z replaced by $z_n{}^n$. For example, if

$$R(s) = \frac{1}{s}$$

then

$$R(z) = \frac{1}{1 - z^{-1}}$$

and

$$R(z_n{}^n) = \frac{1}{1 - z_n^{-n}}$$

As a matter of fact, it should not be surprising that z and z_n are related. On a Laplace-transform basis it is already known that $z = e^{sT}$, and it may be shown that $z_n = e^{sT/n}$, so that in fact $z_n{}^n = z$ and the operation indicated above is a simple change of variable. The transform $G(z_n)$ is the ordinary pulse transfer function of the linear system, based on a sample separation of T/n sec. The variable z_n identifies the period of the samples used in determining $G(z_n)$.

The problem illustrated in Fig. 9.1 is the same as that which results from a search for ripple in the output of a single-rate system, and (9.7) expresses the solution to that problem. A more difficult case, from an analytical point of view, is shown in Fig. 9.2. In this case the continuous output is given by the usual expression of superposition

$$c(t) = \sum_{k=0}^{\infty} r\left(k\frac{T}{n}\right) g\left(t - k\frac{T}{n}\right) \tag{9.8}$$

The output of the second sampler is a periodic impulse train modulated by $c(t)$ with a period of T sec. The corresponding sequence of output values is given by

$$c(lT) = \sum_{k=0}^{\infty} r\left(k\frac{T}{n}\right) g\left(lT - k\frac{T}{n}\right) \tag{9.9}$$

An attempt to take the z transform of (9.9) by multiplying by z^{-l} and summing on l leads to difficulty because it is not possible to make a direct change of variable to separate out that part of the transform which depends on the input from that part of the transform which depends on the system. The source of the difficulty may be readily seen from a graph (shown in Fig. 9.3) of the component signals from $g(t)$ which make up the output $c(t)$. In this graph $n = 3$ and all input samples are taken to be the same value to avoid confusion as far as possible. It is noticed

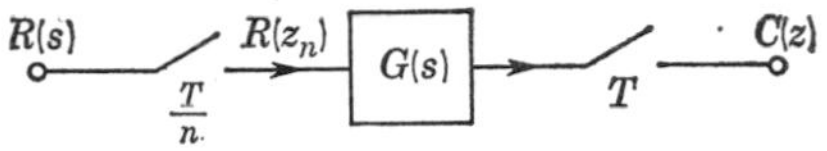

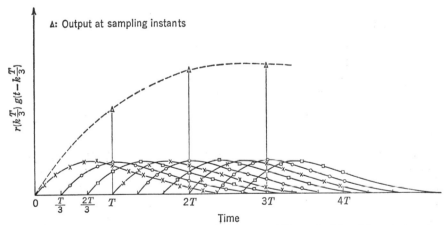

FIG. 9.2. Multirate system with fast input and slow output sampling.

A: Output at sampling instants

FIG. 9.3. Signal components of output of system of Fig. 9.2 with triple-rate input.

from Fig. 9.3 that there are in fact *three distinct sequences* of weights given by the system weighting function $g(t)$ to the input samples. The first weighting sequence is marked with crosses and applies to input samples which occur at 0, T, $2T$, ... This sequence is $g(0)$, $g(T)$, $g(2T)$, ... The second weighting sequence, distinct from the first, is marked with circles and applies to inputs which occur at $T/3$, $T + (T/3)$, $2T + (T/3)$, . . . and consists of the values $g(2T/3)$, $g[T + (2T/3)]$, $g[2T + (2T/3)]$, ... Finally, the third sequence, which is marked with squares, weights inputs applied at $2T/3$, $T + (2T/3)$, $2T + (2T/3)$, ... The sequence of weights for this portion of the input is $g(T/3)$, $g[T + (T/3)]$, $g[2T + (T/3)]$, ... This peculiarity, a sort of segregation of input samples according to their location within a sampling period, is a direct consequence of the multirate system with more frequent input samples than output samples. In any other case all the inputs are treated alike and the simpler methods of earlier chapters apply.

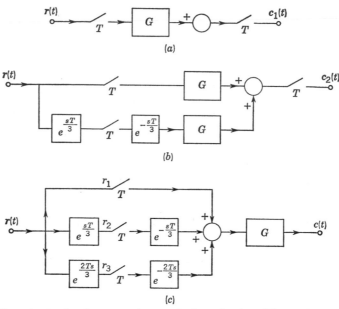

FIG. 9.4. Steps in the development of an equivalent circuit to Fig. 9.2 for $n = 3$ showing switch decomposition.

An analysis of the system illustrated by Fig. 9.2 and Fig. 9.3 can be obtained by separating the input into three—or n—paths, where all samples on a given path will be weighted alike. The separate results are added together at the end to give the total output. For example, again considering Fig. 9.3, the first sequence of samples, $r(0)$, $r(T)$, . . . , is simply obtained by a switch operating at the basic rate of T sec/sample. This sequence is weighted by $g(0)$, $g(T)$, $g(2T)$, . . . and consequently may be applied directly to the system G and added in to the output as shown in Fig. 9.4a. The summing point has been left to permit inclusion of the effects of the other sequences. The second sequence is $r(T/3)$, $r[T + (T/3)]$, $r[2T + (T/3)]$, . . . and is obtained by a sampling switch operating on the input *shifted* $T/3$ sec to the left. This sequence is weighted by 0, $g(2T/3)$, $g[T + (2T/3)]$, . . . , which is the impulse response sequence *shifted* to the *right* by $T/3$ sec. Therefore, the first and the second contributions to the output are obtained by the circuit shown in Fig. 9.4b. Finally, the last contribution necessary to complete the output is given by the sequence $r(2T/3)$, $r[T + (2T/3)]$, $r[2T + (2T/3)]$, . . . , which is obtained from the inputs shifted to the left by $2T/3$ through a transfer function $e^{(2T/ks)}$. This input sequence is weighted by the sequence 0, $g(T/3)$, $g[T + (T/3)]$, . . . , which is effected by passing the input sequence into G and delaying the response by $2T/3$ sec. The total equivalent circuit is shown in Fig. 9.4c, where the common transfer function G is combined in one box. This figure shows clearly that one sampling switch has been "decomposed" into three switches which operate at one-third the rate of the equivalent switch. The method of switch decomposition is general and may be applied to the analysis of any multirate system.

From a mathematical point of view, the switch decomposition is based on the rather obvious fact that a convergent sequence $f_0 + f_1 + f_2 + f_3 + \cdots$ may be summed in parts such as $(f_0 + f_3 + f_6 + \cdots) + (f_1 + f_4 + f_7 + \cdots) + (f_2 + f_5 + f_8 + \cdots)$, or, in general,

$$\sum_{k=0}^{\infty} f(kT) = \sum_{m=0}^{n-1} \sum_{j=0}^{\infty} f[(jn + m)T] \qquad n = 1, 2, \ldots \qquad (9.10)$$

Applying (9.10) to the expression for the output samples, (9.9),

$$c(lT) = \sum_{m=0}^{n-1} \sum_{j=0}^{\infty} f\left[(jn + m)\frac{T}{n} \right] g\left[lT - \frac{T}{n}(jn + m) \right] \qquad (9.11)$$

The z transform of the output is

$$C(z) = \sum_{l=0}^{\infty} c(lT)z^{-l}$$

$$= \sum_{m=0}^{n-1} \sum_{j=0}^{\infty} r\left[(jn + m)\frac{T}{n} \right] \sum_{l=0}^{\infty} g\left(lT - jT - \frac{mT}{n} \right) z^{-l} \qquad (9.12)$$

Making the substitution $l - j = k$ in the last sum of (9.12),

$$C(z) = \sum_{m=0}^{n-1} \sum_{j=0}^{\infty} r\left(jT + \frac{mT}{n} \right) z^{-j} \sum_{k=0}^{\infty} g\left(kT - \frac{mT}{n} \right) z^{-k} \qquad (9.13)$$

In terms of the Laplace transforms of $r(t)$ and $g(t)$, it is possible to write

(9.13) in the form

$$C(z) = \sum_{m=0}^{n-1} \mathcal{Z}[R(s)e^{(mT/n)s}]\mathcal{Z}[G(s)e^{-(mT/n)s}] \tag{9.14}$$

which may be visualized by aid of the block diagram of Fig. 9.5. This figure shows the general case of switch decomposition.

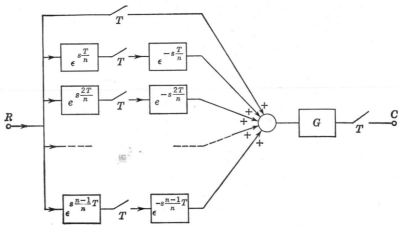

FIG. 9.5. General case of switch decomposition.

EXAMPLE

A simple illustration of the use of the switch-decomposition method for the analysis of an open-loop multirate system will be given by considering a triple-rate system with a single time-constant plant and a step input. That is, for a system like Fig. 9.4, let

$$R(s) = \frac{1}{s}$$

$$G(s) = \frac{1}{s+1}$$

$$T = 1 \text{ sec}$$

$$n = 3$$

Either from inspection of the figure or from Eq. (9.14) one can obtain the output transform as

$$C(z) = \mathcal{Z}\frac{1}{s}\,\mathcal{Z}\frac{1}{s+1} + \mathcal{Z}\frac{e^{s/3}}{s}\,\mathcal{Z}\frac{e^{-s/3}}{s+1} + \mathcal{Z}\frac{e^{2s/3}}{s}\,\mathcal{Z}\frac{e^{-2s/3}}{s+1}$$

$$= \frac{1}{(1-z^{-1})(1-e^{-1}z^{-1})} + \frac{e^{-2/3}z^{-1}}{(1-z^{-1})(1-e^{-1}z^{-1})}$$

$$+ \frac{e^{-1/3}z^{-1}}{(1-z^{-1})(1-e^{-1}z^{-1})}$$

$$= \frac{1 + (e^{-2/3} + e^{-1/3})z^{-1}}{(1-z^{-1})(1-e^{-1}z^{-1})} \tag{9.15}$$

The open-loop system shown in Fig. 9.2 may also be analyzed by the technique illustrated in Fig. 9.6. In this case a mathematical or phantom sampling of the output is done by a switch operating at the rate T/n. The output of this switch, $C(z_n)$, can be readily calculated from single-rate-system theory based on a period of T/n sec. The actual output transform, $C(z)$, can be represented symbolically as the z transform of

FIG. 9.6. Open-loop analysis of multirate system by phantom switch.

$C(z_n)$, or $\mathbb{Z}[C(z_n)]$. This operation is defined as follows. The output has the value $c(kT/n)$ at sampling instants separated by T/n sec. Then transforms are defined as

$$C(z_n) = \sum_{k=0}^{\infty} c\left(k\frac{T}{n}\right) z_n^{-k} \qquad (9.16)$$

and

$$C(z) = \sum_{l=0}^{\infty} c(lT) z^{-l} \qquad (9.17)$$

These transforms are related and, since (9.17) contains only a portion of the samples of (9.16), it should be possible to derive $C(z)$ from $C(z_n)$. This is in fact the case. By the inversion theorem,

$$c\left(k\frac{T}{n}\right) = \frac{1}{2\pi j} \int_{\Gamma} C(z_n) z_n^{k-1} \, dz_n \qquad (9.18)$$

The substitution of (9.18) in (9.17) with $k = ln$ gives

$$C(z) = \sum_{l=0}^{\infty} \left[\frac{1}{2\pi j} \int_{\Gamma} C(z_n) z_n^{ln-1} \, dz_n \right] z^{-l}$$

$$= \frac{1}{2\pi j} \int_{\Gamma} C(z_n) \left[\sum_{l=0}^{\infty} z_n^{ln} z^{-l} \right] \frac{dz_n}{z_n}$$

$$= \frac{1}{2\pi j} \int_{\Gamma} C(z_n) \frac{1}{1 - z_n^{n} z^{-1}} \frac{dz_n}{z_n} \qquad (9.19)$$

The contour Γ on the z_n plane must be so chosen that it encompasses all the poles of $C(z_n)/z_n$ but excludes the poles contributed by the factor $(1 - z_n^{n} z^{-1})$. The reason for this is that in the interchange of summation and integration in (9.19) requires that the infinite sum $\sum_{l=0}^{\infty} (z_n^{n} z^{-1})^l$ be absolutely convergent. This is assured only if $|z_n^{n} z^{-1}|$ is less than unity. Thus the factor $(1 - z_n^{n} z^{-1})$ cannot be zero in the region over which (9.19) is to be valid and the poles introduced by this factor must lie outside the contour of integration.   The condition also implies that the region of the z plane over which the resultant $C(z)$ is valid lies outside the circle whose radius is $z_n{}^n$.   Since Γ contains all the poles of $C(z_n)$ on the z_n plane, the corresponding locus on the z plane contains all the poles of $C(z)$, so that the inversion of $C(z)$ by the usual inversion integral will be correct.   The contour Γ which contains all the poles of $C(z_n)/z_n$ but which excludes the roots of $(1 - z_n{}^n z^{-1})$ thus produces the correct expression for $C(z)$.   In evaluating (9.19), it is possible to do so either by obtaining the residues at the poles of $C(z_n)/z_n$ which are contained inside Γ or by obtaining the residues at the n poles which are the roots of $(1 - z_n{}^n z^{-1})$ which lie outside Γ.   An example will illustrate the evaluation of (9.19).

EXAMPLE

As an example of the use of (9.19), consider again the situation shown in Fig. 9.4c with

$$R(s) = \frac{1}{s}$$

$$G(s) = \frac{1}{s+1}$$

and
$$T = 1$$
$$n = 3$$

One can write down immediately that

$$
\begin{aligned}
C(z_n) &= R(z_n)G(z_n) \\
&= \frac{1}{(1 - z_n{}^{-1})(1 - e^{-1/n}z_n{}^{-1})} \\
&= \frac{z_n{}^2}{(z_n - 1)(z_n - e^{-1/n})}
\end{aligned}
\tag{9.20}
$$

From (9.19) evaluated by obtaining the residues at the poles of $C(z_n)/z_n$,

$$
\begin{aligned}
C(z) &= \frac{1}{2\pi j} \int_\Gamma \frac{z_n{}^2}{(z_n - 1)(z_n - e^{-1/n})} \frac{1}{(1 - z_n{}^n z^{-1})} \frac{dz_n}{z_n} \\
&= \frac{1}{(1 - e^{-1/n})(1 - z^{-1})} + \frac{e^{-1/n}}{(e^{-1/n} - 1)(1 - e^{-1}z^{-1})}
\end{aligned}
$$

and, for $n = 3$,

$$
\begin{aligned}
C(z) &= \frac{(1 - e^{-1}z^{-1}) - e^{-1/3}(1 - z^{-1})}{(1 - e^{-1/3})(1 - z^{-1})(1 - e^{-1}z^{-1})} \\
&= \frac{1 + (e^{-1/3} + e^{-2/3})z^{-1}}{(1 - z^{-1})(1 - e^{-1}z^{-1})}
\end{aligned}
\tag{9.21}
$$

which checks with the previous result obtained by switch decomposition.   The latter form could have been derived by evaluating the residues at the three poles contributed by $(1 - z_3{}^3 z^{-1})$.

In addition to the analysis of systems as illustrated by the example above, the relation (9.19) can be used to show general properties of a z transform in terms of the z_n transform.   For example, if $C(z_n)$ has a pole at $z_n = a$, then $C(z)$ has a pole at $z = a^n$.   The function $C(z_n{}^n)$, formed by replacing z by $z_n{}^n$ in $C(z)$, has n poles of magnitude a located at equal angles around a circle of radius a, as illustrated in Fig. 9.7.   This last result can be obtained from the fact that if $C(z)$ has a pole at $z = a^n$, then $C(z_n{}^n)$ has poles where

$$z_n{}^n = a^n \tag{9.22}$$

Since $e^{j2m\pi} = 1$, (9.22) is equivalent to

$$z_n{}^n = a^n e^{j2\pi m} \qquad m = 0, 1, 2, \ldots$$
and therefore $\qquad z_n = a e^{j2\pi m/n} \qquad m = 0, 1, 2, \ldots \tag{9.23}$

which is the desired result.   In addition to the added insight given by Fig. 9.7 and the relation (9.23) into the characteristics of multirate transforms, these results will be very useful in design problems to be described later.

9.2 Analysis of Closed-loop Multirate Systems

The analysis of closed-loop multirate systems is most readily carried out by the use of the switch-decomposition method described in the last section to reduce the problem to a single-rate system.   Such a reduction is possible only if all sampling rates in the system are integral multiples of a single basic rate.   For example, the rates $2/T$, $3/T$, and $4/T$ are all multiples of the basic rate $1/T$.   The complexity of the analysis problem is directly related to the number of parallel switches which result from the decomposition process.   For the three rates listed above, it would be necessary to perform three decompositions, leading to two, three, and four parallel switches, respectively.

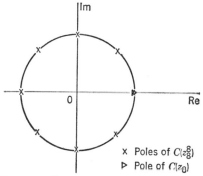

FIG. 9.7. Sketch of corresponding poles of $C(z_n)$ and $C(z_n{}^n)$.

If the rate $3/T$ were missing, then decomposition could be accomplished with respect to a basic rate of $2/T$ and the problem would be greatly simplified.   The method of analysis is straightforward and best illustrated by example.   The techniques used in this example apply to any multiloop single-rate sampled-data system and consist essentially of the following two simple rules:

1. Select as unknown variables all those signals at the inputs to sampling switches. This rule is based on the fact that pulse transfer functions multiply when separated by samplers. The choice of variables at the inputs to switches ensures that switches separate all transfer functions.
2. Use the principle of superposition to obtain the relations between the chosen variables.

Although these rules are obvious and simple to apply, they are very important to the success of the analysis of the system. In certain cases, and particularly when such "natural" variables as the system output or the actuating error are not inputs to switches, a person with limited experience can rapidly become involved in enormous, complicated expressions for no reason except that he failed to follow these rules. The following example will illustrate both the switch decomposition method and the analysis method mentioned above.

EXAMPLE

The block diagram which must be analyzed is shown in Fig. 9.8a and the single-rate equivalent to the system obtained by switch decomposition is shown in Fig. 9.8b. This system will be analyzed to find the response to an input step. The analysis will of necessity include determination of the characteristic equation so that the stability of the system can be checked as the analysis progresses. In Fig. 9.8b the variables at the inputs to the switches have been designated E_1, E_2, C_1, C_2, C_3, and in terms of these variables the system performance is described by the equations

$$E_1(z) = \mathcal{Z}[R(s)] - C_1(z)\mathcal{Z}\left[\frac{1}{s}\right] - C_2(z)\mathcal{Z}\left[\frac{e^{-sT/3}}{s}\right] - C_3(z)\mathcal{Z}\left[\frac{e^{-2sT/3}}{s}\right]$$

$$E_2(z) = \mathcal{Z}[R(s)e^{sT/2}] - C_1(z)\mathcal{Z}\frac{e^{sT/2}}{s} - C_2(z)\mathcal{Z}\frac{e^{-sT/3}e^{sT/2}}{s}$$

$$-C_3(z)\mathcal{Z}\frac{e^{-2sT/3}e^{sT/2}}{s}$$

$$(9.24)$$

$$C_1(z) = E_1(z)\mathcal{Z}\frac{1}{s+1} + E_2(z)\mathcal{Z}\frac{e^{-sT/2}}{s+1}$$

$$C_2(z) = E_1(z)\mathcal{Z}\frac{e^{sT/3}}{s+1} + E_2(z)\mathcal{Z}\frac{e^{-sT/2}e^{sT/3}}{s+1}$$

$$C_3(z) = E_1(z)\mathcal{Z}\frac{e^{2sT/3}}{s+1} + E_2(z)\mathcal{Z}\frac{e^{-sT/2}e^{2sT/3}}{s+1}$$

Equations (9.24) are written by inspection, using superposition. The

14 transforms which are included in (9.24) are simple examples of the "modified" transform discussed in the last chapter in connection with the intersample ripple problem.   The solution of (9.24) for one of the unknowns—$E_1(z)$, for example—is largely a matter of algebra.   For

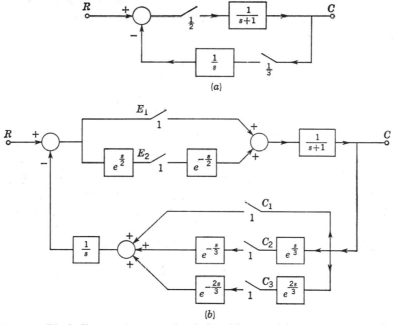

(a)

(b)

FIG. 9.8. Block diagram for example of closed-loop multirate system analysis.

example, substitution of the known functions for $T = 1$ sec into (9.24) and elimination of C_1, C_2, and C_3 leads to the two equations

$$E_1(z) = R(z) - E_1(z) \frac{1 + e^{-1/3}z^{-1} + e^{-2/3}z^{-1}}{(1 - z^{-1})(1 - e^{-1}z^{-1})}$$

$$- E_2(z) \frac{e^{-1/2}z^{-1} + e^{-1/6}z^{-1} + e^{-5/6}z^{-2}}{(1 - z^{-1})(1 - e^{-1}z^{-1})}$$

$$E_2(z) = \mathbb{Z}[R(s)e^{sT/2}] - E_1(z) \frac{1 + e^{-1/3} + e^{-2/3}z^{-1}}{(1 - z^{-1})(1 - e^{-1}z^{-1})}$$

$$- E_2(z) \frac{e^{-1/2}z^{-1} + e^{-5/6}z^{-1} + e^{-1/6}z^{-1}}{(1 - z^{-1})(1 - e^{-1}z^{-1})} \qquad (9.25)$$

Finally, if $R(s) = 1/s$, the response of the error is given by the solution of (9.25) to be

$$E_1(z) = \frac{1 + (e^{-5/6} - e^{-1})z^{-1}}{2 + (-1 - e^{-1} + e^{-1/6} + e^{-2/6} + e^{-4/6} + e^{-5/6})z^{-1} + e^{-1}z^{-2}}$$

$$(9.26)$$

$$E_2(z) = \frac{1 - e^{-2/6} - e^{-1}z^{-1}}{2 + (-1 - e^{-1} + e^{-1/6} + e^{-2/6} + e^{-4/6} + e^{-5/6})z^{-1} + e^{-1}z^{-2}}$$

The algebra involved in obtaining (9.26) from (9.25) is fairly complicated and, in particular, requires that several common factors in the transforms be divided out. In carrying out such an analysis it is helpful to keep the order of the characteristic equation in mind and to continually look for common factors to reduce the expressions. The output of the system is readily calculated from one of the equations in (9.24).

9.3 Synthesis of a Multirate Digital Controller

Methods for the design of digital controllers for control of single-rate sampled-data systems were given in Chap. 7. In that chapter were given several design criteria, such as minimum finite settling time, staleness-factor design, and ripple-free design. All these methods, as developed in that chapter, were applied to systems which are single-rate. The manipulated variable which came from the controllers operated at the same basic rate as the error information fed to the controllers.

In many cases of practical importance the design can be improved by adopting a multirate controller. The block diagram of a system which employs a multirate controller is shown in Fig. 9.9. In this system the error signal, E_1, is sampled at some basic period T which is presumed to be fixed beyond the control of the system designer. The digital controller is designed to operate at a *reduced period*, T/n, so that the samples to the plant G are supplied more frequently than the input is sampled. The properties of such a design are briefly these:

1. Both the output ripple and the response time, or "rise time," are less than in the comparable single-rate system because of the shorter period of the samples at the input to the plant.

2. The input signals to the plant from the multirate controller are larger in amplitude than comparable signals from the single-rate system, with the result that saturation effects are more serious in the multirate system.

3. The multirate controller has the same memory or storage requirements as the corresponding single-rate design, but must operate at a higher speed.

The designer must decide whether or not the improved speed and the ripple performance are worth the price of increased speed of computation of the controller and greater saturation limits in the plant. If the decision is favorable to a multirate controller, then the design may be readily carried out using the procedures to be described here.

The design problem for a multirate controller to be used in the system of Fig. 9.9 consists of the specification of a desired over-all transfer function $K(z_n)$ such that the response will have suitable transient and steady-state behavior and also such that the necessary controller pulse transfer function will be physically realizable. The first step in the design

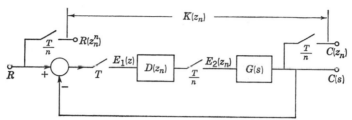

FIG. 9.9. Block diagram of system with multirate controller.

requires the relation between the controller pulse transfer function, $D(z_n)$, and the system transfer function, $K(z_n)$. For the variables as defined in Fig. 9.9 one can readily write

$$E_1(z) = R(z) - C(z) \qquad (9.27)$$

and, using the results expressed in (9.7),

$$C(z_n) = E_1(z_n{}^n) D(z_n) G(z_n) \qquad (9.28)$$

In order to eliminate E_1 from (9.27) and (9.28), it is necessary to take the z transform of (9.28), as defined in (9.19).

$$
\begin{aligned}
C(z) &\triangleq Z[C(z_n)] \\
&= Z[E_1(z_n{}^n) D(z_n) G(z_n)] \\
&= E_1(z) Z[D(z_n) G(z_n)]
\end{aligned}
\qquad (9.29)
$$

where $C(z)$ is the single-rate z transform corresponding to the multirate transform $C(z_n)$.

The last step leading to (9.29) makes use of the fact that the z transform of a product which includes a factor depending on z alone is the product of z transforms. In the case of (9.29), $E_1(z_n{}^n)$ is the factor which depends on z alone and is therefore factored out. If (9.29) is substituted in (9.27), one can solve for $E_1(z)$ as

$$E_1(z) = \frac{R(z)}{1 + Z[D(z_n) G(z_n)]} \qquad (9.30)$$

the expression (9.30) may now be substituted into (9.28) to relate the output to the input

$$C(z_n) = \frac{R(z_n{}^n) D(z_n) G(z_n)}{1 + Z[D(z_n) G(z_n)]} \qquad (9.31)$$

The pulse transfer function of this system is defined as the ratio

$$K(z_n) = \frac{C(z_n)}{R(z_n{}^n)}$$
$$= \frac{D(z_n)G(z_n)}{1 + \mathcal{Z}[D(z_n)G(z_n)]} \tag{9.32}$$

Equation (9.32) is the fundamental equation of analysis for the multirate controller system. If the controller pulse transfer function $D(z_n)$ and the plant transfer function $G(z_n)$ are given, then (9.32) or (9.31) show the response of the system. In order to synthesize the controller transfer function, it is necessary to invert these expressions and solve for $D(z_n)$ in terms of $K(z_n)$ and $G(z_n)$. The first step toward this inversion is to take the z transform corresponding to (9.32).

$$\mathcal{Z}[K(z_n)] = K(z)$$
$$= \frac{\mathcal{Z}[D(z_n)G(z_n)]}{1 + \mathcal{Z}[D(z_n)G(z_n)]} \tag{9.33}$$

In writing (9.33), use has been made of the fact that $1 + \mathcal{Z}[D(z_n)G(z_n)]$ is a function of z and may therefore be factored out of the z transform operation. Solving (9.33) for the term containing the unknown controller transfer function $D(z_n)$,

$$\mathcal{Z}[D(z_n)G(z_n)] = \frac{K(z)}{1 - K(z)} \tag{9.34}$$

$$1 + \mathcal{Z}[D(z_n)G(z_n)] = \frac{1}{1 - K(z)} \tag{9.34a}$$

The solution for the controller pulse transfer function may be completed by substituting (9.34a) into (9.32):

$$K(z_n) = \frac{D(z_n)G(z_n)}{1/[1 - K(z_n{}^n)]} \tag{9.35}$$

therefore $$D(z_n) = \frac{1}{G(z_n)} \frac{K(z_n)}{1 - K(z_n{}^n)} \tag{9.36}$$

Once a desirable over-all transfer function $K(z_n)$ is prescribed, (9.36) gives the transfer function of the multirate controller necessary to produce the desired response. The design of the multirate controller, like that of the single-rate controller, is therefore reduced to the specification of a suitable over-all transfer function $K(z_n)$.

The design objectives and limitations associated with the specification of a suitable over-all pulsed transfer function for use in a multirate control system are essentially the same as those already outlined in Chap. 7 in connection with the design of single-rate systems. Any of the design methods discussed for single-rate systems applies to the design of multirate systems, with the sole exception that the formulas leading to the desired results differ in the two cases. It is possible to design a multirate system for minimum finite settling time with zero steady-state error to a polynomial input, or to design for a "staleness-factor" type of response, or to design for a ripple-free response. Since each of these designs has been discussed in detail in Chap. 7, only the essential parts of the designs will be worked out here to illustrate the special problems introduced by the multirate character of the system.

Three basic requirements on the design of any control system are physical realizability, stability, and steady-state behavior. Each of these requirements will be discussed in turn for the system of Fig. 9.9. The most fundamental of these requirements is that of physical realizability. In its most elementary terms, this limitation of physical equipment is expressed by the statement that to be physical, a device must not respond prior to the application of the excitation. In terms of the multirate control system, the controller pulse transfer function described by (9.36) will be physically realizable if $K(z_n)$ is made to have a zero at infinity of at least the order of the zero of $G(z_n)$ at infinity. That is, if the expansion of $G(z_n)$ about infinity (in powers of z_n^{-1}) starts with the z_n^{-m} term, then the similar expansion of $K(z_n)$ must not start until the z_n^{-m} term.

The requirement that the system be stable is met by having all the poles of $K(z_n)$ lie inside the unit circle and by avoiding the cancellation of poles or zeros of $G(z_n)$ which are outside the unit circle by the controller pulse transfer function $D(z_n)$. This restriction of the poles and zeros of the controller transfer function is equivalent to the similar situation discussed in Chap. 7 in connection with the design of unit-rate systems. For the multirate controller described by (9.36), stability requires that all the zeros of $G(z_n)$ which are on or outside the unit circle be contained as factors of $K(z_n)$ and all poles of $G(z_n)$ which are on or outside the unit circle be contained in $1 - K(z_n{}^n)$. In other words, if

$$G(z_n) = \frac{1 - az_n^{-1}}{1 - bz_n^{-1}} F(z_n) \tag{9.37}$$

where $F(z_n)$ is a ratio of polynomials in z_n containing all its zeros and poles inside the unit circle of the z_n plane and where $|a|$, $|b| \geq 1$. Then, for stability, it is necessary that

$$K(z_n) = (1 - az_n^{-1})A(z_n) \tag{9.38}$$

and
$$1 - K(z_n{}^n) = (1 - b^n z_n^{-n})B(z_n{}^n) \tag{9.39}$$

A peculiarity of the multirate character of the problem is indicated by (9.39). In this equation, because of the nature of $K(z_n{}^n)$, it has been necessary to introduce n roots in the function $1 - K(z_n{}^n)$ in order to remove *one* root from $G(z_n)$. As mentioned in Sec. 9.2, all these roots of

$1 - K(z_n{}^n)$ are equally spaced around a circle of radius b and are therefore outside the unit circle.   The design would be stable if all these extraneous roots but the one in $G(z_n)$ are left in $D(z_n)$ because none of them involve pole or zero cancellation in an unstable region.   The controller transfer function which results from the inclusion of the extra roots of $1 - K(z_n{}^n)$ in $D(z_n)$ is of very high order, however, and the device used to realize this transfer function is unnecessarily complicated.   The design can be greatly simplified by including these extraneous roots from $1 - K(z_n{}^n)$ in the over-all transfer function $K(z_n)$ so that they do not appear in the controller transfer function.   In terms of the design equations, the more practical constraints on the transfer functions for the plant with the transfer function given by (9.37) are

$$K(z_n) = \frac{(1 - az_n{}^{-1})(1 - b^n z_n{}^{-n})A(z_n)}{1 - bz_n{}^{-1}} \qquad (9.40)$$

and $$1 - K(z_n{}^n) = (1 - b^n z_n{}^{-n})B(z_n{}^n) \qquad (9.41)$$

Since physical realizability requires that $K(z_n)$ contain the zeros of the plant which are at infinity, which is certainly outside the unit circle, (9.40) and (9.41) actually express the constraints sufficient to ensure both stability and physical realizability in the design.   In these two equations, the functions $A(z_n)$ and $B(z_n{}^n)$ are general functions which include the design requirements other than removal of the zero at a and the pole at b in the plant.   If there are other poles or zeros in the plant which are outside the unit circle, they must, of course, be treated in the same manner as the two selected in (9.37).   The final constraint on the transfer function which is fairly universal is the specification of the steady-state performance.

The requirement on steady-state response is most conveniently defined in terms of the system response to a polynomial input.   As discussed in Chap. 7, the designer frequently requires that the system follow an input whose transform is $1/s^k$ with zero error at sampling instants in the steady state.   This requirement can be translated into a specification on $K(z_n)$ for the multirate system.   The error of the system of Fig. 9.9 is the variable E_1, which satisfies the relation

$$\begin{aligned} E_1(z_n) &= R(z_n) - C(z_n) \\ &= R(z_n) - R(z_n{}^n)K(z_n) \end{aligned} \qquad (9.42)$$

If $R(s)$ is of the form $1/s^k$, then it is easy to show that

$$R(z_n) = \frac{P(z_n)}{(1 - z_n{}^{-1})^k} \qquad (9.43)$$

and $$R(z_n{}^n) = \frac{P(z_n{}^n)}{(1 - z_n{}^{-n})^k} \qquad (9.44)$$

where (9.44) is obtained in the manner defined earlier, which is to take the z transform of $R(s)$ and replace z by $z_n{}^n$. The functions $P(z_n)$ and $P(z_n{}^n)$ are polynomials in $z_n{}^{-1}$. If (9.43) and (9.44) are substituted in (9.42), one obtains the equation for the z_n transform of the error

$$E_1(z_n) = \frac{P(z_n)}{(1 - z_n{}^{-1})^k} - \frac{P(z_n{}^n)K(z_n)}{(1 - z_n{}^{-n})^k} \qquad (9.45)$$

The steady-state performance one would like to specify is that the final value of $E_1(z_n)$ in response to the polynomial input be zero. The final-value theorem may be used to express this condition in terms of $K(z_n)$. If all poles of $E_1(z_n)$ are inside the unit circle, then

$$e_1(\infty) = \lim_{z_n \to 1} (1 - z_n{}^{-1})E_1(z_n) \qquad (9.46)$$

In order for $E_1(z_n)$ as given by (9.45) to meet the requirements for the application of (9.46), it is necessary, first of all, that $K(z_n)$ contain as zeros all the roots of $(1 - z_n{}^{-n})^k$ except the kth-order root at unity. As discussed in Sec. 9.2, these roots lie equally spaced around the unit circle and must be removed if the final-value theorem is to apply. Therefore, by inspection, it can be stated that for proper steady-state behavior, $K(z_n)$ must be of the form

$$K(z_n) = \frac{(1 - z_n{}^{-n})^k}{(1 - z_n{}^{-1})^k} F(z_n)$$
$$= (1 + z_n{}^{-1} + z_n{}^{-2} + \cdots + z_n{}^{-n+1})^k F(z_n) \qquad (9.47)$$

where the correctness of the polynomial in $z_n{}^{-1}$ can be readily verified by a process of long division and where $F(z_n)$ is as yet arbitrary. Substituting (9.47) in (9.45),

$$E_1(z_n) = \frac{P(z_n)}{(1 - z_n{}^{-1})^k} - \frac{P(z_n{}^n)F(z_n)}{(1 - z_n{}^{-1})^k}$$
$$= \frac{P(z_n) - P(z_n{}^n)F(z_n)}{(1 - z_n{}^{-1})^k} \qquad (9.48)$$

If, now, the final value of $E_1(z_n)$ is to be zero, then (9.48) must have no pole at $z_n = 1$. This means that the numerator of (9.48) must have a kth-order zero at $z_n = 1$. That is, if $Q(z_n)$ is defined as

$$Q(z_n) = P(z_n) - P(z_n{}^n)F(z_n) \qquad (9.49)$$

then the steady-state constraint may be satisfied by requiring that

$$Q(z_n) = (1 - z_n{}^{-1})^k T(z_n) \qquad (9.50)$$

Or, equivalently,

$$\left. \frac{d^m Q(z_n)}{d(z_n{}^{-1})^m} \right|_{z_n = 1} = 0 \qquad m = 0, 1, \ldots, k - 1 \qquad (9.51)$$

Equations (9.47) and either (9.50) or (9.51) express the necessary and sufficient conditions on $K(z_n)$ such that the final value of the error will be zero in response to an input with the transform $1/s^k$. These same conditions take care of the requirement that the steady-state error be zero in response to any $(k-1)$th-order polynomial input.

EXAMPLE

As an example of the application of the steady-state constraints expressed by (9.47) and (9.51), consider the design of a minimum finite-settling-time pulse transfer function which must have zero steady-state error in response to a ramp input. The plant has no poles or zeros outside the unit circle except for a simple zero at infinity. In this case, $k = 2$, and

$$R(s) = \frac{1}{s^2} \tag{9.52}$$

$$R(z_n) = \frac{T}{n} \frac{z_n^{-1}}{(1 - z_n^{-1})^2} \tag{9.53}$$

$$R(z_n{}^n) = T \frac{z_n^{-n}}{(1 - z_n^{-n})^2} \tag{9.54}$$

From (9.53) and (9.54) it is obvious that the numerators of $R(z_n)$ and $R(z_n{}^n)$ are

$$P(z_n) = \frac{T}{n} z_n^{-1}$$

$$P(z_n{}^n) = T z_n^{-n} \tag{9.55}$$

Applying the first of the steady-state constraints, given by (9.47), and the physical-realizability constraint one can write

$$K(z_n) = \frac{(1 - z_n^{-n})^2}{(1 - z_n^{-1})^2} (f_1 z_n^{-1} + f_2 z_n^{-2}) \tag{9.56}$$

Only two terms are included in the arbitrary $F(z_n)$ in (9.56) since the design is to be a minimum settling time, and a look ahead shows that the constraint given by (9.51) requires only two free constants. From (9.55) the function $Q(z_n)$ is formed as

$$Q(z_n) = \frac{T}{n} z_n^{-1} - T z_n^{-n}(f_1 z_n^{-1} + f_2 z_n^{-2}) \tag{9.57}$$

The constraint equations obtained from the application of (9.51) to the function given in (9.57) are

$$\frac{T}{n} - T(f_1 + f_2) = 0$$

$$\frac{T}{n} - T(n + 1)f_1 - T(n + 2)f_2 = 0 \tag{9.58}$$

The solution of the simultaneous equations given in (9.58) is given by

$$f_1 = \frac{n+1}{n}$$
$$f_2 = -1$$

and the final required form of the pulse transfer function is

$$K(z_n) = \left(\frac{1 - z_n^{-n}}{1 - z_n^{-1}}\right)^2 \left(\frac{n+1}{n} z_n^{-1} - z_n^{-2}\right) \tag{9.59}$$

To illustrate the design given above with a numerical example, consider the design of a double-rate controller for the control of a plant with the transfer function

$$G(s) = \frac{1 - e^{-s/2}}{s} \frac{4.6}{s + 4.6} \tag{9.60}$$

with $T = 1$ sec. In this case,

$$G(z_2) = \frac{0.9z_2^{-1}}{1 - 0.1z_2^{-1}} \tag{9.61}$$

and, from (9.59),

$$K(z_2) = (1 + z_2^{-1})^2(1.5z_2^{-1} - z_2^{-2}) \tag{9.62}$$

From (9.62), taking the terms in z_2^{-2},

$$K(z_2{}^2) = 2z_2^{-2} - z_2^{-4} \tag{9.63}$$

The substitution of (9.61), (9.62), and (9.63) in the fundamental design equation (9.36) yields

$$\begin{aligned}
D(z_2) &= \frac{1 - 0.1z_2^{-1}}{0.9z_2^{-1}} \frac{(1 + z_2^{-1})^2}{(1 - z_2^{-2})^2} (1.5z_2^{-1} - z_2^{-2}) \\
&= \frac{(1 - 0.1z_2^{-1})(1.5 - z_2^{-1})}{0.9(1 - z_2^{-1})^2}
\end{aligned} \tag{9.64}$$

The block diagram of the multirate system is shown in Fig. 9.10a, and a single-rate system designed for the same system by the techniques of Chap. 7 is shown in Fig. 9.10b. The responses of the two systems are shown in Fig. 9.11, where the two curves show clearly the advantages of the multirate controller in reducing the output ripple of a sampled-data system. The particular example chosen may seem slightly artificial in that the basic sampling rate is taken to be quite slow compared to the time constant of the plant, but in fact this is the only situation in which ripple is a serious problem anyway.

EXAMPLE

As a second example of the design of a multirate controller, the design of $D(z_n)$ for the finite-settling-time control of a plant with the pulse

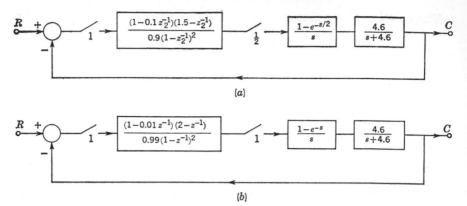

(a)

(b)

FIG. 9.10. Block diagrams of (a) double-rate and (b) single-rate systems designed to the same specifications.

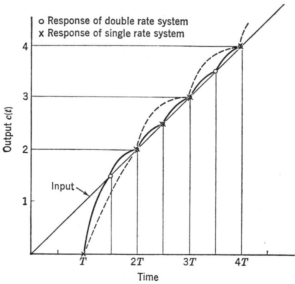

FIG. 9.11. Ramp responses of double- and single-rate systems of Fig. 9.10.

transfer function

$$G(z_n) = \frac{z_n^{-1}}{1 - 2z_n^{-1}} \tag{9.65}$$

to follow a step input with zero steady-state error at sampling instants is considered. In this case, the plant is open-loop unstable, and the design requires the application of the constraints expressed by (9.40), (9.41), (9.47), and (9.51). Combining these equations for the present example, it is found that the over-all pulse transfer function must satisfy the two equations

$$K(z_n) = \frac{1 - z_n^{-n}}{1 - z_n^{-1}} \frac{1 - 2^n z_n^{-n}}{1 - 2z_n^{-1}} (g_1 z_n^{-1} + g_2 z_n^{-2}) \qquad (9.66)$$

$$1 - K(z_n{}^n) = (1 - 2^n z_n^{-n})(b_1 z_n^{-n} + b_2 z_n^{-2n}) \qquad (9.67)$$

The two constants g_1 and g_2 in (9.66) are to be determined from the steady-state requirement and from the fact expressed by (9.67) that $1 - Z[K(z_n)]$ must contain the factor $1 - 2^n z^{-1}$. The constants b_1 and b_2 in (9.67) are only functions of the g's and will automatically fall out of the solution. The essence of the constraint expressed by (9.67) can also be stated in the form

$$Z[K(z_n)]\Big|_{z = 2^n} = 1 \qquad (9.08)$$

The steady-state requirement given by (9.51) requires the formation of the $Q(z_n)$ function from (9.49). In the present example the design requirement is for zero steady-state error to a step, so that one can write immediately

$$R(s) = \frac{1}{s}$$

$$R(z_n) = \frac{1}{1 - z_n^{-1}}$$

$$R(z_n{}^n) = \frac{1}{1 - z_n^{-n}}$$

$$P(z_n) = 1$$

$$P(z_n{}^n) = 1$$

and, from (9.49) and (9.66),

$$Q(z_n) = 1 - \frac{1 - 2^n z_n^{-n}}{1 - 2z_n^{-1}} (g_1 z_n^{-1} + g_2 z_n^{-2})$$

The steady-state requirement of (9.51) reduces to

$$Q(z_n)\Big|_{z_n = 1} = 0$$

for a step input for which $k = 1$. Therefore, the two constants g_1 and g_2 must satisfy the equation

$$g_1 + g_2 = \frac{1}{2^n - 1} \qquad (9.69)$$

The second equation satisfied by g_1 and g_2 is obtained from (9.68) and requires the calculation of $Z[K(z_n)]$. This calculation can be made either by expansion of $K(z_n)$ and selection of the z_n^{-n} terms or else by use of the formula developed earlier that

$$Z[K(z_n)] = \frac{1}{2\pi j} \int_\Gamma \frac{K(z_n)\, dz_n}{(1 - z_n{}^n z^{-1}) z_n} \qquad (9.70)$$

When $K(z_n)$ represents a finite settling time there is little difference in labor involved in the two methods, but when $K(z_n)$ does not represent a finite settling time then (9.70) offers considerable advantage over the direct expansion method. The application of (9.70) is greatly simplified by recognition of the fact that any function of z_n^{-n} may be factored out directly before evaluation of the integral. That is, as may be readily verified from an elementary consideration of Fig. 9.1 and (9.7),

$$Z[F(z_n{}^n)G(z_n)] = F(z)Z[G(z_n)] \tag{9.71}$$

For the present example, substitution of (9.66) in (9.70) leads to the integral

$$Z[K(z_n)] = \frac{1}{2\pi j} \int_\Gamma \frac{1 - z_n^{-n}}{1 - z_n^{-1}} \frac{1 - 2^n z_n^{-n}}{1 - 2 z_n^{-1}} \frac{g_1 z_n^{-1} + g_2 z_n^{-2}}{1 - z_n{}^n z^{-1}} \frac{dz_n}{z_n} \tag{9.72}$$

The application of the results given in (9.71) to the integral in (9.72) simplifies the problem to the form

$$Z[K(z_n)] = \frac{(1 - z^{-1})(1 - 2^n z^{-1})}{2\pi j} \int_\Gamma \frac{(g_1 z_n + g_2)\, dz_n}{(z_n - 1)(z_n - 2)(1 - z_n{}^n z^{-1}) z_n} \tag{9.73}$$

The path of integration Γ for the integral of (9.73) is a circle with radius greater than 2, and the evaluation of the integral is simply done by the method of residues. The final result is that

$$Z[K(z_n)] = \left[(2^n - 1)g_1 + \frac{2^n - 2}{2} g_2 \right] z^{-1} + g_2 2^{n-1} z^{-2} \tag{9.74}$$

The application of the constraint equation (9.68) to (9.74), which requires the evaluation of (9.74) at $z = 2^n$, can be simplified to the equation

$$2g_1 + g_2 = \frac{2^{n+1}}{2^n - 1} \tag{9.75}$$

Finally, the two constants can now be evaluated from the solution of (9.75) and (9.69), with the result

$$g_1 = \frac{2^{n+1} - 1}{2^n - 1}$$

$$g_2 = -2 \tag{9.76}$$

Substitution of (9.76) in (9.66) and (9.74) permits one to calculate the two transfer functions necessary to get the controller pulse transfer function.

$$K(z_n) = \frac{1 - z_n^{-n}}{1 - z_n^{-1}} \frac{1 - 2^n z_n^{-n}}{1 - 2 z_n^{-1}} \left(\frac{2^{n+1} - 1}{2^n - 1} z_n^{-1} - 2 z_n^{-2} \right)$$

$$1 - Z[K(z_n)] = (1 - z_n^{-n})(1 - 2^n z_n^{-n}) \tag{9.77}$$

It should be noted during the algebra leading to (9.77) that $1 - Z[K(z_n)]$

can always be factored because the design has included specification of the roots of this function. Substitution of (9.77) and (9.65) into the basic design equation (9.36) leads to the final design objective, the pulse transfer function of the multirate controller $D(z_n)$.

$$D(z_n) = \left(\frac{2^{n+1} - 1}{2^{n+1} - 2} - z_n^{-1}\right)\frac{2}{1 - z_n^{-1}} \qquad (9.78)$$

The multirate design which has resulted in the specification of the controller pulse transfer function given in (9.78) may be evaluated by comparing the response of the multirate system with that of a single-rate system operating on the same plant and with the same over-all specifications.

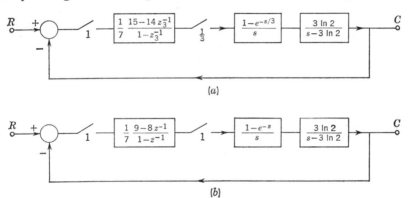

(a)

(b)

FIG. 9.12. (a) Triple-rate and (b) single-rate controllers for an unstable plant.

To illustrate the point, a multirate controller having an output sample rate three times the input sample rate will be used. This means that $n = 3$ in evaluating (9.78). The triple-rate controller is shown in Fig. 9.12a, along with the continuous plant transfer function leading to (9.65). The single-rate system is shown in Fig. 9.12b. It is noted that the complexity of the controller in each case is the same, that is, both controllers require no more than two storage elements. The response of these systems when subjected to a step input is shown in Fig. 9.13, where they may be compared. First of all, the overshoot in both cases is quite large and equal. This is to be expected with an unstable plant used in the example. Also, the triple-rate design does not show much improvement in settling time because the unstable plant can be stabilized only by feedback and the first feedback sample is applied to the error system after 1 sec in either case. A system which is open-loop stable can reach steady state in much less time, as shown in the first example.

Each of the example problems worked out for multirate controller design have been of the minimum-finite-settling-time variety. The application of staleness factors or the design for zero ripple could also be done with a multirate controller, of course. The techniques are the same as for the single-rate case discussed in Chap. 7, except for the change in details of constraint applications as discussed above. The comments regarding the relative merits of each of these designs as given in Chap. 7 apply equally well to the multirate case and need not be repeated here.

9.4 Design of Multirate Controllers with Single-rate Techniques

For the usual problem in control-system design with plants to be controlled which are open-loop stable, the multirate controller may, under certain circumstances, be designed using single-rate techniques. This

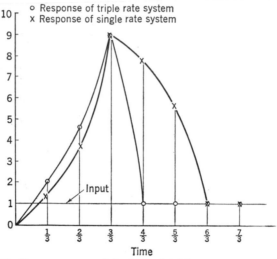

FIG. 9.13. Step responses of single- and triple-rate systems of Fig. 9.12.

design procedure, which was first described by Bertram in a discussion of ref. 30, takes advantage of the fact that for finite-settling-time designs (which include the zero-ripple design) it is always possible to select the speed-up factor n in the multirate controller in such a fashion that all transients in the system at sampling instants are over in one period of length T. Although this technique applies to any finite-settling-time design, the emphasis here will be placed on the zero-ripple case, which, of the several possibilities, is the most attractive in terms of performance and among the most complicated in terms of design steps. For the zero-ripple design, the speed-up factor is so chosen that transients at all instants are made to terminate in one period of length T. To concentrate for the moment on the step response, the operation of a multirate system designed on the basis being proposed here can be described as follows, with reference to Fig. 9.9. Upon application of the step at R, a single pulse of amplitude r_0 is supplied at E_1 to the multirate controller. The controller then applies a sequence of pulses to the plant at intervals of T/n sec, which pulses are so designed in amplitude that the plant output is brought to the new required level or position with no further error detected at E_1. The parameter n must be chosen sufficiently large that the required change in output level can be accomplished in the allotted time. The minimum value of n necessary to do this can be determined by inspection of the design equations.

The reason that single-rate techniques can be used to design the multi-rate controller pulse transfer function for the operation described above is that the entire design is essentially based on open-loop equations. The controller receives a single pulse from E_1 and proceeds to change the output level of the plant sufficiently to reduce the detected error to zero with no feedback at all. Of course, if for any reason the output level did *not* reach the desired position, then a second error pulse would supply the feedback information. In other words, although the system operates on feedback principles, it can be designed on an open-loop basis.

In terms of design equations, the procedure for realizing the pulse transfer function of the multirate controller using these principles is quite simple. The design objective may be realized by requiring the multirate system of Fig. 9.9 to produce an output in response to a step input which is identical to the output of a single-rate system designed for the same plant and a sampling period T/n. The only difference between them is that the multirate controller gets only a single pulse input instead of a sequence of pulses.

To be more specific, the transform of the output of the system of Fig. 9.9 is

$$C(z_n) = E_1(z_n{}^n) D(z_n) G(z_n) \qquad (9.79)$$

and, if n is so chosen that only one pulse appears at E_1, then (9.79) reduces to

$$C(z_n) = r_0 D(z_n) G(z_n) \qquad (9.80)$$

where r_0 is the value of the first error sample supplied to the controller. If the input is a unit step, then r_0 is unity. A single-rate system designed for zero-ripple response with the plant G would have an over-all pulse transfer function $\hat{K}(z_n)$. The output of the single-rate system would be

$$\hat{C}(z_n) = R(z_n)\hat{K}(z_n) \qquad (9.81)$$

If these two system outputs are to be identical, then the multirate controller pulse transfer function must be

$$D(z_n) = \frac{R(z_n)}{r_0} \frac{\hat{K}(z_n)}{G(z_n)} \qquad (9.82)$$

and, if there is to be no transient after T sec, then the output given by (9.81) must have reached the steady state in n samples, and n is chosen accordingly.

It is possible to express (9.81) completely in terms of the plant pulse transfer function if the design is based on zero-ripple step response.   If

$$G(z_n) = \frac{\displaystyle\sum_{i=1}^{n} \alpha_i z_n^{-i}}{\displaystyle\sum_{j=0}^{k} \beta_j z_n^{-j}} \qquad \beta_0 \neq 0 \tag{9.83}$$

Then, from the principles of Chap. 7, $\hat{K}(z_n)$ contains all the zeros of $G(z_n)$ and for proper steady-state behavior $K(1) = 1$.   Therefore

$$\hat{K}(z_n) = \frac{\displaystyle\sum_{i=1}^{n} \alpha_i z_n^{-i}}{\displaystyle\sum_{i=1}^{n} \alpha_i} \tag{9.84}$$

The upper limit on the numerator sums in (9.83) and (9.84) is deliberately taken as n because the order of $K(z_n)$ determines the number of pulses necessary for the output to reach the steady state and this number equals the order of the numerator polynomial in $G(z_n)$.   For example, if $G(z_n)$ has a second-order numerator, then a double-rate system is sufficient.   Substituting (9.84) and (9.83) in (9.82), with the z_n transform of a step for $R(z_n)$, the controller pulse transfer function is found to be

$$D(z_n) = \frac{\displaystyle\sum_{j=0}^{k} \beta_j z_n^{-j}}{\displaystyle\sum_{i=1}^{n} \alpha_i (1 - z_n^{-1})} \tag{9.85}$$

If the plant has an integration, then the $1 - z_n^{-1}$ factor will cancel in (9.85).   It is observed that the *number* of pulses applied to the plant (which number is regulated by the order of the controller transfer function), is determined by the order of the difference equation describing the plant, or, in other words, by the number of poles in the plant pulse transfer function.   The length of time necessary to reach the steady state, however, is determined by the order of the *numerator* polynomial of $G(z_n)$ or by the zeros of the plant pulse transfer function.   Therefore, as mentioned earlier, it is the number of zeros of $G(z_n)$ which determine the speed-up rate n in the multirate system.

EXAMPLE

As an example of the design principle outlined in this section, a second-order plant with zero-order hold is considered. The pertinent transfer function of the continuous element is

$$G(s) = \frac{1 - e^{-sT/n}}{s} \frac{1}{s(s+1)} \tag{9.86}$$

From previous calculations (see Sec. 7.8) it is known that the pulse transfer function of this system has two zeros, so that $n = 2$. If, for

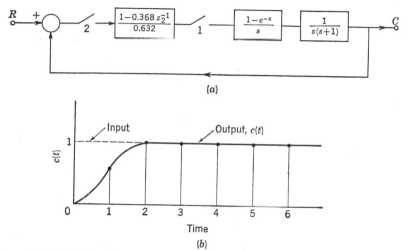

(a)

(b)

FIG. 9.14. (a) Block diagram and (b) step response of a multirate system designed for zero ripple.

purposes of this example, T is taken to be 2 sec, then the previously calculated pulse transfer function can be used, namely,

$$G(z_2) = \frac{0.368z_2^{-1}(1 + 0.718z_2^{-1})}{(1 - z_2^{-1})(1 - 0.368z_2^{-1})} \tag{9.87}$$

Substituting from (9.87) into (9.85),

$$D(z_2) = \frac{(1 - z_2^{-1})(1 - 0.368z_2^{-1})}{0.368(1.718)(1 - z_2^{-1})}$$
$$= \frac{1 - 0.368z_2^{-1}}{0.632} \tag{9.88}$$

A block diagram of this system and the associated step response are shown in Fig. 9.14.

It is possible to generalize the interpretation of the basic design equation given as (9.82) considerably beyond the step-response case worked out in detail in (9.85). In some cases it is desirable, and for plants with two integrations it is necessary, to base the design on zero steady-state response to a ramp rather than a step input. In these cases, the usual single-rate design for $K(z_n)$ is used, but some care must be exercised in the choice of effective input $R(z_n)$ selected to be entered in the formula. The design based on a ramp response will result in a multirate controller which will drive the plant into a ramp upon receipt of a *single error sample* and will settle the output in the steady state on the presumed ramp before being able to check the validity of the assumption. The difficulty of the situation is as shown in Fig. 9.15, where several possible input

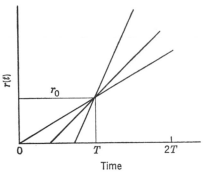

ramps are shown which lead to the *same* first error sample of amplitude r_0. By appropriate choice of $R(z_n)$ entered in (9.82) the designer can drive the plant output to a steady-state correspondence with any of these or with the unlimited other class of inputs which give the same initial sample value. The choice of which first-order polynomial to design for must be made by the designer of the system based on his knowledge or estimate of the best

FIG. 9.15. Three ramp inputs which give the same initial sample value.

case for his system. The decision here is not unlike that of the first-order hold discussed in the early chapters, where one had a choice of designing for full or partial slope correction in a data-hold operation.

A second alternative suggests itself for the design of multirate control systems upon inspection of the dilemma of Fig. 9.15. Since this contemplated design results in a new steady state of the plant being established in each period, there is no reason why the rule for determining this steady state cannot be modified from one period to the next. In other words, it should be possible to set up the controller with provision for selection between designs for zero error to a step and zero error to a ramp. The decision to select one or the other of these possible performance rules could be made by a device which operates on the back difference of E_1. If this back difference is less than some threshold, the slower but smoother step-response design is used, and for rapidly changing inputs the ramp design is used. Further development of this idea is necessary to evaluate its effectiveness in reducing following errors in any particular case.

9.5 Summary

A multirate sampled data system is a system which contains two or more signals which are sampled at different rates. In case the ratios of the different rates are the ratios of small numbers, it is possible to analyze a multirate system by reducing it to an equivalent multiloop single-rate system. This reduction of the multirate problem to a single-rate problem involves the decomposition of a sampling switch which operates with a period T/n into n parallel switches (with delay and advance operators) which operate with the period T. The method, which is called switch decomposition, is practical for pencil-and-paper analyses only if the total number of switches in the equivalent system is relatively small. For multirate systems where an exact equivalent single-rate system would involve a large number of samplers, it is frequently possible to obtain an approximate system which should provide sufficient accuracy to answer the most important questions. For example, switches with sampling rates in the ratio $22:7$ could probably be considered to be in the ratio $3:1$ without a great loss of accuracy.

The theory of multirate control systems is important to the synthesis of new systems as well as to the analysis of existing systems. A multirate controller can be designed which accepts error data at intervals of T sec and supplies data at intervals of T/n sec. This effective speed-up in the data rate into the plant or process means that, in general, the response time of the output will be reduced and the ripple between samples will be lessened. The multirate controller can be designed for the standard prototype response functions, such as minimum finite settling time, staleness factor, or zero ripple, and will in each case effectively speed up the time scale of the response. There is a limitation on the response-time improvement in case the plant is open-loop unstable because such systems can only be stabilized by feedback and the multirate controller does not increase the speed of feedback sampling.

For finite-settling-time designs, it is possible to obtain the pulse transfer function of the multirate controller by using single-rate techniques. With this combined design method, the speed-up factor in the multirate system is included as a design parameter and not left to arbitrary choice. There is some indication that the method can be extended to provide a basis for a nonlinear adaptive control-system design.

CHAPTER 10

SAMPLED DATA SYSTEMS WITH RANDOM INPUTS

In the previous chapters all the input signals have been considered as deterministic, or known, functions of the time. In many cases of practical interest, however, this is not the case, and some or all of the signals must be considered to be random functions of time. That is, one is not able to make a statement such as "$r(t)$ is unity for all positive time and zero for all negative time," but instead must be content with a description in probability such as "$r(t)$ is between 0.9 and 1.1 in 80 per cent of the signals in this class at this time."

Several rather broad treatments of random signals in control systems are readily available (see, for example, ref. 34), and the present chapter contains only a brief review of certain aspects of the theory and an application of these techniques to sampled-data systems. As in the previous chapters, the point of view here is influenced greatly by the simultaneous presence of discrete and continuous signals which characterizes sampled-data systems. The attention of this chapter is accordingly focused on a combination of the analysis of strictly discrete systems and the analysis of strictly continuous systems and signals.

10.1 Review of the Analysis of Random Signals

One can imagine many possible sources or generators of random signals, as, for example, a vacuum tube whose plate current is subject to fluctuations because of the random emission of electrons from the cathode (a phenomenon known as shot noise) or a conductor which contains thermally excited electrons which give rise to thermal noise. A random input to a control system might arise as the command signal from a gyro mounted in an aircraft or ship which is being rocked by wind or waves. All of these signals are examples of random variables which must be described in probabilistic terms.

The mathematical description of a random process depends upon the concepts of a probability-distribution function and probability-density functions of various orders. The first-order probability-density function associated with a random signal $X(t)$ is designated $f_1(x,t)$. This function is defined so that the product $f_1(x,t)\ dx$ is the probability that the variable

$X(t)$ has a value in the infinitesimal range $x \leq X(t) \leq x + dx$ at the time t.   More generally, the probability that $X(t)$ lies in a finite range $a \leq X(t) \leq b$ at the time t is given by the integral

$$P_r[a \leq X(t) \leq b] = \int_a^b f_1(x,t) \, dx \qquad (10.1)$$

The second-order probability-density function associated with a random variable $X(t)$ is designated $f_2(x_1,t_1;x_2,t_2)$ and is defined to be such that the product $f_2(x_1,t_1;x_2,t_2) \, dx_1 \, dx_2$ gives the probability that the variable lies in the range $x_1 \leq X(t_1) \leq x_1 \mid dx_1$ at the time t_1 and also lies in the range $x_2 \leq X(t_2) \leq x_2 + dx_2$ at the time t_2.   Clearly the second-order density function provides a more detailed description of the signal than does the first-order function, and as higher-order density functions are prescribed more and more detail is available about $X(t)$.   It is seldom indeed, however, that one is so fortunate as to know the probability-density functions of all orders which describe a random signal, and in many cases one must settle for much less specific information.

In a typical situation one may know some of the moments of the distributions which describe the random signal being considered.   The first moment is the expected value or average or mean and is defined by the integral

$$E[X(t_1)] = \int_{-\infty}^{\infty} x f_1(x_1,t_1) \, dx \qquad (10.2)$$

This moment depends upon the first-order density function, and gives, in a rough sense, the d-c content of the signal $X(t_1)$.   The generalized second moment of the random variable $X(t)$ is the autocorrelation function, defined by

$$\Phi_{xx}(t_1,t_2) = \overline{X(t_1)X(t_2)} = \int_{-\infty}^{\infty} \int_{-\infty}^{\infty} x_1 x_2 f_2(x_1,t_1;x_2,t_2) \, dx_1 \, dx_2 \qquad (10.3)$$

which is the average of the product of values of the variable at t_1 times the values of the variable at time t_2.   For the special case when t_1 equals t_2, then x_1 equals x_2, and

$$\begin{aligned} \Phi_{xx}(t_1,t_1) &= \int_{-\infty}^{\infty} \int_{-\infty}^{\infty} x_1^2 f_2(x_1,t_1;x_2,t_1) \, dx_1 \, dx_2 \\ &= \int_{-\infty}^{\infty} x_1^2 f_1(x_1,t_1) \, dx_1 \\ &= E[X^2(t_1)] \qquad (10.4) \end{aligned}$$

which is the mean-square value of the variable at t_1.   In the second step of (10.4), use has been made of the fact that the integral of the second-order function f_2 over all values of x_2 is just the first-order density function f_1.   That is, the probability that the variable has a value in the range $x_1 \leq X \leq x_1 + dx_1$ at time t_1 and has any value at all at time t_2 is simply $f_1(x_1,t_1) \, dx_1$.   From the symmetry of (10.3) it is obvious that $\Phi_{xx}(t_1,t_2)$ equals $\Phi_{xx}(t_2,t_1)$.

Where the analysis of two related random processes is involved, as, for example, in the consideration of the input to a filter, $x(t)$, and the output of the filter, $y(t)$, one must define joint probability-density functions to describe the simultaneous characteristics of the two variables. The first joint density function is defined so that the product $f_{11}(x,t_1;y,t_2)\,dx\,dy$ gives the probability that X has a value in the range $x \leq X \leq x + dx$ at time t_1 and Y has a value in the range $y \leq Y \leq y + dy$ at time t_2. The most elementary moment of the first-order joint density function is the cross-correlation function, defined as

$$\Phi_{xy}(t_1,t_2) = E[X(t_1)Y(t_2)]$$
$$= \int_{-\infty}^{\infty} \int_{-\infty}^{\infty} f_{11}(x,t_1;y,t_2)xy\,dx\,dy \qquad (10.5)$$

If the variables X and Y are independent, then the joint density function is the product of the individual first-order density functions for X and Y, and the cross-correlation reduces to

$$\Phi_{xy}(t_1,t_2) = E[X(t_1)]E[Y(t_2)]$$
$$= \overline{X(t_1)}\ \overline{Y(t_2)} \qquad (10.6)$$

Therefore, if the mean value of either of two independent random variables is zero, their cross-correlation is zero. It is important to note that the converse of this statement is false. That is, a zero cross-correlation between two variables, one or both of which have zero mean value, does not imply the independence of the variables. The cross-correlation is the average of the product of values of X at t_1 times the values of Y at t_2. Since this average is unchanged if X is replaced by Y and t_1 by t_2, it follows that $\Phi_{xy}(t_1,t_2)$ equals $\Phi_{yx}(t_2,t_1)$.

In many cases of practical interest it is possible to make the simplifying assumption that the random process is stationary. That is, the probability-density functions do not depend on the origin of time, they are stationary in time. If this assumption can be made, then the expected value given by (10.2) becomes independent of t_1 and is written simply as

$$E(X) = \bar{X} \qquad (10.7)$$

The second-order density function of a stationary process is written $f_2(x_1,x_2,\tau)$ and expresses the probability that the variable X has a value x_1 at some time and a value x_2 τ sec later. The autocorrelation function of a stationary process becomes

$$\Phi_{xx}(\tau) = \int_{-\infty}^{\infty} \int_{-\infty}^{\infty} x_1x_2f_2(x_1,x_2,\tau)\,dx_1\,dx_2 \qquad (10.8)$$

and has even symmetry since $\Phi_{xx}(\tau)$ equals $\Phi_{xx}(-\tau)$. The mean-square value of the stationary variable is independent of the time, and (10.4) reduces to the simple relation that

$$\Phi_{xx}(0) = E(x^2) = \int_{-\infty}^{\infty} x^2 f_1(x) \, dx \tag{10.9}$$

The cross-correlation of two stationary random signals is

$$\Phi_{xy}(\tau) = \int_{-\infty}^{\infty} \int_{-\infty}^{\infty} f_{11}(x,y,\tau) xy \, dx \, dy \tag{10.10}$$

which has such symmetry that $\Phi_{xy}(\tau)$ equals $\Phi_{yx}(-\tau)$.

A further simplifying assumption which is usually made during the analysis of stationary signals is the ergodic property. This hypothesis states that under certain conditions present in many physical cases, the moments of a stationary process obtained by a process of averaging in time on a particular signal are identical to the moments obtained by averaging over the probability-density function. For example, where the ergodic hypothesis applies,

$$E(X) = \bar{X} = <X>$$

where, by definition,

$$<X> = \lim_{T \to \infty} \frac{1}{2T} \int_{-T}^{T} x(t) \, dt \tag{10.11}$$

and furthermore, the autocorrelation function is given by

$$\Phi_{xx}(\tau) = E[X(t)X(t + \tau)]$$

$$= \lim_{T \to \infty} \frac{1}{2T_0} \int_{-T_0}^{T_0} x(t)x(t + \tau) \, dt \tag{10.12}$$

and the cross-correlation may be determined from

$$\Phi_{xy}(\tau) = E[X(t)Y(t + \tau)]$$

$$= \lim_{T \to \infty} \frac{1}{2T_0} \int_{-T_0}^{T_0} x(t)y(t + \tau) \, dt \tag{10.13}$$

It will be assumed that all processes considered hereafter are both stationary and ergodic where necessary. Another property of random signals which is of some interest to the analysis of sampled random signals is that the autocorrelation function of a stationary and ergodic process may be obtained by an average of samples according to

$$\Phi_{xx}(\tau) = \lim_{N \to \infty} \frac{1}{2N + 1} \sum_{n=-N}^{+N} x(nT)x(nT + \tau) \tag{10.14}$$

for positive T.

An important technique in the analysis of linear systems is the resolution of signals into their frequency content by Fourier or Laplace transformation. In the study of random signals this technique is embodied in the concept of the spectral-density function. This function is an average similar to the moments defined above but expresses the average power contained in a signal in an infinitesimal frequency band. Physical interpretations of the spectral density usually speak of averaging the output of a very narrow band filter, whose input is the signal in question. For the purpose of this brief review, the spectral density is defined as the transform of the autocorrelation function

$$S_{xx}(s) = \int_{-\infty}^{\infty} \Phi_{xx}(\tau)e^{-s\tau}\,d\tau \tag{10.15}$$

from which the inverse transform gives the result

$$\Phi_{xx}(\tau) = \frac{1}{2\pi j} \int_{-j\infty}^{j\infty} S_{xx}(s)e^{s\tau}\,ds \tag{10.16}$$

The transform used in (10.15) and (10.16) is the bilateral Laplace transformation, and those familiar with Fourier analysis may replace the variable s by $j\omega$ to obtain possibly more familiar forms for the equations. The form given is chosen because it seems pointless to continually rotate the same complex plane in order to avoid imaginary limits in certain early expressions when one knows they will occur later anyway. By use of the bilateral Laplace transform, bounded time functions for positive time are represented by singularities of the transform in the left half of the s plane and bounded time functions for negative time are represented by singularities in the right half plane. It is noted that the path of integration for the inverse transform (10.16) is the imaginary axis and singularities on this axis are not allowed in the present analysis.

From (10.9) and (10.16) it is seen that the mean-square value of a random variable may be obtained by summing (integrating) the spectral density over all frequencies.

$$\Phi_{xx}(0) = \frac{1}{2\pi j} \int_{-j\infty}^{j\infty} S_{xx}(s)\,ds \tag{10.17}$$

The result expressed by (10.17) is the reason for the name "spectral density" because $S_{xx}(s)$ gives the density of mean-square value of the variable over the spectrum of real frequencies (imaginary s). The cross-spectral density is a function defined for two random variables as the transform of the cross-correlation function.

$$S_{xy}(s) = \int_{-\infty}^{\infty} \Phi_{xy}(\tau)e^{-s\tau}\,d\tau \tag{10.18}$$

As mentioned above, the principal use of the spectral density is in the analysis of random processes in linear systems, where one can use the result that the spectral density of the output of the system is related to the spectral density of the input by the well-known equation

$$S_{yy}(s) = S_{xx}(s)H(s)H(-s) \tag{10.19}$$

where $H(s)$ is the transfer function of the linear filter or the Laplace transform of the response of the filter to a unit impulse.

10.2 Analysis of Sampled Random Signals

In the study of sampled-data systems one is immediately faced with the analysis of the situation shown in Fig. 10.1, where a continuous random signal $x(t)$ is modulating the amplitudes of a train of rectangular pulses of

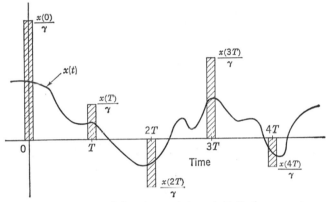

FIG. 10.1. Pulse sequence used for determining statistical parameters of sampled signal.

fixed width γ.   The modulated pulse train represents the sampled signal $x^*(t)$, which has a gain factor of $1/\gamma$ introduced to make the area of the pulses equal to the values of the signal at the sampling instants.   This gain normalization will make the limit process as γ tends to zero simpler to perform later when impulse modulation is introduced.

If the origin of time in the modulated pulse train is random, then the process $x^*(t)$ will be stationary and ergodic if $x(t)$ is stationary and ergodic.   In this case, the autocorrelation of $x^*(t)$ may be found by taking a time average of the product $x^*(t)x^*(t + \tau)$ as follows:

$$\Phi_{x^*x^*}(\tau) = \lim_{T_0 \to \infty} \frac{1}{2T_0} \int_{-T_0}^{T_0} x^*(t)x^*(t + \tau) \, dt \tag{10.20}$$

Sketches of a typical $x^*(t)$ and the shifted $x^*(t + \tau)$ are shown in Fig. 10.2. The integral of (10.20) may be broken up into a sum of integrals, each over one sampling period and expressed in the form

$$\Phi_{x^*x^*}(\tau) = \sum_{k=-\infty}^{\infty} \lim_{N\to\infty} \frac{1}{2N+1} \sum_{n=-N}^{N} x(nT)x(nT+kT)$$
$$\frac{1}{T}\int_{-T/2}^{T/2} p(\sigma)p(\sigma+\tau-kT)\,d\sigma \quad (10.21)$$

where $p(\sigma)$ is a pulse of width γ and height $1/\gamma$. From (10.14) the sample average in (10.21) is recognized to be $\Phi_{xx}(kT)$, so that (10.21) reduces to

$$\Phi_{x^*x^*}(\tau) = \sum_{k=-\infty}^{\infty} \Phi_{xx}(kT) \frac{1}{T}\int_{-T/2}^{T/2} p(\sigma)p(\sigma+\tau-kT)\,d\sigma \quad (10.22)$$

The integral in (10.22) is the convolution of pulse trains and results in a periodic train of triangles of height $1/\gamma T$ and base 2γ centered at "sampling instants" kT. A sketch of the autocorrelation of a typical sampled signal is shown in Fig. 10.3. As mentioned before, the gain factor $1/\gamma$

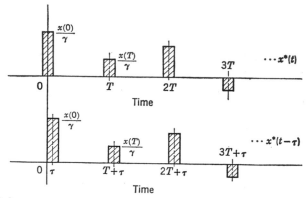

Fig. 10.2. Pulse sequences corresponding to normal and shifted sampled signals.

was introduced in the description of the sampling process to make later limiting processes simpler. If the gain factor is removed for the moment, one is left with a signal consisting of pulses of width γ and height $x(nT)$, and the modified autocorrelation function would be given by the expression of (10.22) multiplied by γ^2. From Fig. 10.3 it is obvious that the value of the modified autocorrelation at the origin which is the mean-square value of the conventional sampled signal with no extra gain is $\gamma/T[\Phi_{xx}(0)]$. That is, the mean-square value of the pulse amplitude-modulated wave equals the mean-square value of the original signal multiplied by a pulse duty factor, γ/T. This result checks with physical reasoning, as it should.

The analysis of the sampled signal shown in Fig. 10.2 gives a physical picture of the results of sampling but leads to an unnecessarily awkward mathematical formulation of the problem.   As in the earlier chapters on the treatment of deterministic signals, it is convenient to let the modulating-pulse width approach zero while the modulator gain approaches

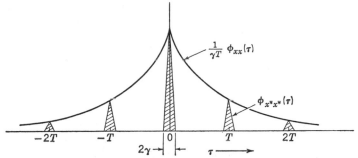

FIG. 10.3. Autocorrelation function of random pulse sequence.

infinity, with the result that the sampling process is approximated by impulse-area modulation.   By inspection of Fig. 10.3 or (10.22) it is obvious that the autocorrelation of the impulse sampled signal reduces to a train of impulses which can be expressed as

$$\Phi_{x^*x^*}(\tau) = \sum_{k=-\infty}^{\infty} \frac{1}{T}\Phi_{xx}(kT)\delta(\tau - kT) \tag{10.23}$$

Following the treatment of deterministic signals, the sampled autocorrelation is defined as the sequence of values

$$\Phi_{xx}^*(kT) = \frac{1}{T}\Phi_{xx}(kT) \tag{10.24}$$

where the $1/T$ factor is arbitrarily introduced in the definition (10.24) to simplify later expressions.

The spectral density of the signal whose autocorrelation function is given by (10.23) is the transform of this equation and has the form

$$S_{xx}^*(s) = \int_{-\infty}^{\infty} \sum_{k=-\infty}^{\infty} \Phi_{xx}^*(kT)\delta(\tau - kT)e^{-s\tau}\, d\tau$$

$$= \sum_{k=-\infty}^{\infty} \Phi_{xx}^*(kT)e^{-skT} \tag{10.25}$$

This function is called the sampled spectral density, or the *sampled power spectrum*, of the signal $x(t)$.   If e^{sT} is replaced by z, it is recognized that the sampled power spectrum of the signal is simply the two-sided z transform of the sampled autocorrelation function, $\Phi_{xx}^*(kT)$.

The discussion of sampled signals thus far has been concerned with the interpretation of sampling as a process of amplitude modulation of continuous signals. For discrete signals which are number sequences only the situation is exactly the same as in the case of deterministic signals. The autocorrelation of a sequence of numbers $r(nT)$ is defined as

$$\Phi_{rr}^*(kT) = \frac{1}{T} \lim_{N \to \infty} \frac{1}{2N+1} \sum_{n=-N}^{N} r(nT)r(nT - kT) \qquad (10.26)$$

and the sampled power spectrum of the sequence is defined as the z transform of the autocorrelation,

$$S_{rr}(z) = \sum_{k=-\infty}^{\infty} \Phi_{rr}^*(kT)z^{-k} \qquad (10.27)$$

The factor $1/T$ in (10.26) is arbitrarily introduced to simplify later expressions.

The mean-square value of a sequence of numbers or of a continuous signal $x(t)$ may be obtained from the sampled power spectrum using the inversion formula derived in Chap. 4 and either (10.27) or (10.25), which relate the sampled autocorrelation function to the desired mean-square value. By (10.24) and the inversion formula (4.20),

$$\Phi_{xx}(0) = T\Phi_{xx}^*(0)$$

$$= \frac{T}{2\pi j} \int_{\Gamma} S_{xx}(z)z^{-1}\, dz \qquad (10.28)$$

where the path of integration, Γ, is the unit circle. The formula (10.28) is equivalent to the expression

$$\Phi_{xx}(0) = \frac{T^2}{2\pi} \int_{-\pi/T}^{\pi/T} S_{xx}^*(j\omega)\, d\omega \qquad (10.29)$$

which is sometimes given for the mean-square value of a discrete variable. The equivalence of (10.29) to (10.28) may be shown by a change of variable $z = e^{j\omega T}$ in (10.28).

Although the forms for the sampled power spectrum [given by (10.25) and (10.27)] find the greatest use in the analysis of sampled random signals it is also possible to view this spectrum as the summation of harmonics introduced by the sampling process. If the complex Fourier series representation of the modulated impulse train in (10.25) is used, one obtains

$$S_{xx}^*(s) = \frac{1}{T^2} \sum_{n=-\infty}^{\infty} S_{xx}(s + jn\omega_0) \qquad (10.30)$$

where $S_{xx}(s)$ is the spectral density of the continuous signal $x(t)$.

10.3 Calculation of the Sampled Power Spectrum

Since the sampled power spectrum defined in (10.25) is required in the analysis of sampled random signals, it is desirable to be able to calculate this function easily from given data. For example, one may be given the power spectrum of the continuous signal $x(t)$ and be required to find the sampled power spectrum. A simple formula is possible in this case if $S_{xx}(s)$, the given power spectrum, is a rational function of s. Suppose the known power spectrum is

$$S_{xx}(s) = \int_{-\infty}^{\infty} \Phi_{xx}(\tau)e^{-s\tau}\, d\tau$$

which may be written

$$S_{xx}(s) = \int_{-\infty}^{0} \Phi_{xx}(\tau)e^{-s\tau}\, d\tau + \int_{0}^{\infty} \Phi_{xx}(\tau)e^{-s\tau}\, d\tau$$

Since $\Phi(\tau)$ is an even function, the change of variable $\sigma = -\tau$ in the first integral leads to

$$S_{xx}(s) = \int_{0}^{\infty} \Phi_{xx}(\sigma)e^{\sigma s}\, d\sigma + \int_{0}^{\infty} \Phi_{xx}(\tau)e^{-s\tau}\, d\tau$$
$$= G(-s) + G(s) \tag{10.31}$$

Where all the poles of $G(s)$ lie in the left half plane and all the poles of $G(-s)$ lie in the right half plane.

From (10.24) and (10.25) the sampled power spectrum is given by

$$S_{xx}(z) = \frac{1}{T} \sum_{n=-\infty}^{\infty} \Phi_{xx}(nT)z^{-n}$$

$$= \frac{1}{T}\left[\sum_{n=-\infty}^{0} \Phi_{xx}(nT)z^{-n} + \sum_{n=0}^{\infty} \Phi_{xx}(nT)z^{-n} - \Phi_{x}(0) \right]$$

by substitution of $k = -n$ in the first sum

$$S_{xx}(z) = \frac{1}{T}\left[\sum_{k=0}^{\infty} \Phi_{xx}(kT)z^{k} + \sum_{n=0}^{\infty} \Phi_{xx}(nT)z^{-n} - \Phi_{x}(0) \right] \tag{10.32}$$

The formula for the sampled power spectrum depends upon the ability to express each of the three terms in (10.32) in terms of the function $G(s)$ given in (10.31). A comparison of these two equations shows immediately that

$$\sum_{n=0}^{\infty} \Phi_{xx}(nT)z^{-n} = Z[G(s)]$$

which may be evaluated by complex convolution (4.10) as

$$Z[G(s)] = \frac{1}{2\pi j} \int_{c-j\infty}^{c+j\infty} G(\lambda)\, \frac{d\lambda}{1 - e^{-T(s-\lambda)}} \tag{10.33}$$

It is also noted that

$$\sum_{k=0}^{\infty} \Phi_{xx}(kT)z^k = \mathcal{Z}[G(-s)]$$

$$= \frac{1}{2\pi j} \int_{c-j\infty}^{c+j\infty} G(\lambda) \frac{d\lambda}{1 - e^{-T(-s-\lambda)}} \qquad (10.34)$$

and $$\Phi_{xx}(0) = \frac{1}{2\pi j} \int_{c-j\infty}^{c+j\infty} G(s)\, ds \qquad (10.35)$$

The substitution of (10.33), (10.34), and (10.35) in (10.32) gives

$$S_{xx}(z) = \frac{1}{T2\pi j} \int_{c-j\infty}^{c+j\infty} G(\lambda) \frac{(1 - e^{2T\lambda})\, d\lambda}{[1 - e^{-T(s-\lambda)}][1 - e^{T(s+\lambda)}]} \qquad (10.36)$$

The combination of three terms in the one integral (10.36) requires that a common path of integration be found for all the terms. This requirement will be met if the function $G(s)$ [which is half the partial-fraction expansion of $S_{xx}(s)$ as expressed in (10.31)] has no poles on or to the right of the imaginary axis. The desired common path is then the imaginary axis itself. The evaluation of (10.36) may be effected by equating the desired contour integral to the closed integral around the left half plane, in which case the poles of the integrand are the poles of $G(\lambda)$. A difficulty arises if $G(\lambda)$ tends to zero as λ tends to infinity only as $1/\lambda$. In this case the integral around the semicircle completing the closed contour does *not* vanish unless a slight shift of $g(t)$ α sec to the left is made, which introduces a factor $e^{\alpha\lambda}$ in the integrand which forces the integral over the semicircle to be zero. This artifice is necessary because of the way the z transform is defined and leads to no real difficulty.

EXAMPLE

As an example of the application of the technique developed above, suppose it is desired to find the sampled power spectrum of the random signal whose spectral density is

$$S_{xx}(s) = \frac{2\omega_1}{{\omega_1}^2 - s^2} = \frac{1}{\omega_1 + s} + \frac{1}{\omega_1 - s} \qquad (10.37)$$
$$= G(s) + G(-s)$$

Substituting (10.37) in (10.36),

$$S_{xx}(z) = \frac{1}{T2\pi j} \int_{-j\infty}^{j\infty} \frac{1}{\omega_1 + \lambda} \frac{(1 - e^{-2T\lambda})\, d\lambda}{[1 - e^{-T(s-\lambda)}][1 - e^{+T(s+\lambda)}]}$$
$$= \frac{1}{T} \frac{1 - e^{-2T\omega_1}}{[1 - e^{-T(s+\omega_1)}][1 - e^{+T(s-\omega_1)}]}$$
$$= \frac{1}{T} \frac{1 - e^{-2T\omega_1}}{(1 - e^{-T\omega_1}z^{-1})(1 - e^{-T\omega_1}z)} \qquad (10.38)$$

The usual substitution $z = e^{sT}$ is made in the last step of the reduction of (10.38).

10.4 Random Signals in Sampled Systems

The principal use of the foregoing analysis is in the study of signals in linear sampled-data systems. For this purpose, consider the system represented by the block diagram of Fig. 10.4 and the problem of calculating the autocorrelation function, cross-correlation functions, and the power spectra defined for the various continuous and sampled signals ap-

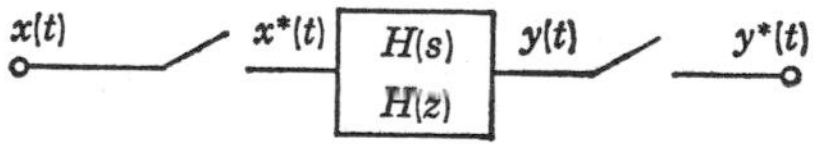

FIG. 10.4. Open-loop sampled-data system with input and output variables defined.

pearing in this elementary system on the assumption that the autocorrelation function of the input $x(t)$ and the system function of the network are given. It follows immediately from the analysis of Sec. 10.3 and conventional analysis expressed by (10.19) that the power spectrum of the output is given by

$$S_{yy}(s) = S_{xx}^*(s)H(s)H(-s) \tag{10.39}$$

or, in terms of the real frequency,

$$S_{yy}(j\omega) = S_{xx}^*(j\omega)|H(j\omega)|^2 \tag{10.40}$$

if one assumes that the sampled signal $x^*(t)$ may be sufficiently well approximated by the periodic impulse modulation of $x(t)$. If pulse modulation of finite width γ is a better approximation to the sampled signal, this effect can be generated by passing the (nonexistent) impulse-modulated signal through a filter whose response is a rectangular pulse of the proper width. In this case the output of this particular system has an autocorrelation function of the type sketched in Fig. 10.3 and a spectrum

$$S_{yy}(s) = S_{xx}^*(s)\frac{1 - e^{-s\gamma}}{s}\frac{1 - e^{s\gamma}}{-s} \tag{10.41}$$

A more common situation is the use of a clamp, or zero-order hold, for the system or filter, in which case the spectral density of the output is

$$S_{yy}(s) = S_{xx}^*(s)\frac{1 - e^{-sT}}{s}\frac{1 - e^{sT}}{-s} \tag{10.42}$$

Before going further into the analysis of the signals in Fig. 10.4 in general terms, it is instructive to observe some of the characteristics of a particular random signal and to consider the effects of passing this signal through a particular system. For example, consider the signal $x(t)$ with the autocorrelation function and power spectrum given by

$$\Phi_{xx}(\tau) = e^{-\omega_1|\tau|}$$

$$S_{xx}(s) = \frac{2\omega_1}{\omega_1{}^2 - s^2} \tag{10.43}$$

The sampled power spectrum for this function was obtained in Sec. 10.3 as

$$S_{xx}(z) = \frac{1}{T} \frac{1 - e^{-2\omega_1 T}}{(1 - e^{-\omega_1 T}z^{-1})(1 - e^{-\omega_1 T}z)} \tag{10.38}$$

which can be written in terms of the real frequency as

$$S_{xx}^*(j\omega) = \frac{1}{T} \frac{\sinh \omega_1 T}{\cosh \omega_1 T - \cos \omega T} \tag{10.44}$$

Certain characteristics of this spectrum are immediately evident from an inspection of (10.44). The spectrum is periodic in the variable ω as expected and, since the maximum value of $\cos \omega T$ is unity and minimum value of $\cosh \omega T$ is also unity, the magnitude of the fluctuations in the spectrum depend greatly on the value of $\omega_1 T$. If this quantity $\omega_1 T$, which is proportional to the ratio between the signal bandwidth and the sampling frequency $1/T$, is large, then $\cosh \omega_1 T$ is large and the spectrum is virtually constant. From another point of view, this means that if the sampling period is long compared to the signal fluctuations, the samples are nearly uncorrelated and the spectrum is "almost white," that is, almost constant. On the other hand, as the sampling period becomes very short, (10.44) becomes indeterminate and a limiting process must be followed. Although the form of power spectrum given by (10.44) correctly represents the impulse-modulated signal, it is clear from (10.29) that a multiplying factor of T^2 must be included in $S_{xx}^*(j\omega)$ to maintain a comparative amplitude as T approaches zero. For small T, consider

$$\lim_{T \to 0} T^2 S_{xx}^*(j\omega) = \lim_{T \to 0} \frac{T \sinh \omega_1 T}{\cosh \omega_1 T - \cos \omega T}$$

$$= \frac{2\omega_1}{\omega_1{}^2 + \omega^2} = S_{xx}(j\omega) \tag{10.45}$$

The limiting process as $T \to 0$ given in (10.45) shows that with the proper amplitude modifying factor, the sampled power spectrum has the shape of the continuous power spectrum as the sampling operation is made faster and faster.

Another approach to the same problem of fast sampling may be made through consideration of (10.42), which expresses the power spectrum of the signal at the output of a zero-order-hold circuit. Substituting (10.44) in (10.42) and manipulating the expression slightly, one obtains, in terms of the real frequency,

$$S_{yy}(j\omega) = \frac{1}{T}\frac{\sinh \omega_1 T}{\cosh \omega_1 T - \cos \omega T}\frac{2(1-\cos \omega T)}{\omega^2} \qquad (10.46)$$

It is possible to verify by integration of (10.46) over all frequencies that the mean-square value of the output is unity, which is the same as the mean-square value of the input. This particular calculation is really

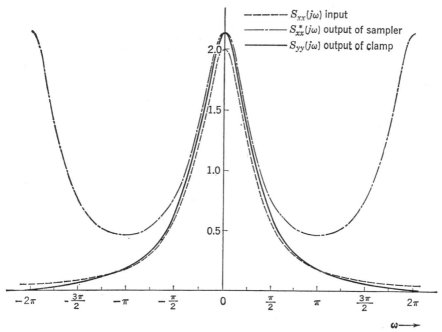

FIG. 10.5. Plots of spectra showing the effects of sampling and clamping.

unnecessary, however, because by inspection of Fig. 10.3 with the gain factor removed and $\gamma = T$ it is obvious that the mean-square value of the output of a zero-order hold is always equal to the mean-square value of the input signal. For very small T, the spectrum of the output closely resembles that of the input and, in the limit as $T \to 0$, one obtains

$$\lim_{T\to 0} S_{yy}(j\omega) = \lim_{T\to 0} \frac{1}{T}\frac{\sinh \omega_1 T}{\cosh \omega_1 T - \cos \omega T}\frac{2(1-\cos \omega T)}{\omega^2}$$

$$= \frac{2\omega_1}{\omega_1^2 + \omega^2}$$

$$= S_{xx}(j\omega) \qquad (10.47)$$

Plots of $S_{xx}(j\omega)$, $T^2 S_{xx}^*(j\omega)$, and $S_{yy}(j\omega)$ for the example under consideration are given in Fig. 10.5 for the particular case of $\omega_1 = 1$, $T = 1$. The ratio of sampling frequency, $1/T$, to signal "bandwidth," $\omega_1/2\pi$, is 2π in this case, which is a moderate sampling ratio, neither fast nor slow. The mean-square value of the signal $x(t)$ is given by the area under $T^2 S_{xx}^*(j\omega)$ between $-\pi < \omega < \pi$. From the plot of Fig. 10.5 it is not easy to obtain a quantitative idea of the closeness with which the output of the zero-order hold approximates the original signal. Later, a comparison based on the mean-square error will be made between this system and other somewhat more sophisticated schemes for the reconstruction of random signals, but before a discussion of the filtering problem can be begun, some more results must be derived from Fig. 10.4. In particular, expressions are needed for the autocorrelation function or sampled power spectrum of the sampled output of the system and for the cross-correlation between output and input.

Since $y^*(t)$ is the impulse-modulated $y(t)$, one would expect from (10.24) and (10.25) that the sampled power spectrum of $y^*(t)$ would be the two-sided z transform of $S_{yy}(j\omega)$. In other words, intuitively, one would expect that

$$
\begin{aligned}
S_{yy}(z) &= \mathbb{Z}[S_{xx}^*(s)H(s)H(-s)] \\
&= S_{xx}(z)H(z)H(z^{-1})
\end{aligned}
\tag{10.48}
$$

This result will be derived directly from the fundamental relations between the signals and the filter impulse response $h(t)$. The first step toward finding $S_{yy}(z)$ is to find $\Phi_{yy}(kT)$, the autocorrelation function of $y(t)$ at integral values of τ/T.

By definition of impulse sampling,

$$
y^*(t) = \sum_{k=-\infty}^{\infty} y(kT)\delta(t - kT)
\tag{10.49}
$$

and, from the convolution integral,

$$
y(kT) = \sum_{n=0}^{\infty} h(nT)x(kT - nT)
\tag{10.50}
$$

Since the process $y(t)$ is ergodic the autocorrelation function of this process may be obtained from the time average

$$
\begin{aligned}
\Phi_{yy}(kT) &= \lim_{N\to\infty} \frac{1}{2N+1} \sum_{l=-N}^{N} y(lT)y(lT + kT) \\
&= \langle y(lT)y(lT + kT) \rangle
\end{aligned}
\tag{10.51}
$$

If (10.50) is substituted in (10.51),

$$\Phi_{yy}(kT) = \left\langle \sum_{n=0}^{\infty} h(nT)x(lT - nT) \sum_{j=0}^{\infty} h(jT)x(lT + kT - jT) \right\rangle$$

$$= \sum_{n=0}^{\infty} h(nT) \sum_{j=0}^{\infty} h(jT) \langle x(lT - nT)x(lT + kT - jT) \rangle \quad (10.52)$$

$$= \sum_{n=0}^{\infty} h(nT) \sum_{j=0}^{\infty} h(jT)\Phi_{xx}(nT + kT - jT)$$

where, in the last step, the ergodic nature of the processes is used along with (10.14).

By the definition (10.27), the sampled power spectrum of $y^*(t)$ is the z transform of $\Phi_{yy}^*(kT) = \dfrac{1}{T} \Phi_{yy}(kT)$.   Therefore,

$$S_{yy}(z) = \frac{1}{T} \sum_{k=-\infty}^{\infty} z^{-k} \sum_{n=0}^{\infty} h(nT) \sum_{j=0}^{\infty} h(jT)\Phi_{xx}(nT + kT - jT)$$

$$= \sum_{n=0}^{\infty} h(nT) \sum_{j=0}^{\infty} h(jT) \sum_{k=-\infty}^{\infty} \Phi_{xx}^*(nT + kT - jT)z^{-k} \quad (10.53)$$

$$= H(z)H(z^{-1})S_{xx}(z)$$

which is the desired result.   As before, the sampled power spectrum, $S_{yy}(z)$, is the power spectrum of the *impulse-modulated* $y(t)$.   The mean-square value of $y(t)$ may be obtained from $S_{yy}(z)$ by the use of either (10.28) or (10.29).

The cross-correlation between a sampled and a continuous signal may also be computed directly.   Let $x^*(t) = \displaystyle\sum_{k=-\infty}^{\infty} x(t)\delta(t - kT)$ represent a sampled signal and $y(t)$ represent the nonsampled signal.   Then

$$\Phi_{xy}(\tau) = \lim_{T_0 \to \infty} \frac{1}{2T_0} \int_{-T_0}^{T_0} x(t)y(t + \tau) \sum_{k=-\infty}^{\infty} \delta(t - kT) \, dt \quad (10.54)$$

The right side of (10.54) contains an integral over the limits from $-T_0$ to T_0 of a train of uniformly spaced impulses extending over all time.   Those impulses falling outside the limits of integration cannot contribute to the value of the integral, and one can terminate the summations on k at $N = \pm(T_0/T)$, the largest integer contained in T_0/T.   If the summation is terminated at these limits, then the integration limits may be extended to infinity in both directions without affecting the results. It is also noticed that the interval length T_0 is within one period of $(2N + 1)T$. In view of the above remarks,

$$\Phi_{x^*y}(\tau) = \lim_{N \to \infty} \frac{1}{(2N + 1)T} \sum_{k=-N}^{N} \int_{-\infty}^{\infty} x(t)y(t + \tau)\delta(t + \tau - kT) \, dt$$

$$= \frac{1}{T} \lim_{N \to \infty} \frac{1}{2N + 1} \sum_{k=-N}^{N} x(kT)y(kT + \tau) \tag{10.55}$$

For the special case where $y(t)$ is the output of a linear filter whose input is $x^*(t)$ and whose impulse response is $h(t)$, the relation

$$y(t) = \sum_{n=-\infty}^{\infty} h(t - nT)x(nT) \tag{10.56}$$

applies, and therefore

$$\Phi_{x^*y}(\tau) = \frac{1}{T} \lim_{N \to \infty} \frac{1}{2N + 1} \sum_{k=-N}^{N} x(kT) \sum_{n=-\infty}^{\infty} h(\tau + kT - nT)x(nT)$$

If a change of index is made on the second summation from n to $l + k$ then

$$\Phi_{x^*y}(\tau) = \frac{1}{T} \sum_{l=-\infty}^{\infty} h(\tau - lT) \lim_{N \to \infty} \frac{1}{2N + 1} \sum_{k=-N}^{N} x(kT)x(kT + lT)$$

$$= \frac{1}{T} \sum_{l=-\infty}^{\infty} h(\tau - lT)\Phi_{xx}(lT)$$

$$= \sum_{l=-\infty}^{\infty} h(\tau - lT)\Phi_{xx}^*(lT) \tag{10.57}$$

the transform of (10.57) yields

$$S_{x^*y}(s) = S_{xx}^*(s)H(s) \tag{10.58}$$

which states simply that the cross power spectrum between the sampled input to a linear filter and the output of the filter depends only on the sampled power spectrum of the input and the continuous transfer function of the filter.

In a manner similar to that used to find (10.58) one can obtain the other spectra relating the variables which are defined in Fig. 10.4. A tabulation of these spectra is given in (10.59). The variable z is used in the second and the last of the expressions in (10.59) because all of the functions involved in these particular expressions are sampled functions.

$$S_{yy}(s) = S_{xx}^*(s)H(s)H(-s)$$
$$S_{yy}(z) = S_{xx}(z)H(z)H(z^{-1})$$
$$S_{xy}(s) = \frac{1}{T}S_{xx}(s)H(s)$$
$$S_{xy^*}(s) = \frac{1}{T}S_{xx}(s)H^*(s) \qquad (10.59)$$
$$S_{x^*y}(s) = S_{xx}^*(s)H(s)$$
$$S_{x^*y^*}(z) = S_{xx}(z)H(z)$$

10.5 Linear Filtering of Sampled Random Data

In this section attention is turned from the analysis problem to the synthesis problem. Sections 10.3 and 10.4 were concerned with analyzing the random signals which might appear in sampled-data systems and determining the effects of the system on the signal characteristics. The

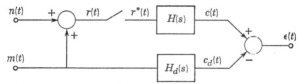

FIG. 10.6. Block diagram illustrating formulation of the linear filtering problem.

present section is concerned with the design or synthesis of systems intended to operate in the presence of random sampled data. The design of any system depends on the characteristics of the signals on which the system operates, on the constraints placed on the system behavior, on the desired operation required, and on the criterion used to evaluate the actual performance. The value of the design to the "consumer" will depend upon how closely these four conditions match his situation. Although a variety of problems suitable for different situations in the filtering of discrete data have been treated in the literature,[2,11,12,37,45] only one of these will be discussed here. That one is the linear least-squares filtering—smoothing and prediction—of sampled random data in the presence of additive random noise. The approach used is that of "spectral shaping," introduced by Zadeh and Ragazzini,[67] and is closely related to the method of Bode and Shannon.[5]

The filtering problem under consideration is most easily visualized by considering Fig. 10.6. The design objective is the selection of a filter with the transfer function $H(s)$ which will operate on the sampled signal $r^*(t)$ in such a way as to minimize the mean-square value of the error $\epsilon(t)$. The input signal is assumed to be the periodic impulse modulation of the sum of a random message, $m(t)$, and a random noise, $n(t)$, and the error is defined as the difference between the filter output and the ideal or *desired* output, $c_d(t)$. Typically the desired output is the result of a linear operation on the input message, such as ideal prediction, differentiation, or, in general,

$$c_d(t) = \int_{-\infty}^{\infty} h_d(\tau) m(t - \tau) \, d\tau$$

where $h_d(\tau)$ is the impulse response of the filter (which is not necessarily physically realizable) which will perform the desired operation. As this problem is formulated, the only information concerning the input which is required in order to perform the minimization is the autocorrelation functions of noise and message and their cross-correlation.

The problem diagramed in Fig. 10.6 is particularly simple to solve when the successive samples of the input are statistically independent. In that case the autocorrelation of the input is zero for $|\tau|$ equal to or greater than the sampling period T and the input sampled power spectrum is a constant for all z. Such an input spectrum is said to be "almost white."

The mean-square value of the error defined in Fig. 10.6 is

$$\begin{aligned}
\langle \epsilon^2(t) \rangle &= \langle [c(t) - c_d(t)]^2 \rangle \\
&= \langle c^2(t) \rangle - 2\langle c(t) c_d(t) \rangle + \langle c_d{}^2(t) \rangle \\
&= \Phi_{cc}(0) - 2\Phi_{cc_d}(0) + \Phi_{c_d c_d}(0)
\end{aligned} \tag{10.60}$$

Each of the terms in (10.60) will be evaluated separately in terms of the relations defined by Fig. 10.6.

The mean-square value of the output of the filter, $\Phi_{cc}(0)$, can be obtained from the inversion of (10.39) as

$$\Phi_{cc}(0) = \frac{1}{T} \int_0^{\infty} h(x) \, dx \int_0^{\infty} h(y) \, dy \, \Phi_{rr}(x - y) \sum_{k=-\infty}^{\infty} \delta(x - y - kT) \tag{10.61}$$

On the assumption that the input is white, the autocorrelation function $\Phi_{rr}(kT)$ is zero for $k \neq 0$ and

$$\begin{aligned}
\Phi_{cc}(0) &= \frac{1}{T} \int_0^{\infty} h(x) \, dx \int_0^{\infty} h(y) \, dy \, \Phi_{rr}(x - y) \delta(x - y) \\
&= \frac{1}{T} \int_0^{\infty} [h(x)]^2 \, \Phi_{rr}(0) \, dx
\end{aligned} \tag{10.62}$$

The second term in (10.60) is given by

$$\begin{aligned}
\Phi_{cc_d}(0) &= \lim_{T_0 \to \infty} \frac{1}{2T_0} \int_{-T_0}^{T_0} c(t) c_d(t) \, dt \\
&= \lim_{T_0 \to \infty} \frac{1}{2T_0} \int_{-T_0}^{T_0} \left[\int_0^{\infty} h(x) r(t - x) \sum_{k=-\infty}^{\infty} \delta(t - x - kT) \, dx \right] c_d(t) \, dt
\end{aligned} \tag{10.63}$$

If the order of integration with respect to x and t is reversed,

$$\Phi_{cc_d}(0) = \int_0^\infty dx\, h(x) \lim_{T_0 \to \infty} \frac{1}{2T_0} \int_{-T_0}^{T_0} r(t-x)c_d(t) \sum_{k=-\infty}^{\infty} \delta(t-x-kT)\, dt$$

$$= \int_0^\infty dx\, h(x) \lim_{N \to \infty} \frac{1}{(2N+1)T} \sum_{k=-N}^{N} r(kT)c_d(kT+x) \qquad (10.64)$$

$$= \frac{1}{T} \int_0^\infty h(x)\Phi_{rc_d}(x)\, dx$$

With the substitution of (10.63) and (10.64) in (10.60)

$$\langle \epsilon^2(t) \rangle = \frac{\Phi_{rr}(0)}{T} \int_0^\infty [h(x)]^2\, dx - \frac{2}{T} \int_0^\infty h(x)\Phi_{rc_d}(x)\, dx + \Phi_{c_d c_d}(0)$$

$$= \frac{\Phi_{rr}(0)}{T} \int_0^\infty \left[h(x) - \frac{\Phi_{rc_d}(x)}{\Phi_{rr}(0)} \right]^2 dx$$

$$- \frac{1}{T} \int_0^\infty \frac{[\Phi_{rc_d}(x)]^2}{\Phi_{rr}(0)}\, dx + \Phi_{c_d c_d}(0) \qquad (10.65)$$

Since the last two terms in (10.65) do not include the unknown $h(x)$ at all, and since the first term is either positive or zero, it is obvious that the least squared error will result if, and only if,

$$h(x) = \frac{\Phi_{rc_d}(x)}{\Phi_{rr}(0)} \qquad x \geq 0 \qquad (10.66)$$

which leads to the transfer function

$$H(s) = \int_0^\infty \frac{\Phi_{rc_d}(x)e^{-sx}}{\Phi_{rr}(0)}\, dx \qquad (10.67)$$

A filter with the transfer function given by (10.67) will perform least-squares smoothing on inputs which are almost white, in the sense discussed previously. For arbitrary input spectra, an extension is possible.

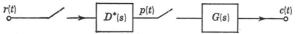

FIG. 10.7. Block diagram for spectral shaping to form almost white noise.

The extension discussed here is based on the ability to shape the spectrum of a signal with a realizable filter so that the output of the filter is almost white and consequently has a constant sampled power spectrum. A block diagram of the shaping operation is shown in Fig. 10.7. The pulse transfer function $D(z)$ is assumed to be chosen such that the sampled power spectrum of the signal $p(t)$ is unity. This shaping operation is possible with a realizable discrete filter if the original signal, $r(t)$, has a spectrum which is rational in the frequency s (or ω). If the optimum transfer function between $r^*(t)$ and $c(t)$ is $H(s)$, then the optimum transfer function between $p^*(t)$ and $c(t)$ must be

$$G(s) = \frac{H(s)}{D^*(s)} \tag{10.68}$$

If (10.68) represents a realizable transfer function, the output, $c(t)$, is the same for the two cases. That is, if $G(s)$ in Fig. 10.7 satisfies (10.68), then the output $c(t)$ shown in Fig. 10.7 would be the same as the output $c(t)$ shown in Fig. 10.6 in the presence of identical inputs. This transfer function $G(s)$ is then optimum in the same sense that $H(s)$ is optimum.

Conversely, if $G(s)$ is realized as the optimum filter with the input $p^*(t)$, then the optimum filter with input $r^*(t)$ has the transfer function.

$$H(s) = D^*(s)G(s) \tag{10.69}$$

if this is realizable. If both (10.68) and (10.69) are to be the transfer functions of realizable filters, then $D^*(s)$ must have neither poles nor zeros in the right half plane. Equivalently, $D(z)$ must have neither poles nor zeros outside the unit circle. The conditions that $D(z)$ have neither poles nor zeros outside the unit circle and that the sampled power spectrum of $p^*(t)$ be constant are sufficient to determine $D(z)$.

From (10.53) the sampled power spectrum of $p^*(t)$ is

$$S_{pp}(z) = D(z)D(z^{-1})S_{rr}(z) \tag{10.70}$$

If $S_{pp}(z)$ is to be unity then

$$D(z)D(z^{-1}) = \frac{1}{S_{rr}(z)} \tag{10.71}$$

From (10.71) and the conditions that $D(z)$ have neither poles nor zeros outside the unit circle, it is clear that

$$D(z) = \frac{1}{[S_{rr}(z)]^+} \tag{10.72}$$

where the superscript $+$ indicates that factor of $S_{rr}(z)$ whose poles and zeros lie inside the unit circle. The optimum form for the transfer function between $p^*(t)$ and $c(t)$ will, by (10.69), complete the design.

From (10.66), if the mean-square value of $p(t)$ is unity, the optimum impulse response of the filter from $p^*(t)$ to $c(t)$ is

$$g(t) = \Phi_{pc_d}(t) \qquad t \geq 0 \tag{10.73}$$

The cross-correlation $\Phi_{pc_d}(t)$ may be determined by the average

$$\Phi_{pc_d}(t) = \lim_{N \to \infty} \frac{1}{2N+1} \sum_{n=-N}^{N} p(nT)c_d(nT + t) \tag{10.74}$$

and, by convolution, the output of the shaping filter at sampling instants is given by

$$p(nT) = \sum_{k=0}^{\infty} d(kT)r(nT - kT) \tag{10.75}$$

Substitution of (10.75) in (10.74) yields, after some rearrangement,

$$\Phi_{pc_d}(t) = \lim_{N \to \infty} \frac{1}{2N + 1} \sum_{n=-N}^{N} \sum_{k=0}^{\infty} d(kT)r(nT - kT)c_d(nT + t) \tag{10.76}$$

The system function of the optimum filter is implicit in (10.69), (10.72), (10.73), and (10.76). This transfer function $H(s)$ may be made explicit by expressing all these equations in their equivalent frequency-domain forms.

The cross power spectrum of the signal $p(t)$ and the desired output $c_d(t)$ is the transform of (10.76):

$$S_{pc_d}(s) = \int_{-\infty}^{\infty} \Phi_{pc_d}(t)e^{-st}\, dt$$

$$= \int_{-\infty}^{\infty} \sum_{k=0}^{\infty} d(kT)\Phi_{rc_d}(kT + t + dt \tag{10.77}$$

Integrating term by term and substituting $x = t + kT$,

$$S_{pc_d}(s) = \sum_{k=0}^{\infty} d(kT)e^{kTs} \int_{-\infty}^{\infty} \Phi_{rc_d}(x)e^{-sx}\, dx$$

$$= D^*(-s)S_{rc_d}(s)$$

$$= \frac{S_{rc_d}(s)}{[S_{rr}^*(s)]^-} \tag{10.78}$$

where, in the last step, use has been made of (10.71) and (10.72) and the symmetry of the sampled power spectrum about the imaginary axis of the s plane.

From (10.78) and (10.73), the optimum transfer function between $p^*(t)$ and $c(t)$ in Fig. 10.7 is

$$G(s) = \int_0^{\infty} dt\, e^{-st} \frac{1}{2\pi j} \int_{-j\infty}^{j\infty} D^*(-\lambda)S_{rc_d}(\lambda)e^{\lambda t}\, d\lambda \tag{10.79}$$

$$= \int_0^{\infty} dt\, e^{-st} \frac{1}{2\pi j} \int_{-j\infty}^{j\infty} \frac{S_{rc_d}(\lambda)e^{\lambda t}}{[S_{rr}^*(\lambda)]^-}\, d\lambda \tag{10.80}$$

The superscript $^-$ in (10.78) and (10.80) indicates the factor of the input sampled power spectrum whose poles and zeros lie in the right half plane.

The entire optimum filter transfer function can be written from (10.80), (10.72), and (10.69) in two parts:

$$H(s) = \frac{1}{[S_{rr}^*(s)]^+} \int_0^\infty \psi(t)e^{-st}\,dt$$

where
$$\psi(t) = \frac{1}{2\pi j} \int_{-j\infty}^{j\infty} \frac{S_{rc_d}(\lambda)e^{\lambda t}}{[S_{rr}^*(\lambda)]^-}\,d\lambda \qquad (10.81)$$

It is frequently convenient to express the desired output as the result of passing the message through an ideal filter, as shown in Fig. 10.6.   If the ideal filter is linear and has the impulse response $h_d(t)$, then cross-correlating the total input of message and noise $[m(t) + n(t)]$ and the desired output $c_d(t)$ expressed in terms of its convolution integral, the cross-correlation function $\Phi_{rc_d}(\tau)$ is

$$\Phi_{rc_d}(\tau) = \lim_{T_0 \to \infty} \frac{1}{2T_0} \int_{-T_0}^{T_0} \left\{ [m(t) + n(t)] \int_{-\infty}^\infty h_d(x)m(t + \tau - x)\,dx \right\} dt$$
$$= \int_{-\infty}^\infty h_d(x)\Phi_{mm}(\tau - x)\,dx + \int_{-\infty}^\infty h_d(x)\Phi_{nm}(\tau - x)\,dx \qquad (10.82)$$

The cross power spectrum between input and desired output on the assumption (10.59) is given by the transform of (10.82), which is

$$S_{rc_d}(\lambda) = H_d(\lambda)[S_{mm}(\lambda) + S_{nm}(\lambda)] \qquad (10.83)$$

which may be substituted in (10.81) for calculation of the optimum transfer function, if desired.

Before working out an example of optimum least-squares filtering, it is instructive to determine an expression for the mean-square value of the error between the desired output and the output of the optimum filter. The mean-square value of the error in terms of an internal signal $p(t)$ whose mean-square value as expressed by $\Phi_{pp}(0)$ is unity may be obtained by a substitution of p for r and the optimum impulsive response for $h(x)$, which causes the first integral of (10.65) to be zero.   Thus,

$$\langle \epsilon^2(t) \rangle = \Phi_{c_d c_d}(0) - \frac{1}{T} \int_0^\infty [\Phi_{pc_d}(x)]^2\,dx \qquad (10.84)$$

However, $\Phi_{pc_d}(x)$ is simply the inverse transform of 10.78, which is the $\psi(t)$ defined in (10.81), so that,

$$\langle \epsilon^2(t) \rangle = \Phi_{c_d c_d}(0) - \frac{1}{T} \int_0^\infty [\psi(t)]^2\,dt \qquad (10.85)$$

The transfer function for the optimum filter given in (10.81) is identical in form to the corresponding Wiener filter, but in the case of the sampled-data filter the factor $1/[S_{rr}^*(s)]^+$ corresponds to the transfer function of a discrete filter or digital controller of the type described in previous chapters.   It is also possible to realize a transfer function of the type required here with a tapped delay line, under certain circumstances.

EXAMPLE

A block diagram of an illustrative problem is shown in Fig. 10.8. The objective of the problem is to design a linear filter which will pre-

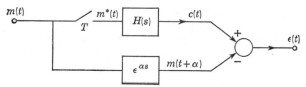

FIG. 10.8. Error formation of example problem.

dict or delay in the absence of noise a message whose spectrum is given by

$$S_{rr}(s) = \frac{2\omega_1}{\omega_1{}^2 - s^2} \tag{10.86}$$

From the results of Sec. 10.4 the sampled power spectrum of this signal is

$$S_{rr}(z) = \frac{1 - e^{-2T\omega_1}}{(1 - e^{-T\omega_1}z^{-1})(1 - e^{-T\omega_1}z)} \tag{10.87}$$

The factors of this sampled power spectrum having zeros and poles inside and outside the unit circle respectively, are

$$[S_{rr}(z)]^+ = \frac{(1 - e^{-2\omega_1 T})^{1/2}}{1 - e^{-T\omega_1}z^{-1}} \tag{10.88}$$

$$[S_{rr}(z)]^- = \frac{(1 - e^{-2\omega_1 T})^{1/2}}{1 - e^{-T\omega_1}z} \tag{10.89}$$

For prediction or delay the ideal transfer function is $e^{\alpha s}$, which, when substituted in (10.83) with (10.86) gives the cross-correlation between the input and the desired output as

$$S_{rc_d}(s) = \frac{2\omega_1 e^{\alpha s}}{\omega_1{}^2 - s^2} \tag{10.90}$$

where positive values of α correspond to prediction and negative values of α correspond to delay.   The substitution of (10.90) and (10.89) in (10.81) gives

$$\psi(t) = \frac{(1 - e^{-2\omega_1 T})^{1/2}}{2\pi j} \int_{-j\infty}^{j\infty} \frac{2\omega_1}{\omega_1{}^2 - \lambda^2} e^{\alpha\lambda}(1 - e^{T\lambda}e^{-T\omega_1})e^{\lambda t} \, d\lambda \tag{10.91}$$

The integral (10.91) can be evaluated over three ranges of time, depending on the values of α and T.   The evaluation, which is relatively simple, leads to the result that

$$\psi(t) = 0 \qquad -\infty \le t \le -(\alpha + T) \qquad (10.92a)$$

$$= \frac{e^{\alpha\omega_1}}{(1 - e^{-2\omega_1 T})^{1/2}} [e^{\omega_1 t} - e^{-2\omega_1(T+\alpha)}e^{-\omega_1 t}] \qquad -(\alpha + T) \le t \le -\alpha$$

$$(10.92b)$$

$$= (1 - e^{-2\omega_1 T})^{1/2}e^{-\alpha\omega_1}e^{-\omega_1 t} \qquad -\alpha \le t \le \infty \qquad (10.92c)$$

A sketch of $\psi(t)$ is shown in Fig. 10.9 with no designation of the time origin since this depends on the particular value of α. From (10.81) it is noted that the optimum transfer function contains the unilateral Laplace transform of $\psi(t)$ so that only the portion of the function over positive time is of interest.

For positive α, the ideal operation is one of prediction and, in this case, the entire positive time axis is contained in (10.92c). Substitution of this expression in (10.81) gives the optimum transfer function

$$H_{opt}(s) = \frac{1 - e^{-\omega_1 T}e^{-sT}}{(1 - e^{-2\omega_1 T})^{1/2}} e^{-\omega_1 \alpha}(1 - e^{-2\omega_1 T})^{1/2} \int_0^\infty e^{-\omega_1 t}e^{-st} \, dt$$

$$= e^{-\alpha\omega_1} \frac{1 - e^{-\omega_1 T}e^{-sT}}{s + \omega_1} \qquad (10.93)$$

It is interesting to compare the optimum filter whose transfer function is given by (10.93) with the transfer function of the optimum filter for the prediction (without sampling) of the signal whose spectrum is given by (10.86). In the absence of sampling, the Wiener theory gives

$$\hat{H}_{opt}(s) = e^{-\alpha\omega_1} \qquad (10.94)$$

At sampling instants, the operation of the filter whose transfer function is given by (10.93) is expressed by the z transform of this transfer function; that is, by

$$H_{opt}(z) = e^{-\alpha\omega_1} \qquad (10.95)$$

Comparison of (10.95) with (10.94) indicates at once that the outputs of the two filters at sampling instants are identical. Between sampling instants, the output of the filter whose input is sampled is an exponential decay of time constant $1/\omega_1$.

The mean-square error of prediction of the sampled-data filter calculated from (10.92c) and (10.85) is

$$\langle \epsilon^2(t) \rangle = 1 - \frac{1}{T} \int_0^\infty e^{-2\omega_1 \alpha}(1 - e^{-2\omega_1 T})e^{-2\omega_1 t} \, dt$$

$$= 1 - e^{-2\omega_1 \alpha} \frac{1 - e^{-2\omega_1 T}}{2\omega_1 T}$$

$$= 1 - e^{-2\omega_1 \alpha} + e^{-2\omega_1 \alpha} \left[\frac{2\omega_1 T}{2!} - \frac{(2\omega_1 T)^2}{3!} + \cdots \right] \qquad (10.96)$$

The mean-square value of the error of prediction for the filter whose transfer function is given by (10.94) is

$$\langle \hat{e}^2(t) \rangle = 1 - e^{-2\omega_1\alpha} \qquad (10.97)$$

The expression for the error of the sampled-data filter is written deliberately as the sum of three terms. The first two of these terms are independent of the sampling period T and, furthermore, are identical to the error of prediction of the filter whose input is *not sampled*. It is reasonable, then, to describe these error terms as the error of prediction, as contrasted to the error due to sampling, which is termed ripple. The ripple is the third term of (10.96) and is an always positive quantity which increases monotonically with the sampling period T and vanishes as T approaches zero.

For negative values of α the ideal operation is one of delay, and the physical system is trying to reproduce the message continuously with a delay of α sec. In the absence of noise, a filter operating on the continuous signal can obviously perform this function exactly, and no error results. With sampled-data inputs, however, the ripple effect remains, and for a specified sampling rate T there is a specific minimum value of mean-square error in the reproduction despite the fact that no noise is present with the signal.

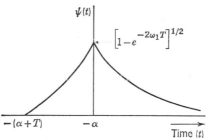

FIG. 10.9. Sketch showing general shape of $\psi(t)$ function for example problem.

A calculation of this minimum error will permit the designer to select the lowest sampling rate possible for a given specification of error.

From an inspection of the expression for the minimum mean-square value of the error given in (10.85), it is clear that the error will decrease as long as the area under $[\psi(t)]^2$ for $t \geq 0$ increases, which usually continues as the delay time is increased. The $\psi(t)$ function for the example problem is sketched in Fig. 10.9, which shows clearly that if $\alpha = -T$ all of the nonzero portion of $\psi(t)$ is included in positive time and no further reduction in error may be realized by longer delays. This result merely expresses the well-known fact that two samples from a first-order Markov process supply all the information that is useful for the extrapolation of the process. A delay of one sampling period permits these two samples to be collected, and a longer delay, which would introduce more samples, would not reduce the error of extrapolation. This situation only applies to the particular problem chosen for this example of course, and for another problem the error will normally decrease as the delay is increased.

The minimum mean-square error for all delay less than $-T$ is given by the substitution of (10.92) in (10.85)

$$\langle \epsilon^2(t) \rangle_{\min} = 1 - \int_{-\alpha-T}^{-\alpha} \frac{e^{\alpha\omega_1}}{(1 - e^{-2\omega_1 T})^{1/2}} \left[e^{\omega_1 T} - e^{-2\omega_1(T)}e^{+o-\omega_1 t} \right]^2 dt$$
$$- \int_{-\alpha}^{\infty} \left[(1 - e^{-2\omega_1 T})^{1/2} e^{-\omega_1\alpha}e^{-\omega_1 t} \right]^2 dt \quad (10.98)$$

After some simplification, (10.98) reduces to

$$\langle \epsilon^2(t) \rangle_{\min} = \frac{1 + e^{-2\omega_1 T}}{1 - e^{-2\omega_1 T}} - \frac{1}{\omega_1 T} \quad (10.99)$$

The mean-square error given by (10.99) is independent of the actual value of delay α, as was expected, and represents the absolute minimum error for this particular example. That is, no value of α outside the

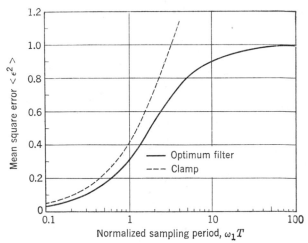

Fig. 10.10. Plot of normalized mean-square error for optimum filter and for clamp for illustrative example.

range $\alpha \leq -T$ will result in an error as small as that given by (10.99). A plot of this error as a function of $\omega_1 T$ is given in Fig. 10.10, which could be used to select the sampling period T for the reproduction after sampling, with specified error, and at least T sec delay of some process whose spectrum is given by (10.86). For values of $\omega_1 T$ outside the range of the plot in Fig. 10.10, the asymptotic behavior of the error is given by

$$\langle \epsilon^2(t) \rangle_{\min} \approx \frac{\omega_1 T}{3} \qquad\qquad \omega_1 T \ll 1 \qquad\qquad (10.100)$$

$$\langle \epsilon^2(t) \rangle_{\min} \approx \frac{\omega_1 T - 1}{\omega_1 T} \qquad\qquad \omega_1 T \gg 1 \qquad\qquad (10.101)$$

It is interesting to work out a numerical example using (10.100). Suppose one is required to reproduce from samples a signal whose spectrum is given by (10.86) with a bandwidth $\omega_1/2\pi$ of 1 cps to an accuracy of 1 per cent, that is, it is necessary to maintain the rms error of the reproduction less than or equal to 10^{-2}. The mean-square error must then be equal to or less than 10^{-4}. Substitution of these values in (10.100) gives

$$10^{-4} = \frac{2\pi T}{3}$$

$$T = \frac{3 \times 10^{-4}}{2\pi} = 0.0477 \times 10^{-3} \text{ sec}$$

$$1/T = f_s \approx 20{,}000 \text{ cps}$$

In words, to be able to reproduce a signal described by the spectrum of (10.86) with an rms error of 1 per cent, it is necessary to sample approximately 20,000 times the bandwidth frequency of the signal! Later calculation will show how a simple clamp compares with the optimum filter on a mean-square-error basis.

The simplest filter which will realize the absolute minimum error given by (10.99) is that designed for a delay of one sampling period. The optimum transfer function could be obtained for arbitrary delays, of course, but the case of an ideal delay of exactly one sampling period illustrates clearly all the important details with a minimum of unnecessary mathematics. For $\alpha = -T$, (10.92) reduces to

$$
\begin{aligned}
\psi(t) &= 0 & -\infty \le t \le 0 \\
&= \frac{e^{-\omega_1 T}}{(1 - e^{-2\omega_1 T})^{1/2}} (e^{\omega_1 t} - e^{-\omega_1 t}) & 0 \le t \le T \\
&= (1 - e^{-2\omega_1 T})^{1/2} e^{\omega_1 T} e^{-\omega_1 T} & T \le t \le \infty \qquad (10.102)
\end{aligned}
$$

substitution of (10.102) and (10.88) in (10.81) leads to the optimum transfer function

$$H_{\text{opt}}(s) = \frac{2\omega_1 e^{-\omega_1 T}}{1 - e^{-2\omega_1 T}} \frac{(1 - e^{-sT}e^{-\omega_1 T})(1 - e^{-sT}e^{\omega_1 T})}{s^2 - \omega_1{}^2} \qquad (10.103)$$

The z transform of (10.103) reveals

$$H_{\text{opt}}(z) = z^{-1} \qquad\qquad (10.104)$$

which indicates that this filter delays each sample by one sampling period, as indicated by the design requirement that the output equal the input delayed by one period.   Between sampling periods, however, the continuous signal output is composed of a combination of a growing and a decaying exponential.   The unstable plant or continuous portion of the filter is kept under control by the digital controller which precedes it, but this control depends upon the exact cancellation of a pole outside the unit circle, which is not physically possible.   A solution to

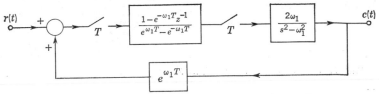

FIG. 10.11. Block diagram of stabilized optimum filter.

the problem may be obtained by realizing the filter as a closed-loop error-sampled system which has been adjusted to avoid the unstable cancellation, as discussed in Chap. 7.   In the case of a filter such as is being discussed here, the system must be designed so as to maintain the transfer function given by (10.103).   In this situation the necessary degree of freedom for avoiding the unstable cancellation is introduced by the addition of a feedback constant in the system.   This additional constant is selected in such a manner that the digital controller in the closed loop is not required to cancel the unstable pole of the plant transfer function.   A block diagram of the stabilized system is shown in Fig. 10.11.

The example problem which has been worked out consists essentially of the design of a data hold or extrapolator for random data.   It is instructive to compare the operation of the optimum filter with that of a simpler and more common device.   For example, how does the mean-square error of the optimum system compare with that of a clamp, or zero-order hold? This question can be answered simply by calculating the mean-square value of the difference between the output of the zero-order hold and the ideal output.   As discussed in Chap. 6, the zero-order hold closely resembles a delay of half a sampling period, so that the error will be calculated based on an ideal system of a half-period delay.   A block diagram of the situation is shown in Fig. 10.12.   For the configuration shown in Fig. 10.12,

$$\begin{aligned}
\langle \epsilon^2(t) \rangle &= \langle [c(t) - c_d(t)]^2 \rangle \\
&= \langle c^2(t) \rangle - 2 \langle c(t) c_d(t) \rangle + \langle c_d{}^2(t) \rangle \\
&= \Phi_{cc}(0) - 2\Phi_{cc_d}(0) + \Phi_{c_d c_d}(0)
\end{aligned} \qquad (10.105)$$

where $c_d(t)$ equals $r[t - (T/2)]$.   If $r(t)$ is a stationary random signal, then the mean-square value of $r(t)$ delayed by half a sampling period,

$\langle r^2[t - (T/2)]\rangle$, is the same as the mean-square value of $r(t)$. Also, from the results of Sec. 10.4, it is clear that the mean-square value of the out-

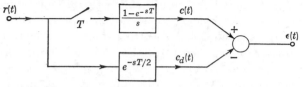

FIG. 10.12. Error formulation for evaluation of clamp as a filter.

put of a zero-order hold equals the mean-square value of the unsampled input as shown in (10.47). Therefore,

$$\Phi_{cc}(0) = \Phi_{c_d c_d}(0) = \Phi_{rr}(0) \tag{10.106}$$

If the input is assumed to have the spectrum of (10.86) then $\Phi_{rr}(0)$ equals unity. Also

$$\begin{aligned}
\Phi_{cc_d}(0) &= \langle c(t)c_d(t)\rangle \\
&= \langle c(t)r[t - (T/2)]\rangle \\
&= \Phi_{rc}(T/2) \tag{10.107}
\end{aligned}$$

From (10.59)

$$S_{rc}(s) = \frac{1}{T} S_{rr}(s)H(s) = \frac{1}{T} \frac{2\omega_1}{\omega_1{}^2 - s^2} \frac{1 - e^{-Ts}}{s} \tag{10.108}$$

and, by definition,

$$\begin{aligned}
\Phi_{rc}(T/2) &= \frac{1}{2\pi j} \int_{-j\infty}^{j\infty} S_{rc}(s)e^{sT/2}\, ds \\
&= \frac{1}{2\pi j} \int_{-j\infty}^{j\infty} \frac{1 - e^{-Ts}}{Ts} \frac{2\omega_1}{\omega_1{}^2 - s^2} e^{sT/2}\, ds \\
&= \frac{1}{2\pi j} \int_{-j\infty}^{j\infty} \frac{e^{(s/\omega_1)(\omega_1 T/2)} - e^{-(s/\omega_1)(\omega_1 T/2)}}{\omega_1 T(s/\omega_1)} \frac{2}{1 - (s/\omega_1)^2} \frac{ds}{\omega_1} \tag{10.109}
\end{aligned}$$

With the substitutions $s/\omega_1 = \lambda$ and $\omega_1 T = a$, (10.109) becomes

$$\begin{aligned}
\Phi_{rc}(T/2) &= \frac{1}{2\pi j} \int_{j\infty}^{-j\infty} \frac{e^{a\lambda/2} - e^{-a\lambda/2}}{a\lambda} \frac{2}{1 - \lambda^2}\, d\lambda \\
&= 2\frac{1 - e^{-a/2}}{a} \tag{10.110}
\end{aligned}$$

The mean-square value of the error is found by the substitution of (10.106) and (10.110) in (10.105):

$$\langle \epsilon^2(t)\rangle = 2 - 4\frac{1 - e^{-\omega_1 T/2}}{\omega_1 T} \tag{10.111}$$

The expression (10.111) is plotted in Fig. 10.10 for comparison with (10.99). For small values of $\omega_1 T$, (10.111) is approximately

$$\langle \epsilon^2(t)\rangle \approx \frac{\omega_1 T}{2} \tag{10.112}$$

The asymptotic expression given by 10.112 should be compared with (10.99), which gives the absolute minimum mean-square value of the error that can be obtained by the use of a linear filter to reconstruct the particular random signal under consideration.   In the case being considered, the zero-order hold has an error which is at least 50 per cent greater than the optimum.   To reconstruct a signal with a bandwidth of 1 cps with a zero-order hold one needs 30,000 samples/sec instead of the 20,000 samples required by the optimum filter.   In many cases this increase in sampling rate is not a severe price to pay for the great reduction in complexity of the zero-order hold as compared with the optimum filter.   As is the case in continuous filter theory, the optimum filter represents a standard for comparison and not a very practical filter design.

10.6 Summary

The analysis of random signals in linear sampled-data systems can be as easily performed as the analysis of random signals in linear continuous systems.   The use of the sampled power spectrum to describe impulse-modulated random signals permits the immediate extension of ideas from continuous systems to sampled systems in much the same way that the z transform and the pulse transfer function carry over familiar relations from continuous to sampled-data systems.   A method is given for the calculation of the sampled power spectrum which corresponds to a given continuous signal spectrum if the given spectrum is a rational function of frequency s.   This method shows that the sampled power spectrum is a rational function of z if the power spectrum of the continuous signal is a rational function of s.   The mean-square value of a continuous signal can be calculated from the sampled power spectrum, and formulas are given for this purpose.

The relation between the spectra of the signals at the input and the output of a sampler-and-filter combination is not obviously related to the continuous case, and a table of formulas is given as (10.59) to facilitate the use of the sampled power spectrum.   The technique for calculating the spectra is straightforward, and additional relations are readily determined.

It is possible to apply the theory of linear time-varying networks to the analysis of random signals in sampled-data systems, but this technique does not add any particular insight into the problem.   The special character of the time variation in sampled-data systems permits the use of specialized formulas and techniques which lead quickly to the answers most generally required.   It is obvious, of course, that the special techniques used for sampled-data systems do not apply to as broad a class of problems as do the methods of variable network theory.

One example of system synthesis has been given, that of the Wiener filter for sampled data. This synthesis technique leads to the transfer function of the linear filter which will minimize the mean-square error of prediction or smoothing. An example which is worked out shows that under certain circumstances a simpler filter, such as a zero-order hold, may be more desirable than the optimum filter. The optimum filter always remains as a guide, however, to indicate how well the practical filter performs.

CHAPTER 11

MISCELLANEOUS APPLICATIONS
OF SAMPLED-DATA THEORY

The theory which has been developed in previous chapters was applied specifically to linear dynamical systems containing one or more samplers operating periodically. Taken more abstractly, however, the z transformation bears the same relation to linear difference equations as does the Laplace transformation to linear differential equations. For this reason, sampled-data theory can serve to solve any problem which is represented exactly by a linear difference equation, as is the case in sampled-data systems, or approximately, as in other cases, where the difference equation is only an approximation to a differential equation. An advantage of the linear difference equation is that it can be integrated directly by use of desk calculators or digital computers.

Linear continuous dynamical systems are described approximately by means of linear difference equations. The error which is incurred can be controlled by choice of quadrature interval and interpolation technique employed. The former corresponds to the sampling interval and the latter to the form of data hold in a sampled-data system. For instance, a polygonal approximation, while physically unrealizable, serves as a good means of improving the computational accuracy, as contrasted to the use of a zero-order data-hold approximation.

Methods of adapting sampled-data theory to the numerical solution of systems which can be approximated by difference equations will be considered. There are a number of approaches to this problem, each having certain advantages and disadvantages. The use of a sampled-data model which bears topological similarity to the actual continuous system has the advantage of making possible a direct relation between the location of the samplers and the frequency content of the signal at those points. On the other hand, a direct approximation of the inverse Laplace transform of the variable of interest is convenient because it takes into account some initial conditions. In addition, this approach can be applied to time-varying systems. It will also be shown that sampled-data theory can also be used to evaluate certain infinite summations by application of the Poisson summation rule. Generally, this chapter will deal with some of the uses of sampled-data theory as applied to continuous systems which do not include a sampler but which can be so approximated.

11.1 Approximation of Open-loop Continuous Systems by a Sampled Model

Continuous dynamical systems are characterized by a set of differential equations containing derivatives with respect to time. The response in the time domain to a test input is studied by integrating the differential equations and plotting the resultant solution. An alternative is the experimental approach, using an analogue computer which is so programmed that its describing equations are identical to those of the actual system, except for scale factors. Still another alternative is to program a digital computer or to use manual computation, employing desk calculators, which solves an acceptably accurate difference equation derived from the differential equation. This section deals with techniques adapted from the theory of sampled-data systems which can be used to set up numerical routines for solving the continuous differential equations of linear systems.

If the system is linear, the solution of the differential equations describing it can be carried out in a straightforward manner. The Laplace transform of the output variable is obtained analytically and is inverted into the time domain by the use of tables or by contour integration. The resultant analytical expression is not readily interpreted and is generally plotted in order to obtain significant information required by the designer. The plotting is done by computing the value of the output variable at selected instants of time, plotting the points on a graph, and fitting a smooth curve connecting these points. It is noted that, in spite of the analytic nature of the solution, the final graph is obtained by employing some form of numerical computation at the selected time instants.

The alternate approach to the problem is to convert the differential equations into difference equations that can be solved numerically by the application of a recursion formula. There are well-known techniques for accomplishing this, but it so happens that, for linear systems, sampled-data theory can be applied directly.[50,B17] The technique is to replace the continuous system with an acceptably accurate sampled-data model. The z transform of the output sequence is readily obtained by the usual methods and its inversion accomplished either by contour integration or by the process of long division, easily implemented by digital-computer programming or by means of desk calculators.

To describe the technique, a simple open-cycle system will be used. Referring to Fig. 11.1a, it is desired to obtain the response of the linear system whose transfer function is $G_p(s)$ to an input function whose

Laplace transform is $R(s)$. In this case, the problem can be solved by computing the Laplace transform of the output, $C(s)$, from the simple relation

$$C(s) = G_p(s)R(s) \qquad (11.1)$$

The time-domain expression for the output $c(t)$ is obtained exactly from the inverse Laplace transformation,

$$c(t) = \mathcal{L}^{-1}[C(s)] \qquad (11.2)$$

The output $c(t)$ is then sketched by substituting a sequence of values of time t into the expression and plotting the result point by point.

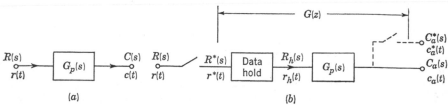

(a)   (b)

FIG. 11.1. Open-cycle approximate sampled model.

The other approach is that of constructing the equivalent approximate sampled model shown in Fig. 11.1b. Here the continuous input $r(t)$ is applied to the system through a sampler which closes every T sec. A data hold reconstructs the function as $r_h(t)$, which is an acceptably accurate reproduction of the continuous function $r(t)$, and applies it to the system whose transfer function is $G_p(s)$. The output of this element is $c_a(t)$, which is an approximation of $c(t)$. The errors in $c_a(t)$ are caused by the imperfect reproduction of the function $r(t)$, in other words, by the difference between $r(t)$ and $r_h(t)$. The approximate output function $c_a(t)$ is then sampled synchronously, as shown in Fig. 11.1b, to produce a pulse sequence $c_a^*(t)$.

The advantage of the simulation of the continuous system by this equivalent sampled-data system is that the relation between $C^*(s)$ and $R^*(s)$ can be obtained by the application of sampled-data theory. The variable s is replaced by z to give the generating function for the output $C(z)$ as follows:

$$C(z) = G(z)R(z) \qquad (11.3)$$

where $G(z)$ is the z transform corresponding to the Laplace transform of the process $G_p(s)$ and the data hold in cascade. The pulse sequence obtained by the inversion of $C(z)$ will give a sequence of numbers representing the output values at sampling instants. If the sampling interval T and the form of the data hold are judiciously chosen, the output will be acceptably accurate. In mathematical terms, what has been done is the replacement of the linear differential equation implied by $G_p(s)$ by the difference equation implied by $G(z)$ with a quadrature interval of T.

The accuracy of the output sequence obtained from the sampled model depends on the sophistication of the data-hold element in conjunction with the sampling interval T. The selection of this element is analogous to the selection of an interpolation technique in numerical methods for the integration of differential equations. In relating the choice of this element as well as the sampling interval, the use of a sampled model is generally clearer to the engineer and designer. For instance, if the input as expressed by $r(t)$ contains significant spectral components up to some frequency F, the sampling frequency should be high enough to pass them all, which means a sampling frequency more than $2F$. The combined data hold and $G_p(s)$ also enter into the choice of sampling frequency. If their combined frequency response effectively filters out high-frequency components of $r(t)$, the sampling frequency can be chosen with this in mind. Relating the numerical method to the physical problem in this manner has advantages. The application of the method can be shown by means of an example.

EXAMPLE

The response of a simple system whose transfer function $G_p(s)$ is

$$G_p(s) = \frac{1}{s+1}$$

to a unit step function is to be found. The data hold which is selected is a zero-order hold whose transfer function is

$$H(s) = \frac{1 - e^{-Ts}}{s}$$

The sampling interval T is chosen to be 1 sec, resulting in a sampling frequency of 1 cps. This frequency is approximately six times the half-energy frequency of the system.

If the input function is a unit step, it is evident from physical reasoning that the reconstructed function $r_h(t)$ is perfect, so that it is anticipated that the output obtained from the sampled model is perfect. The z transform of the input $R(z)$ is

$$R(z) = \frac{1}{1 - z^{-1}}$$

The z transform of the process, $G(z)$, is

$$G(z) = \mathrm{Z} \frac{1 - e^{-Ts}}{s(s+1)}$$
$$= \frac{0.632z^{-1}}{1 - 0.368z^{-1}}$$

The z transform of the output $C(z)$ is thus

$$C_a(z) = G(z)R(z)$$
$$= \frac{0.632z^{-1}}{1 - 1.368z^{-1} + 0.368z^{-2}}$$

This transform is inverted numerically by use of long division to yield the sequence

$$C_a(z) = 0.632z^{-1} + 0.865z^{-2} + 0.950z^{-3} + \cdots$$

A check will show that the values of the samples obtained from this sequence are exact, as expected.

For purposes of comparison, the response of the system to a unit ramp will be obtained, using the same sampled model and interval. It is immediately evident that the reconstructed input will be a "staircase" which differs considerably from the actual input. It is expected that the output from the sampled model will be in error. For this input, $R(z)$ is

$$R(z) = \frac{z^{-1}}{(1 - z^{-1})^2}$$

The z transform of the output $C(z)$, using $G(z)$ obtained previously, is

$$C_a(z) = \frac{0.632z^{-1}}{1 - 2.37z^{-1} + 1.74z^{-2} - 0.37z^{-3}}$$

Inverting this transform by the method of long division,

$$C_a(z) = 0.632z^{-2} + 1.5z^{-3} + 2.44z^{-4} + 3.42z^{-5} + 4.52z^{-6} + \cdots$$

The exact solution obtained by inversion of $C(s)$ gives the following values at the same sampling instants:

$$C(z) = 0.368z^{-1} + 1.135z^{-2} + 2.05z^{-3} + 3.00z^{-4} + \cdots$$

Comparison of the approximate and exact solutions shows that the former is always smaller than the latter at comparable sampling instants. This is due to the "staircase" approximation of the ramp produced by the zero-order hold which, aside from ripple, produces a time delay equal to $T/2$. Advancing the approximate solution by $\frac{1}{2}$ sec in this example improves the accuracy of the resultant points.

The illustrative example points up the fact that the data hold which is used to obtain a numerical solution must be chosen with care and with some regard as to the character of the input function $r(t)$ and the transfer function $G(s)$. In view of the fact that the problem at hand is to compute and not to implement physically, there is no reason why a desirable data hold which is not physically realizable should not be used. In this category, one of the more useful data-interpolation formulas is the one leading to a polygonal approximation of the continuous function. This approximation is shown in Fig. 11.2, where it is seen that the reconstructed function $r_h(t)$ is obtained by connecting the sample values $r(nT)$ by means of straight lines. The approximation is better than the one produced by

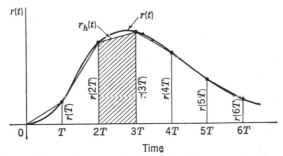

FIG. 11.2. Polygonal approximation of continuous time function.

either the zero-order or first-order data holds under the same conditions. The difficulty that would be experienced in attempting to construct physical devices embodying this form of data hold is that one would require physically unrealizable elements, as will be shown. For purposes of computation, however, this is of no consequence.

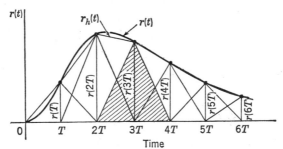

FIG. 11.3. Generating triangles for polygonal approximation.

In order to utilize the polygonal approximation in sampled-data models of continuous systems, it is necessary to derive the transfer function for the process. Referring to Fig. 11.3, it is seen that the polygonal approximation can be obtained by means of a sequence of generating triangles so constructed that their altitudes are equal to the value of the ordinate at the sampling instant and their bases are twice the sampling interval. A particular generating triangle at the third sampling instant is shown shaded in Fig. 11.3. Using the impulse approximation, a system must be found whose impulsive response is a generating triangle of the form shown here.

Referring to Fig. 11.4, the impulsive response $b(t)$ of a data hold of this type is a triangle-shaped function whose apex is at zero, its altitude equal to unity, and its base equal to $2T$. It is clear that this is the impulsive response of a physically unrealizable system since an output is produced before the application of the impulse at $t = 0$. To find the transfer func-

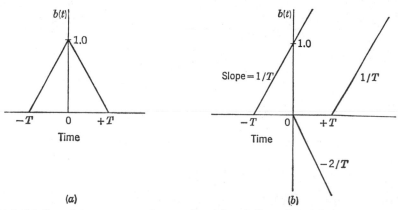

(a)   (b)

Fɪɢ. 11.4. (a) Impulsive response of generating triangle for polygonal approximation. (b) Decomposition of generating triangle into ramp functions.

tion, the impulsive response is decomposed into three elementary ramp functions, as shown in Fig. 11.4b, the sum of which is the triangle of Fig. 11.4a. The Laplace transform of these three components is

$$B(s) = \frac{1}{Ts^2} e^{Ts} - \frac{2}{Ts^2} + \frac{1}{Ts^2} e^{-Ts} \qquad (11.4)$$

Combining these terms and simplifying,

$$B(s) = \frac{e^{Ts}}{Ts^2} (1 - e^{-Ts})^2 \qquad (11.5)$$

The use of the polygonal or "triangle" hold having the transfer function given in (11.5) results in increased accuracy of computation in most cases. To illustrate the point, the same illustrative example considered previously will be repeated with the triangle hold in place of the simple data clamp.

EXAMPLE

The transfer functions of the data hold $B(s)$ and the continuous element $G_p(s)$ are as follows

$$B(s) = \frac{e^s(1 - e^{-s})^2}{s^2}$$

and

$$G_p(s) = \frac{1}{1 + s}$$

for a sampling interval T of unity. The pulse transfer function of the combination is

$$G(z) = Z \frac{e^s(1 - e^{-s})^2}{s^2(1 + s)}$$

which simplifies to

$$G(z) = \frac{0.368 + 0.264z^{-1}}{1 - 0.368z^{-1}}$$

If the input is a unit ramp function as previously, the z transform of the output $C(z)$ becomes

$$C(z) = \frac{0.368z^{-1}(1 + 0.72z^{-1})}{1 - 2.37z^{-1} + 1.74z^{-2} - 0.372z^{-3}}$$

Inverting $C(z)$ by the method of long division, there results the sequence

$$C(z) = 0.368z^{-1} + 1.14z^{-2} + 2.05z^{-3} + 3.00z^{-4} + 4.00z^{-5} + \cdots$$

As expected, this sequence is exact because the polygonal approximation reproduces the ramp function perfectly before it is applied to the

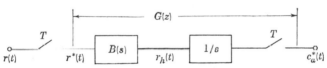

FIG. 11.5. Integration process using polygonal approximation.

continuous element. This demonstrates the effectiveness of relating the numerical method used to integrate the differential equation to the sampled-data model.

In Sec. 4.6, it was shown how the pulse transfer function can be used to describe a numerical process and, by example, a number of well-known numerical integration formulas were so expressed. The physical interpretation of these numerical processes can further be clarified by considering them in terms of the preceding discussions. For instance, if the polygonal approximation is used, the process of integration can be represented by the block diagram of Fig. 11.5, where $B(s)$ represents a triangle data hold. The over-all pulse transfer function of the operation is given by

$$G(z) = Z \frac{e^{Ts}(1 - e^{-Ts})^2}{Ts^3} \tag{11.6}$$

which, by reference to the table in Appendix I, is found to be

$$G(z) = \frac{T}{2} \frac{1 + z^{-1}}{1 - z^{-1}} \tag{11.7}$$

This is the same formula which was derived in the example in Sec. 4.6 from purely mathematical considerations.

The advantage of viewing the numerical integration process from the physical properties described in this section is that it is possible to relate the accuracy of the process to the properties of the function being integrated. In the case of this particular integration formula using the polygonal data hold, the error is caused by the difference between the actual function to be integrated, $r(t)$, and the reconstructed function, $r_h(t)$,

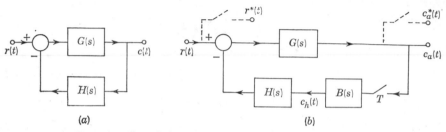

FIG. 11.6. Sampled model of continuous feedback system.

actually applied to the filter, in this case, a pure integrator. The difference function is "scalloped" in shape, as can be seen from Fig. 11.2, and contains periodic components having a fundamental frequency equal to the sampling frequency. If the filter which follows the data hold has a frequency response which is well below the sampling frequency, the error in the sampled model is not excessive. In the case of pure integration, the error is the area contained between the actual function and the polygonal approximation. It is evident that the error can be reduced by sampling more frequently, which is equivalent to stating that in a numerical process the quadrature error is reduced by reducing the quadrature interval. Some measure of the error can be obtained in more complex cases by integrating in the frequency domain the power contained in the error components, although an exact interpretation of the result is not always clear.

11.2 Approximation of Closed-loop Continuous Systems by a Sampled Model

The same general procedure which is applied to open-loop continuous systems can be used for closed-loop systems as well. The block diagram of such a system is shown in Fig. 11.6a, where $G(s)$ is the feedforward and $H(s)$ the feedback transfer functions, respectively. In converting the system to a sampled model, it is assumed that polygonal data reconstruction is adequate.[50] An important consideration is the location of these fictitious elements in the loop. As contrasted to the open-cycle case, where the sampler and data hold had to be placed in cascade with the continuous element, a number of locations are possible in the closed-loop case. For instance, the sampler could be placed in the error line, in the feedback line, or at some intermediate point in $G(s)$ or $H(s)$.   In view of the fact that the sampler and data hold are most accurate for the lower-frequency components of a signal, it follows that the best location is always at that point where the frequency content of the signal is lowest.

Assuming that the feedforward component of the system, $G(s)$, is low-pass, it is evident that the most restricted bandwidth for the signal will be found at the output of this element.   If $H(s)$ is also low-pass, then the bandwidth at the output of this element is even more restricted.   Figure 11.6b shows the sampler and data-hold elements placed at the output of $G(s)$, on the assumption that $G(s)$ is low-pass and that $H(s)$ is not.   The accuracy of the computations based on this sampled model depends on the accuracy with which $c_h(t)$ is reproduced from a sequence of samples derived from $c(t)$ by the triangle data hold.   To compute the output $c_a^*(t)$, the z transform of the output $C_a(z)$ is found from the expression

$$C_a(z) = \frac{RG(z)}{1 + HBG(z)} \tag{11.8}$$

Inversion of $C_a(z)$ by one of the standard methods will yield the desired output sequence $c_a^*(t)$ of the sampled model at sampling instants.   To illustrate the technique, an example will be given.

EXAMPLE

The simple feedback system shown in Fig. 11.7a has a unit step $r(t)$ applied to its input.   It is desired to compute the output $c(t)$.   As an arbitrary practical rule, the bandwidth of the system will be assumed to extend from zero frequency to an upper frequency at which the output is down 30 to 40 db below this level.   It is assumed, therefore, that all components above this value are not significant.   For the system used in the example, this frequency is 1 cps, at which frequency the response is down 32 db.   The sampling frequency will be chosen at 1 cps mainly for convenience, even though a higher frequency should have been chosen on the basis of using twice the frequency of the highest significant frequency component to be passed.

The sampled model which will be used is shown in Fig. 11.7b, where it is seen that the triangle hold is placed in the feedback path to be consistent with the requirement that sampling take place at the point where the most restricted spectrum is found.   If the input $r(t)$ is a unit step function, then the elements to be substituted in (11.8) become

$$RG(z) = \mathbb{Z} \frac{1}{s^2(s + 1)}$$

which is, from the table in Appendix I,

$$RG(z) = \frac{z^{-1}}{1 - z^{-1}} \frac{0.3679 + 0.2642z^{-1}}{(1 - z^{-1})(1 - 0.3679z^{-1})}$$

The term $HBG(z)$ is given by

$$HBG(z) = Z \frac{e^{s}(1 - e^{-s})^2}{s^2(s + 1)}$$

which is, from the table in Appendix I,

$$HBG(z) = \frac{0.1321 + 0.4198z^{-1} + 0.0802z^{-2}}{(1 - z^{-1})(1 - 0.3679z^{-1})}$$

Substituting the component terms in (11.8), $C_a(z)$ becomes

$$C_a(z) = \frac{0.3679z^{-1} + 0.2642z^{-2}}{1.1321 - 2.0802z^{-1} + 1.3962z^{-2} - 0.4481z^{-3}}$$

This z transform is inverted by the method of long division, using a desk calculator, resulting in the sequence

$$C_a(z) = 0.3250z^{-1} + 0.8305z^{-2} + 1.125z^{-3} + 1.1721z^{-4} + 1.094z^{-5}$$
$$+ 1.011z^{-6} + 0.9718z^{-7} - \cdots$$

The coefficients of the various z^{-1} terms are the values of the output at the sampling instants corresponding to the powers of z^{-1}. The result-

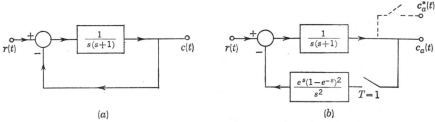

(a)   (b)

FIG. 11.7. (a) Closed-loop system used in example. (b) Sampled model of closed-loop system.

ing points are plotted in Fig. 11.8a on the same graph with the continuous curve obtained from the direct inversion of $C(s)$. The errors are not large, as is seen from this curve and from the error plot shown in Fig. 11.8b. The maximum error is 2 per cent, which is within the required accuracy for most engineering computations.

One of the usual problems in the application of numerical methods to the solution of continuous systems lies in an estimation of the errors which are incurred. In the context of this discussion, it is desirable to obtain an estimate or possibly an upper bound to the error in the output at sampling instants produced by the sampled model.   For engineering approximations, maximum advantage can be taken of the relationship which is established between the sampled model and the actual physical system.   The definition of the computational error can best be understood by referring to Fig. 11.9, where the difference between the output

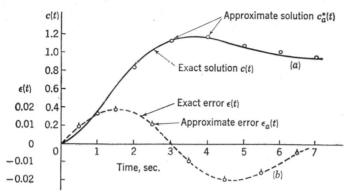

FIG. 11.8. Exact and approximate response of system to unit step function.

of the actual system $c(t)$ and the sampled model output $c_a(t)$ is $\epsilon(t)$.   For the linear system, the Laplace transform of the error $\epsilon(s)$ is given by

$$\epsilon(s) = C(s) - C_a(s) \qquad (11.9)$$

The problem is to evaluate or approximate this transform.

To approximate $\epsilon(s)$, a number of steps are taken, the first of which is to

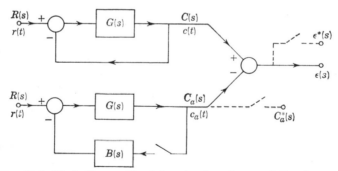

FIG. 11.9. Block diagram for determination of computational error.

note that the Laplace transform of the output $C_a^*(s)$ is given by the summation

$$C_a^*(s) = \frac{1}{T} \sum_{n=-\infty}^{\infty} C_a(s + nj\omega_0) \qquad (11.10)$$

Taking only the central term of the summation as being an adequate approximation depends on the contributions of the sidebands being small, a condition which will be true if the sampling frequency is chosen high enough.   Thus,

$$C_a(s) \approx \frac{1}{T} C(s) \tag{11.11}$$

Substituting the central term only in (11.9), the Laplace transform of the system error becomes

$$\epsilon(s) = \frac{G(s)R(s)}{1 + G(s)} - \frac{G(s)R(s)}{1 + [(1/T)B(s)G(s)]} \tag{11.12}$$

Simplifying this expression and making use of the fact that $G(s)$ and $B(s)G(s)/T$ are approximately equal, the approximate expression for $\epsilon(s)$ becomes

$$\epsilon(s) = \frac{[(1/T)B(s) - 1][G(s)]^2 R(s)}{[1 + G(s)]^2} \tag{11.13}$$

It is noted that if $B(s)/T$ were exactly equal to unity, a situation which would obtain if the data reconstruction were perfect, there would be no computational error.   In order to make (11.13) more tractable, $B(s)$,

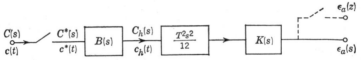

Fig. 11.10. Reduced sampled model for determination of computational error.

which is given in (11.5) in terms of exponential operators, can be expanded into a power series in s.   If this is done by expanding each exponential into its power series and if the terms of the series so obtained are substituted in (11.13), the Laplace transform of the error becomes

$$\epsilon(s) = \frac{T^2 s^2}{12} K(s)C(s) + \frac{T^4 s^4}{360} K(s)C(s) + \cdots \tag{11.14}$$

where $K(s)$ is defined by

$$K(s) = \frac{G(s)}{1 + G(s)}$$

For the likely case that the sampling interval is small, and consistent with the approximation made in (11.11), only the first term of (11.14) need be considered to obtain an estimate of error.   Even with these simplifications, the inversion of the first term of (11.14) involves the same difficulties as the main problem itself.   Applying the same techniques, the sampled error may be obtained from the model shown in Fig. 11.10. $C_h(s)$ is the Laplace transform of the reconstructed output function, using the polygonal approximation.   For purposes of error computation, $c_h(t)$ differs only slightly from the actual output $c(t)$. Thus, it may be stated that

$$C_h(s) = C^*(s)B(s) \approx C(s) \tag{11.15}$$

From which it follows that the Laplace transform of the error function $\epsilon_a(s)$ may be represented with reasonable accuracy by

$$\epsilon_a(s) = \frac{T^2 s^2}{12} B(s)K(s)C^*(s) \tag{11.16}$$

Taking the z transform of both sides of (11.16),

$$\epsilon_a(z) = \frac{T}{12} (z - 2 - z^{-1})K(z)C(z) \tag{11.17}$$

where $B(s)$ is taken as the transfer function of the triangle hold.

If the original solution being computed was the response of the system to a unit step function, $K(z)$ can be approximated by obtaining the first back difference of the approximate output already computed. This introduces a delay of one-half a sampling interval, but this is readily eliminated by shifting forward the first difference by one-half a sampling interval. Thus,

$$K_a(z) = z^{1/2}\left[\frac{1}{T}(1 - z^{-1})C_a(z)\right] \tag{11.18}$$

where the term $z^{1/2}$ is used loosely to indicate the advance of the resultant sample points by one-half a sampling interval.

If this technique is applied to the illustrative example worked out previously, the resultant error samples result in the points shown in Fig. 11.8b. The dashed line is an exact computation of the error. It is seen that a remarkable accuracy in error computation exists in this case. The procedure used to evaluate the computational error was related closely to the physical properties of the system. It would have been much more difficult for the engineer to arrive at these results had only abstract mathematical procedures been employed.

11.3 Approximation of the Inverse Laplace Transform

In the previous sections, the numerical process was correlated with a sampled physical system which simulates the mathematical operation. It has been shown[B17] that numerical computation methods can also be related to the approximate evaluation of the inverse Laplace transform without using a physical model. The inverse Laplace transform is given by

$$f(t) = \frac{1}{2\pi j} \int_{c-j\omega}^{c+j\omega} F(s)e^{st}\,ds \tag{11.19}$$

For practical stable systems, the poles of $F(s)$ are contained within the left half plane so that the path of integration can be the imaginary axis, which means that c is equal to zero. The integral (11.19) can be separated into two component integrals

$$f(t) = \frac{1}{2\pi j} \int_{-j\pi/T}^{+j\pi/T} F(s)e^{st}\,ds + \frac{1}{2\pi j} \int_{j\pi/T}^{j\infty} F(s)e^{st} + F(-s)e^{-st}\,ds \quad (11.20)$$

The path of integration for the first integral of (11.20) is shown in Fig. 11.11a, where the heavy line on the $j\omega$ axis represents this portion of the

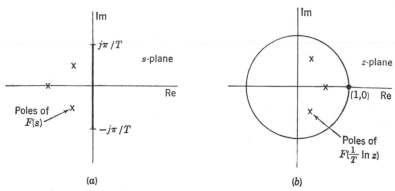

(a)   (b)

FIG. 11.11. (a) Truncated integration path for inversion of Laplace transform. (b) Map of truncated integration path on z plane.

path. If $1/T$ is chosen sufficiently large so that the limit of integration $j\pi/T$ is well-removed from the location of the poles of $F(s)$, the contribution of the second integral of (11.20) may be discarded.

Assuming that the error produced by the omission of the second integral of (11.20) is acceptable, then $f_a(t)$, an approximation of $f(t)$, is given by

$$f_a(t) = \frac{1}{2\pi j} \int_{-j\pi/T}^{+j\pi/T} F(s)e^{st}\,ds \quad (11.21)$$

If the output at sampling instants only is desired, then $t = nT$ in (11.21) and

$$f_a(nT) = \frac{1}{2\pi j} \int_{-j\pi/T}^{+j\pi/T} F(s)e^{nTs}\,ds \quad (11.22)$$

A change of variable from s to z is made, where z is defined by the usual expression, $z = e^{sT}$. Replacing s by $1/T \ln z$ in (11.22),

$$f_a(nT) = \frac{1}{2\pi j} \int_{\Gamma} F\left(\frac{1}{T}\ln z\right) e^{nT(1/T)\ln z}\,d(1/T \ln z) \quad (11.23)$$

which simplifies to

$$f_a(nT) = \frac{1}{2\pi j} \int_{\Gamma} \frac{1}{T} F\left(\frac{1}{T}\ln z\right) z^{n-1}\,dz \quad (11.24)$$

The contour Γ is the map of the truncated imaginary axis shown in Fig. 11.11a on the z plane.   The map is the unit circle on the z plane, as shown in Fig. 11.11b.   The poles of $F(s)$ are shown to lie on the left half of the s plane, and these map inside of the unit circle of the z plane.   The integral of (11.24) is recognized to be the standard inversion integral for a pulse transfer function $M(z)$ given by

$$M(z) = \frac{1}{T} F\left(\frac{1}{T} \ln z\right) \qquad (11.25)$$

It is relatively difficult to evaluate (11.24) because $M(z)$ is a transcendental function rather than the ratio of polynomials in z which permits numerical inversion by the method of long division.

To facilitate the inversion of $M(z)$, $\ln z$ will be approximated by a convenient series as follows:

$$\ln z = 2(u + \tfrac{1}{3}u^3 + \tfrac{1}{5}u^5 + \cdots) \qquad (11.26)$$

where

$$u = \frac{1 - z^{-1}}{1 + z^{-1}}$$

This particular series converges rapidly for regions of the z plane where z is large.   To apply this approximation, the Laplace transform will be expressed as a polynomial in s^{-1}, the latter variable being more desirable, as will be seen.   From the definition $z = e^{Ts}$,

$$s^{-1} = 1/s = T/\ln z \qquad (11.27)$$

Substituting the series expression for $\ln z$ from (11.26) into (11.27),

$$s^{-1} = \frac{T/2}{u + u^3/3 + u^5/5 + \cdots} \qquad (11.28)$$

Expanding (11.28) into powers of u by the simple process of long division,

$$s^{-1} = T/2(1/u - u/3 - 4u^3/45 - 44u^5/945 - \cdots) \qquad (11.29)$$

To obtain the general term s^{-k}, (11.29) is raised to the power k and is expanded by means of the binomial theorem, where $1/u$ is considered the first term and the remainder of the expression the second term.   For instance, taking $k = 2$,

$$s^{-2} = T^2/4[(1/u) - (u/3 + 4u^3/45 + \cdots)]^2 \qquad (11.30)$$

which expands to

$$s^{-2} = T^2/4[(1/u)^2 - (2/u)(u/3 + 4u^3/45 - \cdots) + \cdots] \qquad (11.31)$$

Taking only the first term of the series contained in the third parenthesis of (11.31) and ignoring all other terms,

$$s^{-2} = T^2/4[(1/u^2) - (2/3)] \qquad (11.32)$$

Substituting the expression for u from (11.26), there results the so-called z form

$$s^{-2} = \frac{T^2}{12} \frac{1 + 10z^{-1} + z^{-2}}{(1 - z^{-1})^2} \tag{11.33}$$

Higher orders of s^{-1} may be similarly evaluated, leading to a table of z forms given in Table 11.1. It is seen that the expression for s^{-k} will con-

TABLE 11.1*

s^{-k}	z form
s^{-1}	$\dfrac{T}{2} \dfrac{1 + z^{-1}}{1 - z^{-1}}$
s^{-2}	$\dfrac{T^2}{12} \dfrac{1 + 10z^{-1} + z^{-2}}{(1 - z^{-1})^2}$
s^{-3}	$\dfrac{T^3}{2} \dfrac{z^{-1} + z^{-2}}{(1 - z^{-1})^3}$
s^{-4}	$\dfrac{T^4}{6} \dfrac{z^{-1} + 4z^{-2} + z^{-3}}{(1 - z^{-1})^4} - \dfrac{T^4}{720}$
s^{-5}	$\dfrac{T^5}{24} \dfrac{z^{-1} + 11z^{-2} + 11z^{-3} + z^{-4}}{(1 - z^{-1})^5}$

* Reproduced in part from R. Boxer and S. Thaler, A Simplified Method of Solving Linear and Nonlinear Systems, *Proc. IRE*, vol. 44, no. 1, pp. 89–101, January, 1956.

tain a pole of order k at $z = 1$ in the z plane and at $s = 0$ in the s plane. Since the unit circle represents the other periodic strips of the s plane as well as the first strip, there are additional poles displaced by $jk\pi/T$ as well on the corresponding map on the s plane. If the sampling period T is small enough, the additional poles on the s plane are sufficiently removed from the region of interest extending from $-\pi/T$ to π/T to introduce negligible errors so long as π/T is considerably greater than the highest frequency of interest in the system. It might appear that the inclusion of additional terms from (11.31) would improve the accuracy of the approximation. However, this would introduce additional poles in the z form, which would lead to increased rather than decreased errors. To make the approximation accurate, it is necessary to use a sampling frequency sufficiently higher than the maximum significant frequency passed by the system and then to employ the simpler forms. In the context of this discussion, this means that the frequency π/T must be high enough to place the spurious poles introduced by the periodicity of (11.25), when plotted in the s plane, far away from the region of interest. By doing so, the approximation to the exact Laplace transform is adequate.

A property of the z forms which are listed in Table 11.1 is that the expressions obtained by replacing z by e^{sT} have the same initial terms when expanded into a power series in s about zero. For instance, considering the z form for the second integral given by (11.33), an error transform can be formed

$$\epsilon(s) = \frac{T^2}{12} \frac{1 + 10e^{-sT} + e^{-2sT}}{(1 - e^{-sT})^2} - \frac{1}{s^2} \qquad (11.34)$$

If $\epsilon(s)$ is differentiated twice, it will be found that the first two derivatives are zero for $s = 0$. Higher-order z forms have this property also, except that more derivatives are involved. The significance of this result is that, in the frequency domain, there will be a close coincidence in frequency response between the approximate and exact forms in the region of zero frequency. As the frequencies under consideration become

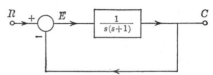

FIG. 11.12. Feedback system used in example.

higher, there will be more and more deviation between the frequency-response characteristics of the exact and approximate forms. This is another manifestation of the fact that sampled models are most accurate at frequencies which are well below the sampling frequency.

Application of the z forms listed in Table 11.1 is fairly simple. The Laplace transform of the desired variable, including initial conditions, is obtained and is expressed in terms of powers of s^{-1} as follows:

$$F(s) = \frac{a_m s^{-m} + a_{m-1} s^{-(m-1)} + \cdots + a_0}{b_n s^{-n} + b_{n-1} s^{-(n-1)} + \cdots + b_0} \qquad (11.35)$$

The significance of (11.35) in the time domain is that an equality is established between the weighted sum of the time integrals of the input and output variables. The approach is to approximate each of these integrals by a z form from Table 11.1 and to invert the resultant z transform. This is done directly by substituting for each of the terms in (11.35) the appropriate z form obtained from Table 11.1, as illustrated by means of an example.

EXAMPLE

A simple type I servomechanism is represented by the block diagram shown in Fig. 11.12. The input to the system $r(t)$ is a unit step function. The over-all transfer function $K(s)$ is given by

$$K(s) = \frac{C(s)}{R(s)} = \frac{1}{s^2 + s + 1}$$

and
$$R(s) = 1/s$$

The Laplace transform of the output $C(s)$ is thus

$$C(s) = \frac{1}{s^3 + s^2 + s}$$

Following the procedure which permits the use of the z forms given in Table 11.1, both numerator and denominator are divided by the highest order of s, resulting in

$$C(s) = \frac{s^{-3}}{s^{-2} + s^{-1} + 1}$$

Substituting for each term the z form from Table 11.1, there results the equivalent z transform of the output $C(z)$:

$$C(z)$$
$$= \frac{6T^2(z^{-1} + z^{-2})}{\begin{array}{l}(12 + 6T + T^2) - (36 + 6T - 9T^2)z^{-1} \\ \quad + (36 - 6T - 9T^2)z^{-2} - (12 - 6T + T^2)z^{-3}\end{array}}$$

The sampling interval T is chosen on the basis of frequency-response considerations similar to those used in previous sections. In this case, T is chosen as 1 sec, based on the criterion that frequency components below -30 db are negligible. If T is taken as 1 sec, then

$$C(z) = \frac{6z^{-1} + 6z^{-2}}{19 - 33z^{-1} + 21z^{-2} - 7z^{-3}}$$

Inverting $C(z)$ by the process of long division there results the sequence

$$C(z) = 0.316z^{-1} + 0.864z^{-2} + 1.15z^{-3} + 1.16z^{-4} + 1.06z^{-5}$$
$$+ 0.987z^{-6} + \cdots$$

The computed response at sampling instants is given by the coefficients of the terms of this sequence. These are plotted as the marked points in Fig. 11.13.

To show how a reduction of sampling interval can improve accuracy, a sampling interval T of 0.5 sec is used in the expression for $C(z)$. The result is

$$C(z) = \frac{1.5z^{-1} + 1.5z^{-2}}{15.25 - 36.75z^{-1} + 30.75z^{-2} - 9.25z^{-3}}$$

which, upon expansion by long division, becomes

$$C(z) = 0.0984z^{-1} + 0.335z^{-2} + 0.610z^{-3} + 0.853z^{-4} + \cdots$$

It is noted that every second term in this expression corresponds to that of the sequence obtained for a 1-sec sampling interval. These points are plotted on Fig. 11.13, where it is seen that the accuracy is improved over that obtained with the 1-sec interval.   This is especially true in those regions where the second and higher-order derivatives of the output are high.

11.4 Equations with Time-varying Coefficients

The techniques used in the previous section can be adapted to the case of time-varying systems.[B17]   These systems are described by differential equations containing coefficients which are functions of time.   One form of equation is

$$g_n \frac{d^n y}{dt^n} + g_{n-1} \frac{d^{n-1} y}{dt^{n-1}} + \cdots + g_0 y = f(t) \qquad (11.36)$$

where the various g_i are functions of time.   If the g_i are slowly varying

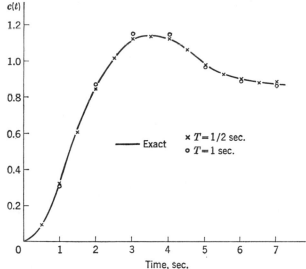

FIG. 11.13. Exact and approximate response of system in example.

with time, (11.36) can be expressed in terms of an approximation.   In general, it is readily shown that the nth derivative $d^n(g_n y)/dt^n$ is given by

$$\frac{d^n(g_n y)}{dt^n} = \sum_{k=0}^{n} C_k{}^n \frac{d^k g_n}{dt^k} \frac{d^{n-k} y}{dt^{n-k}} \qquad (11.37)$$

where the various C_k are the binomial coefficients.   If g_n is slowly varying, the contributions of the derivatives of g_n are negligible, so that the approximation can be made that

$$\frac{d^n(g_n y)}{dt^n} \approx g_n \frac{d^n y}{dt^n} \tag{11.38}$$

If this approximation is acceptable, then (11.36) can be expressed as

$$\frac{d^n(g_n y)}{dt^n} + \frac{d^{n-1}(g_{n-1} y)}{dt^{n-1}} + \cdots + g_0 y = f(t) \tag{11.39}$$

Equations of the form in (11.39) can be solved by numerical methods which are set up using z forms. The procedure is to take the Laplace transform of both sides of (11.39)

$$s^n G_n(s) + s^{n-1} G_{n-1}(s) + \cdots + G_0(s) = F(s) \tag{11.40}$$

where $G_n(s)$ is $\mathcal{L}(g_n y)$. It is assumed here that all initial conditions on $g_n y$ are zero. If this does not obtain, the initial conditions can be inserted in the usual manner. Dividing (11.40) through by s^n,

$$G_n(s) + \frac{1}{s} G_{n-1}(s) + \cdots + \frac{1}{s^n} G_0(s) = \frac{1}{s^n} F(s) \tag{11.41}$$

This relation can be interpreted as being an equality between various integrals on the left side of the equation and integrals on the right side. The various $1/s^k$ terms can be approximated by the z forms of Table 11.1. Clarification of the approximation of the various $G_i(s)$ is required.

It is recalled that $G_i(s)$ is the Laplace transform of the time function $g_i(t)y(t)$, which has been abbreviated in this development as $g_i y$. The Laplace transform is, by definition,

$$G_i(s) = \int_0^\infty g_i(t) y(t) e^{-st} \, dt \tag{11.42}$$

The integral can be approximated by the summation

$$G_i(s) \approx \sum_{n=0}^\infty g_i(nT) y(nT) e^{-snT} T \tag{11.43}$$

This summation is recognized as

$$G_i(s) \approx T G_i(z) \tag{11.44}$$

and, similarly,

$$F(s) \approx T F(z) \tag{11.45}$$

The procedure is to replace the various $1/s^k$ terms by the z forms and the Laplace transforms by the approximate z transforms. Abbreviating the symbol for the z forms as ZF_k to represent the z form corresponding to $1/s^k$, (11.41) becomes, after dividing through by T,

$$G_n(z) + ZF_1 G_{n-1}(z) + \cdots + ZF_n G_0(z) = ZF_n F(z) \tag{11.46}$$

(11.46) is interpreted as a z transform relation which is directly converted to a recursion formula between the variables. This is best shown by means of an example.

EXAMPLE

The time-varying differential equation of first order is expressed as follows:

$$\frac{d^2y}{dt^2} + \frac{d}{dt}(ty) = u(t)$$

where $u(t)$ is the unit step function. The equation is reduced to the form of (11.40):

$$Y(s) + \frac{1}{s}G_1(s) = \frac{1}{s^2}U(s)$$

where $G_1(s)$ is $\mathcal{L}[ty(t)]$ and $U(s)$ is the Laplace transform of the unit step function. Since the Laplace transform of the independent variable is, in this case, in the form of $1/s^k$, it is possible to apply the z forms directly to the right side of the equation. Reducing the equation to the form of (11.45) with the slight change that the z form $1/s^3$ is used on the right side, the relation is obtained that

$$TY(z) + \frac{T(1+z^{-1})}{2(1-z^{-1})}TG_1(z) - \frac{T^3(z^{-1}+z^{-2})}{2(1-z^{-1})^3}$$

This relation represents a difference equation or recursion formula between samples. To obtain this relation, both sides of the equation are multiplied by $(1-z^{-1})^3$, and, canceling out T, there results

$$(1-z^{-1})^3 Y(z) + T/2(1+z^{-1})(1-z^{-1})^2 G_1(z) = T^2/2(z^{-1}+z^{-2})$$

The recursion relationship represented by this equation is, after combination of terms,

$$[2y(nT) + Tg_1(nT)] - [6y(n-1)T + Tg_1(n-1)T]$$
$$+ [6y(n-2)T - Tg_1(n-2)T] - [2y(n-3)T - Tg_1(n-3)T]$$
$$= T^2u(n-1)T + T^2u(n-2)T$$

where $g_1(nT)$ is from the definition of $G_1(s)$ given by

$$g_1(nT) = nT[y(nT)]$$

Thus, the recursion relation can be written

$$[2+T(nT)]y(nT) - [6+T(n-1)T]y(n-1)T$$
$$+ [6-T(n-2)T]y(n-2)T - [2-T(n-3)T]y(n-3)T$$
$$= T^2u(n-1)T + T^2u(n-2)T$$

For instance, if T is unity, the first ordinate $y(0)$ is zero and the other terms are

$$y(1) = \tfrac{1}{3}$$
$$y(2) = \tfrac{10}{12}$$
$$\text{etc.}$$

11.5 Problems Involving Initial Conditions

In the developments of the previous sections, the systems were generally considered to be initially relaxed so that initial values and derivatives of the variables were assumed to be zero. Techniques for inserting initial conditions in the problem will now be considered. In the first place, the use of z forms described in Sec. 11.3 permits the insertion of initial conditions readily because the technique consists of approximating the Laplace transform of the variable of interest with a z transform. This means that, if initial conditions are nonzero, they may be inserted directly into the Laplace transform by the standard methods and then conversion into a z transform carried out. In the approach which replaces the continuous system with a sampled model a general technique will be developed which permits the application of initial conditions directly into the model rather than into the Laplace transform.

A typical element of the system represents a process given by the exact integral

$$y(t) = \int_{-\infty}^{t} x(t)\, dt \tag{11.47}$$

This integral is approximated by considering values at every T sec, as described in Chap. 4. Thus, (11.47) can be written

$$y[(n+1)T] = \int_{-\infty}^{nT} x(t)\, dt + \int_{nT}^{(n+1)T} x(t)\, dt \tag{11.48}$$

This simplifies to

$$y[(n+1)T] = y(nT) + \int_{nT}^{(n+1)T} x(t)\, dt \tag{11.49}$$

The integral in (11.49) is approximated by means of the polygonal approximation to produce an approximate value of $y[(n+1)T]$ as follows:

$$y_a[(n+1)T] = y_a(nT) + T/2\{x(nT) + x[(n+1)T]\} \tag{11.50}$$

To obtain the z transform of (11.50), both sides are multiplied by z^{-n} and summed over all positive values of n

$$\sum_{n=0}^{\infty} y_a[(n+1)T]z^{-n} = \sum_{n=0}^{\infty} y_a(nT)z^{-n} + T/2 \sum_{n=0}^{\infty} x(nT)z^{-n}$$

$$+ T/2 \sum_{n=0}^{\infty} x[(n+1)T]z^{-n} \tag{11.51}$$

Substituting $k = n + 1$ in the first and last sums,

$$\sum_{k=1}^{\infty} y_a(kT)z^{-k}z = \sum_{n=0}^{\infty} y_a(nT)z^{-n} + T/2 \sum_{n=0}^{\infty} x(nT)z^{-n}$$

$$+ T/2 \sum_{k=1}^{\infty} x(kT)z^{-k}z \quad (11.52)$$

By adding and subtracting the initial terms in the first and last sums in (11.52), this equation can be written in terms of the z transforms of $y(nT)$ and $x(nT)$

$$z[Y_a(z) - y(0)] = Y_a(z) + T/2[X(z)] + T/2\{z[X(z) - x(0)]\} \quad (11.53)$$

Simplifying this expression, $Y_a(z)$ becomes

$$Y_a(z) = \frac{T(1 + z^{-1})[X(z)]}{2(1 - z^{-1})} + \frac{y(0)}{1 - z^{-1}} - \frac{Tx(0)}{2(1 - z^{-1})} \quad (11.54)$$

In this manner, the z transform is corrected for the initial values of the independent and dependent variables.

The operations indicated by (11.54) are shown schematically in Fig. 11.14. The input or independent variable $x(t)$ is applied at the input,

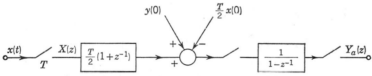

FIG. 11.14. Sampled model of integration process with initial conditions.

while the initial conditions are inserted as inputs at the intermediate summing point, as shown. This equivalent system suggests the technique which is used to insert initial conditions in problem solutions. The system equations are written in terms of Laplace transforms, and a system block diagram is drawn containing only elementary integration operations. This type of reduction is much the same as that which would be applied if the problem were to be set up on an analogue computer containing only summers and integrators. Each integrator is then replaced by the sampled equivalent circuit shown in Fig. 11.14 and the initial conditions inserted. The sampled model which results can be solved by the usual z-transform inversion methods. This is best illustrated by means of a simple example.

EXAMPLE

The resistance-inductance circuit shown in Fig. 11.15 is subjected to a unit step voltage applied at time $t = 0$. It is desired to set up a computational model which permits the insertion of an initial current condition.　The differential equation for the system is

$$e_1(t) = L\frac{di}{dt} + Ri$$

Taking the Laplace transform of both sides, there results

$$E_1(s) = L[sI(s) - i(0)] + RI(s)$$

where $i(0)$ is the initial value of the current.　Solving for $I(s)$,

$$I(s) = \frac{E_1(s)}{Ls + R} + \frac{Li(0)}{Ls + R}$$

If the output voltage $e_o(t)$ is desired,

$$E_o(s) = RI(s) = \frac{RE_1(s)}{Ls + R} + \frac{RLi(0)}{Ls + R}$$

It is readily ascertained that the model shown in Fig. 11.16a has an over-all relationship between $E_o(s)$ and $E_1(s)$ given by this expression.

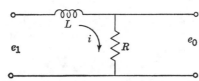

It is seen that the only dynamical element is a perfect integrator, which can be replaced by a sampled approximant.　The initial condition $i(0)$ is inserted as an impulse applied as shown.

Fig. 11.15. Resistance-capacitance circuit used in example.

Figure 11.16b shows the integration process replaced by a numerical equivalent using the polygonal approximation.　The initial conditions are applied at the intermediate point, and it is noted that not only must the initial condition $i(0)$ be inserted but also $T/2$ times the derivative of the current $i'(0)$.　This corresponds to the quantity $x(0)$ in Fig. 11.14 and Eq. (11.54), which, being the integrand in the integration process, is also the derivative of the integral $y(t)$.　Thus, to solve the problem by numerical methods with an initial condition of current, the initial rate change of current must also be ascertained.　In this simple problem, this rate change is easily shown to be $e_L(0)/L$, where $e_L(0)$ is the initial value of the voltage across the inductance. In this problem, this initial voltage is the entire voltage $e_1(0)$.

If, for this problem, it is assumed that the input $e_1(t)$ is a unit step and the initial current $i(0)$ (but not the initial rate change of current) is zero, then the z transform of the output voltage $E_o(z)$ is

$$E_o(z) = \frac{\dfrac{RT}{2L}\dfrac{1 + z^{-1}}{(1 - z^{-1})^2} - \dfrac{RT}{2L}\dfrac{1}{1 - z^{-1}}}{1 + \dfrac{RT}{2L}\dfrac{1 + z^{-1}}{1 - z^{-1}}}$$

If the sampling period is chosen to be half the time constant of the circuit so that $RT/L = \frac{1}{2}$, then the relation for $E_o(z)$ reduces to

$$E_o(z) = \frac{0.400z^{-1}}{(1 - z^{-1})(1 - 0.600z^{-1})}$$

The output sequence can be obtained by a process of long division and the results are found to agree to within better than 1 per cent of the exact solution.

It is evident that the procedure used in the illustrative example is far too complex to be used to solve problems of this simplicity.   The fact of

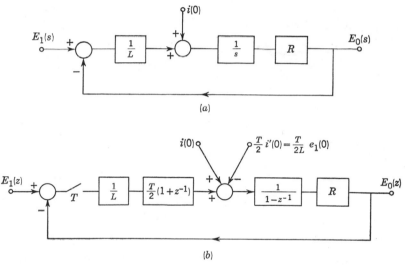

(a)

(b)

FIG. 11.16. (a) Continuous model giving exact input-output relations for circuit.   (b) Sampled model which replaces continuous model.

the matter is that the problem is actually made to seem more difficult than is warranted but, for that matter, so does any method of numerical analysis.   The true test of the method is how well it provides organization of complicated problems, and on that basis, the procedure does offer significant advantages.   So long as in the analysis of networks the block diagram is set up with all the condenser voltages and all the inductor currents as unknown variables, the initial conditions can readily be inserted. This can be shown more readily by a more complex example.

EXAMPLE

An RLC network is shown in Fig. 11.17.   There is no forcing voltage applied to the input to the network, but the initial conditions determine the response of the network after the initial instant.   In this case, it is assumed that the voltage across the condenser is zero and the current through the inductor is unity. Thus, $e_c(0) = 0$, $i(0) = 1$. The block diagram for the system is obtained as shown in Fig. 11.18a. This diagram can be obtained step by step from the relationships between the transforms of the variables. Replacing the integration operations by the numerical equivalent as expressed by the sampled elements using the polygonal approximation of Fig. 11.14, a sampled model shown in

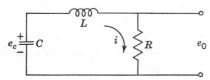

FIG. 11.17. Resistance-capacitance-inductance network used in example.

Fig. 11.18b is obtained. From the original assumptions and the differential equations for the system are obtained the following series of relationships:

$$e_c(0) = 0$$
$$e_c'(0) = -\tfrac{1}{2}$$
$$i(0) = 1$$
$$i'(0) = -2$$

These constitute the inputs to the sampled model in Fig. 11.18b. The z transform of the output $E_o(z)$ is obtained directly from this model and is found to be

$$E_o(z) = \frac{(1 + T + T^2/4) - z^{-1}(1 + T - T^2/4)}{(1 + T + T^2/4) + (T^2/2 - 2)z^{-1} + (1 - T + T^2/4)z^{-2}}$$

If T is chosen to be 0.314, then $E_o(z)$ is found to be

$$E_o(z) = \frac{1 - 0.964z^{-1}}{1 - 1.46z^{-1} + 0.531z^{-2}}$$

Inversion of this expression by the method of long division generates a sequence of sample values which differ from the exact solution by no more than 1 per cent.

11.6 Evaluation of Infinite Series

One of the relationships developed in connection with the Laplace transform of an impulse-modulated sequence is useful in the evaluation of infinite series. It has been shown in Chap. 2 that the Laplace transform $F^*(s)$ of an impulse-modulated signal whose continuous Laplace transform is $F(s)$ can be expressed in the form of two different infinite series. This relation expressed in (2.27) was stated to be equivalent to the Poisson summation rule and was used as the basis of alternate forms of expression for impulse-modulated sequences.   This expression is

$$F^*(s) = \frac{1}{T} \sum_{n=-\infty}^{+\infty} F(s + nj\omega_0) = \sum_{n=0}^{+\infty} f(nT)e^{-nTs} \qquad (11.55)$$

This equivalence can be useful in the evaluation in closed form of some infinite series.   For instance, if the series can be closed more readily in

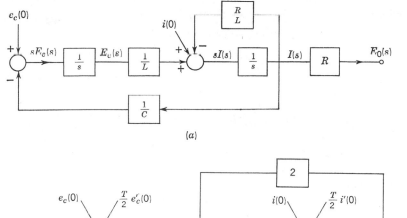

(a)

(b)

FIG. 11.18. (a) Continuous model giving exact input-output relations for circuit.   (b) Sampled model which replaces continuous model.

one of the alternate forms of (11.55) than the other, conversion of the series into the preferred form by means of (11.55) is useful.

The steps in adapting the summation rule consist of first setting T, the sampling interval, equal to unity.   Doing so,

$$\sum_{n=0}^{+\infty} f(n)e^{-sn} = \sum_{n=-\infty}^{+\infty} F(s + jn2\pi) \qquad (11.56)$$

where it will be recalled that ω_0 is equal to $2\pi/T$.   Selecting a particular value of s equal to zero, (11.56) becomes

$$\sum_{n=0}^{+\infty} f(n) = \sum_{n=-\infty}^{+\infty} F(jn2\pi) \qquad (11.57)$$

The technique used in the evaluation of an infinite sum is to express it in terms of one of the forms of (11.57), usually the right-hand term. Working backwards, the equivalent Laplace transform $F(s + jn2\pi)$ is found and from this $F(s)$. The z transform corresponding to $F(s)$ is obtained from the table and stated in terms of e^{Ts}, where both T and s are set equal to unity. The resultant closed form is that corresponding to the left-hand side of (11.57). This is best illustrated by means of an example.

EXAMPLE

It is desired to evaluate the following infinite series:

$$S = \sum_{n=-\infty}^{+\infty} \frac{1}{n^2 + a^2}$$

The general term in the summation is expressed as

$$\frac{1}{n^2 + a^2} = \frac{1}{(a + jn)(a - jn)}$$

which is identical to

$$\frac{4\pi^2}{(2\pi a + j2\pi n)(2\pi a - j2\pi n)}$$

This, in turn, is equal to

$$\frac{4\pi^2}{[2\pi a + s + (j2\pi/T)n][2\pi a - s - (j2\pi/T)n]} \bigg|_{\substack{T=1 \\ s=0}}$$

The summation of terms of the latter type constitutes the right-hand side of (11.56). This latter expression stems from a Laplace transform $F(s)$, given by

$$F(s) = \frac{4\pi^2}{(2\pi a + s)(2\pi a - s)}$$

which can be expanded into partial fractions

$$F(s) = \frac{\pi}{a}\left(\frac{1}{s + 2\pi a} - \frac{1}{s - 2\pi a}\right)$$

The z transform corresponding to $F(s)$, setting T to unity and s to zero after replacing z by e^{Ts}, is

$$F(e^{Ts})\bigg|_{\substack{T=1 \\ s=0}} = \frac{\pi}{a}\left(\frac{1}{1 - e^{-2\pi a}} - \frac{1}{1 - e^{+2\pi a}}\right)$$

This is the value of the summation of the form on the left-hand side of (11.57), which is equal to the desired summation.

For instance, if the constant a were unity, then the value of the summation is

$$S = \frac{\pi}{1}\left(\frac{1}{1 - e^{-2\pi}} - \frac{1}{1 - e^{+2\pi}}\right)$$

which is equal closely to π.   On the other hand, if a were 0.1, the sum would be equal to 34π.

11.7 Summary

Theory which was developed for sampled-data systems has been adapted to other uses.   Most important among these is the orderly approach to the setting up of a difference equation which approximates the differential equation of a system.   If the system is linear, this difference equation can be solved by means of a recursion formula.   The interpretation of the process of numerical approximation by a physical sampled equivalent model assists considerably in setting up the numerical technique.   For instance, the selection of quadrature interval is related to the choice of sampling interval in the physical model.   Considerations of frequency response of the various elements and input functions affect the choice of sampling interval directly.   The use of polygonal approximations is equivalent to insertion of the triangle hold, which, though physically unrealizable, is useful for purposes of computation.

The approach to the numerical solution of linear dynamical systems can take one of several forms.   The first one replaces the continuous system with a sampled model containing samplers and data holds in carefully chosen places.   This method is most closely related to the physical system itself.   The next method approximates the Laplace transform of the desired variable, including all initial conditions.   The use of z forms to approximate this transform makes possible its numerical inversion, but the relationship to the actual physical system is not so clear.   Finally, for systems, particularly networks, where the initial conditions are associated with initial voltages across condensers or currents in inductances, a technique which reduces the actual system to a set of interconnected integrators and summers is employed.   Each of the integrators is then replaced by an approximate integration process with initial conditions introduced.   This approach makes it relatively simple to apply initial conditions of the type mentioned.

Linear systems with time-varying coefficients can also be solved by methods related to the theory of sampled-data systems.   The setting up of a recursion formula in which the coefficients take on different values at each sampling instant is a relatively straightforward procedure.   Finally, the evaluation of certain forms of infinite series, particularly those which are even rational polynomials of the index, can be evaluated by applying the Poisson summation rule. The theory of sampled-data systems in which two alternate forms of the transform of a sampled variable is useful in this case. These applications of sampled-data theory all arise because sampled-data systems are described by difference equations and z transforms are applicable to the solution of these equations.

APPENDIXES

APPENDIX I

TABLE OF Z TRANSFORMS

Note: $F_s(s)$ is the Laplace transform, $f(nT)$ is the number sequence obtained upon inversion of the corresponding z transform and $F_z(z)$ is the associated z transform. If, in the column headed $f(nT)$, the variable nT is replaced by t, the inverse of the associated Laplace transform is obtained. This table was constructed by drawing from references 1, 2, 19, and 49.

No.	$F_s(s)$	$f(nT)$	$F_z(z)$
1	1	$1,\ n = 0;\ 0,\ n \neq 0$	z^{-0}
2	e^{-kTs}	$1,\ n = k;\ 0,\ n \neq k$	z^{-k}
3	$\dfrac{1}{s}$	1	$\dfrac{1}{1 - z^{-1}}$
4	$\dfrac{1}{s^2}$	nT	$\dfrac{Tz^{-1}}{(1 - z^{-1})^2}$

	$F(s)$	$f(nT)$	$F(z)$
5	$\dfrac{1}{s^3}$	$\dfrac{1}{2!}(nT)^2$	$\dfrac{T^2}{2}\dfrac{z^{-1}(1+z^{-1})}{(1-z^{-1})^3}$
6	$\dfrac{1}{s^4}$	$\dfrac{1}{3!}(nT)^3$	$\dfrac{T^3}{6}\left[\dfrac{3z^{-2}(\_+z^{-1})}{(1-z^{-1})^4}+\dfrac{z^{-1}(1+2z^{-1})}{(1-z^{-1})^3}\right]$
7	$\dfrac{1}{s^m}$	$\lim_{a\to 0}\dfrac{(-1)^{m-1}}{(m-1)!}\dfrac{\delta^{m-1}}{\delta a^{m-1}}(e^{-anT})$	$\lim_{a\to 0}\dfrac{(-1)^{m-1}}{(m-1)!}\dfrac{\delta^{m-1}}{\delta a^{m-1}}\dfrac{1}{1-e^{-aT}z^{-1}}$
8	$\dfrac{1}{s+a}$	e^{-anT}	$\dfrac{1}{1-\epsilon^{-aT}z^{-1}}$
9	$\dfrac{1}{(s+a)^2}$	nTe^{-anT}	$\dfrac{Te^{-aT}z^{-1}}{(1-e^{-aT}z^{-1})^2}$
10	$\dfrac{1}{(s+a)^3}$	$\dfrac{1}{2}(nT)^2e^{-anT}$	$\dfrac{T^2}{2}\dfrac{e^{-aT}z^{-1}(1+e^{-aT}z^{-1})}{(1-e^{-aT}z^{-1})^3}$
11	$\dfrac{1}{(s+a)^m}$	$\dfrac{(-1)^{m-1}}{(m-1)!}\dfrac{\delta^{m-1}}{\delta a^{m-1}}(e^{-anT})$	$\dfrac{(-1)^{m-1}}{(m-1)!}\dfrac{\delta^{m-1}}{\delta a^{m-1}}\dfrac{1}{1-e^{-aT}z^{-1}}$
12	$\dfrac{a}{s(s+a)}$	$1-e^{-anT}$	$\dfrac{(1-\epsilon^{aT})z^{-1}}{(1-z^{-1})(1-e^{-aT}z^{-1})}$
13	$\dfrac{a}{s^2(s+a)}$	$\dfrac{1}{a}(anT-1+e^{-anT})$	$\dfrac{Tz^{-1}}{(1-z^{-1})^2}-\dfrac{(1-e^{-aT})z^{-1}}{a(1-z^{-1})(1-e^{-aT}z^{-1})}$
14	$\dfrac{a}{s^3(s+a)}$	$\dfrac{1}{a^2}\left[\dfrac{1}{2}(anT)^2-anT+1-e^{-anT}\right]$	$\dfrac{T^2}{2}\dfrac{z^{-1}(1+z^{-1})}{(1-z^{-1})^3}-\dfrac{T}{a}\dfrac{z^{-1}}{(1-z^{-1})^2}+\dfrac{(1-e^{-aT})z^{-1}}{a^2(1-z^{-1})(1-e^{-aT}z^{-1})}$

No.	$F_s(s)$	$f(nT)$	$F_z(z)$
15	$\dfrac{b-a}{(s+a)(s+b)}$	$(e^{-anT} - e^{-bnT})$	$\dfrac{(e^{-aT} - e^{-bT})z^{-1}}{(1 - e^{-aT}z^{-1})(1 - e^{-bT}z^{-1})}$
16	$\dfrac{s}{(s+a)^2}$	$(1 - anT)e^{-anT}$	$\dfrac{1 - e^{-aT}(1 + aT)z^{-1}}{(1 - e^{-aT}z^{-1})^2}$
17	$\dfrac{a^2}{s(s+a)^2}$	$1 - e^{-anT}(1 + anT)$	$\dfrac{1}{1 - z^{-1}} - \dfrac{1 - (1 - aT)e^{-aT}z^{-1}}{(1 - e^{-aT}z^{-1})^2}$
18	$\dfrac{(b-a)s}{(s+a)(s+b)}$	$be^{-bnT} - ae^{-anT}$	$\dfrac{(b-a) - z^{-1}(be^{-aT} - ae^{-bT})}{(1 - e^{-aT}z^{-1})(1 - e^{-bT}z^{-1})}$
19	$\dfrac{a}{s^2 + a^2}$	$\sin anT$	$\dfrac{\sin aT z^{-1}}{1 - (2\cos aT)z^{-1} + z^{-2}}$
20	$\dfrac{s}{s^2 + a^2}$	$\cos anT$	$\dfrac{1 - (\cos aT)z^{-1}}{1 - (2\cos aT)z^{-1} + z^{-2}}$
21	$\dfrac{a}{s^2 - a^2}$	$\sinh anT$	$\dfrac{\sinh aT z^{-1}}{1 - (2\cosh aT)z^{-1} + z^{-2}}$
22	$\dfrac{s}{s^2 - a^2}$	$\cosh anT$	$\dfrac{1 - (\cosh aT)z^{-1}}{1 - (2\cosh aT)z^{-1} + z^{-2}}$

23	$\dfrac{s+a}{(s+a)^2+b^2}$	$e^{-anT}\cos bnT$	$\dfrac{1-e^{-aT}\cos bT\,z^{-1}}{1-2e^{-aT}(\cos bT)z^{-1}+e^{-2aT}z^{-2}}$
24	$\dfrac{b}{(s+a)^2+b^2}$	$e^{-anT}\sin bnT$	$\dfrac{e^{-aT}\sin bT\,z^{-1}}{1-2e^{-aT}(\cos bT)z^{-1}+e^{-2aT}z^{-2}}$
25	$\dfrac{ab}{s(s+a)(s+b)}$	$1-\dfrac{be^{-anT}-ae^{-bnT}}{(b-a)}$	$\dfrac{1}{1-z^{-1}}+\dfrac{(be^{-bT}-ae^{-aT})z^{-1}-(b-a)}{(b-a)(1-e^{-aT}z^{-1})(1-e^{-bT}z^{-1})}$
26	$F_s(s+a)$	$e^{-anT}f(nT)$	$F_z(e^{aT}z)$
27	$e^{-ksT}F_s(s)$	$f(n-k)T$	$z^{-k}F_z(z)$

TABLE OF ADVANCED Z TRANSFORMS

Note: $F_s(s)$ is the Laplace transform of the time function and $F_s(s)e^{\Delta Ts}$ is the Laplace transform of the same time function advanced by a time ΔT. $F_z(z,\Delta)$ is the z transform of the pulse sequence resulting from sampling the advanced time function with a period T. This table was constructed by drawing from references 1, 3, and 20.

No.	$F_s(s)e^{\Delta Ts}$	$F_z(z,\Delta)$
1	$\dfrac{1}{s}e^{\Delta Ts}$	$\dfrac{1}{1 - z^{-1}}$
2	$\dfrac{1}{s^2}e^{\Delta Ts}$	$\dfrac{\Delta T + T(1 - \Delta)z^{-1}}{(1 - z^{-1})^2}$
3	$\dfrac{1}{s^3}e^{\Delta Ts}$	$T^2\left[\dfrac{z^{-2}}{(1 - z^{-1})^3} + \dfrac{(1 + 2\Delta)z^{-1}}{2(1 - z^{-1})^2} + \dfrac{\Delta^2}{2(1 - z^{-1})}\right]$
4	$\dfrac{1}{s + a}e^{\Delta Ts}$	$\dfrac{e^{-a\Delta T}}{1 - e^{-aT}z^{-1}}$
5	$\dfrac{1}{(s + a)^2}e^{\Delta Ts}$	$T\left[\dfrac{\Delta e^{-a\Delta T}}{1 - e^{-aT}z^{-1}} + \dfrac{e^{-a(1+\Delta)T}z^{-1}}{(1 - e^{-aT}z^{-1})^2}\right]$
6	$\dfrac{1}{(s + a)^3}e^{\Delta Ts}$	$T^2e^{-a\Delta T}\left[\dfrac{\Delta^2}{2(1 - e^{-aT}z^{-1})} + \dfrac{(1 + 2\Delta)e^{-aT}z^{-1}}{2(1 - e^{-aT}z^{-1})^2}\right.$ $\left. + \dfrac{e^{-2aT}z^{-2}}{(1 - e^{-aT}z^{-1})^3}\right]$
7	$\dfrac{a}{s(s + a)}e^{\Delta Ts}$	$\dfrac{1}{1 - z^{-1}} - \dfrac{e^{-a\Delta T}}{1 - e^{-aT}z^{-1}}$
8	$\dfrac{a}{s^2(s + a)}e^{\Delta Ts}$	$\dfrac{Tz^{-1}}{(1 - z^{-1})^2} + \dfrac{a\Delta T - 1}{a(1 - z^{-1})} + \dfrac{e^{-a\Delta T}}{a(1 - e^{-aT}z^{-1})}$

No.	$F_s(s)e^{\Delta Ts}$	$F_z(z,\Delta)$
9	$\dfrac{a^2}{s(s+a)^2}e^{\Delta Ts}$	$\dfrac{1}{1-z^{-1}} - \dfrac{(1-a\Delta T)e^{-a\Delta T}}{1-e^{-aT}z^{-1}} + \dfrac{aTe^{-a(1-\Delta)T}z^{-1}}{(1-e^{-aT}z^{-1})^2}$
10	$\dfrac{a}{s^2+a^2}e^{\Delta Ts}$	$\dfrac{\sin a\Delta T + \sin(1-\Delta)aTz^{-1}}{1-2\cos aTz^{-1}+z^{-2}}$
11	$\dfrac{s}{s^2+a^2}e^{\Delta Ts}$	$\dfrac{\cos a\Delta T + \cos(1-\Delta)aTz^{-1}}{1-2(\cos aT)z^{-1}+z^{-2}}$
12	$\dfrac{b}{(s+a)^2+b^2}e^{\Delta Ts}$	$\dfrac{e^{-a\Delta T}\sin b\Delta T + [e^{-a(1+\Delta)T}\sin(1-\Delta)bT]z^{-1}}{1-2e^{-aT}(\cos bT)z^{-1}+e^{-2aT}z^{-2}}$
13	$\dfrac{s+a}{(s+a)^2+b^2}e^{\Delta Ts}$	$\dfrac{e^{-a\Delta T}\cos b\Delta T - [e^{-a(1+\Delta)T}\cos(1-\Delta)bT]z^{-1}}{1-2e^{-aT}(\cos bT)z^{-1}+e^{-2aT}z^{-2}}$

OUTPUT TRANSFORMS FOR BASIC
SAMPLED-DATA SYSTEMS*

System	Laplace transform of output $C(s)$	z-Transform of output $C(z)$
(1)	$R^*(s)$	$R(z)$
(2)	$GR^*(s)$	$GR(z)$
(3)	$G(s)R^*(s)$	$G(z)R(z)$
(4)	$\dfrac{G(s)\ R^*(s)}{1+HG^*(s)}$	$\dfrac{G(z)\ R(z)}{1+HG(z)}$
(5)	$\dfrac{G^*(s)R^*(s)}{1+H^*(s)G^*(s)}$	$\dfrac{G(z)R(z)}{1+H(z)G(z)}$
(6)	$G(s)\left[R(s)-\dfrac{H(s)RG^*(s)}{1+HG^*(s)}\right]$	$\dfrac{RG(z)}{1+HG(z)}$
(7)	$\dfrac{G_2(s)RG_1^*(s)}{1+HG_1G_2^*(s)}$	$\dfrac{G_2(z)RG_1(z)}{HG_1G_2(z)}$
(8)	$\dfrac{G_2(s)G_1^*(s)R^*(s)}{1+G_1^*(s)G_2H^*(s)}$	$\dfrac{G_1(z)G_2(z)R(z)}{1+G_1(z)G_2H(z)}$

* Reproduced from J. R. Ragazzini and L. A. Zadeh, The Analysis of Sampled-data Systems, *Trans. AIEE*, vol. 71, pt. II, pp. 225-234, November, 1952.

REFERENCES

1. Barker, R. H.: The Pulse Transfer Function and Its Application to Sampling Servo Systems, *Proc. IEE*, pt. IV, monograph 43, July 15, 1952.
2. Barker, R. H.: The Theory of Pulse-monitored Servos and Their Use for Prediction, *rept.* 1046, *Signals Research and Development Establishment*, Christchurch, Hants, England, November, 1950.
3. Bergen, A. R., and J. R. Ragazzini: Sampled-data Processing Techniques for Feedback Control Systems, *Trans. AIEE*, vol. 73, 1954.
4. Bertram, J. E.: Factors in the Design of Digital Controllers for Sampled-data Feedback Control Systems, *Trans. AIEE*, paper 56-209, 1956.
5. Bode, H. W., and C. E. Shannon: A Simplified Derivation of Linear Least Squares Smoothing and Prediction Theory, *Proc. IRE*, vol. 38, no. 44, pp. 417–425, April, 1950.
6. Brown, B. M.: Application of Finite Difference Operators to Linear Systems, *Proc. D.S.I.R. Conf. on Automatic Control* (A.Tustin, ed.), Butterworth's Scientific Publications, London, 1952.
7. Brown, R. G., and G. L. Murphy: An Approximate Transfer Function for the Analysis and Design of Pulsed Servos, *Trans. AIEE*, vol. 71, pt. II, pp. 435–440, 1952.
8. Chow, C. K.: Contactor Servomechanism Employing Sampled-data, *Trans. AIEE*, vol. 74, pt. II, pp. 51–62, March, 1953.
9. Demoivre, A.: "Miscellanea Analytica de Seriebus et Quadraturis," London, 1730.
10. Franklin, G. F.: Filtering Deterministic Messages from Sampled-data, *Tech. Note* TN-3/127, Department of Electrical Engineering, Columbia University, New York, June, 1956.
11. Franklin, G. F.: Linear Filtering of Sampled-data, *Tech. Rept.* T-5/B, Department of Electrical Engineering, Columbia University, New York, December, 1954.
12. Franklin, G. F.: The Optimum Synthesis of Sampled-data Systems, *Tech. Rept.* T-6/B, Department of Electrical Engineering, Columbia University, New York, May 2, 1955.
13. Friedland, B.: A Technique for the Analysis of Time-varying Sampled-data Systems, *Tech. Rept.* T-10/B, Department of Electrical Engineering, Columbia University, New York, Sept. 15, 1955, also *Trans. AIEE*, vol. 76, pt. II, January, 1956.
14. Friedland, B.: Transformation Techniques for Time-varying Sampled-data Systems, *Tech. Rept.* T-13/B, Department of Electrical Engineering, Columbia University, New York, Jan. 2, 1956.
15. Holt Smith, C., D. F. Lawden, A. E. Bailey: Characteristics of Sampling Servo Systems, *Proc. D.S.I.R. Conf. on Automatic Control* (A. Tustin, ed.), Butterworth's Scientific Publications, London, 1952.

16. Huggins, W. H.: A Low-pass Transformation for Z-transforms (correspondence), *IRE, P.G.C.T. Trans.*, September, 1954.
17. Hurewicz, W.: "Filters and Servo Systems with Pulsed Data," in James, H. M., N. B. Nichols, and R. S. Phillips: "Theory of Servomechanisms," chap. 5, Radiation Laboratory Series, vol. 25, McGraw-Hill Book Company, Inc., New York, 1947.
18. Johnson, G. W., and D. P. Lindorff: Transient Analysis of Sampled-data Control Systems, *Trans. AIEE*, vol. 74, pt. II, pp. 147–153, July, 1954.
19. Jury, E. I.: Analysis and Synthesis of Sampled-data Control Systems, *Trans. AIEE*, vol. 73, pt. I, 1954.
20. Jury, E. I.: Synthesis and Critical Study of Sampled-data Control Systems, *Trans. AIEE*, pt. II, paper 56-208, July, 1956.
21. Jury, E. I.: The Effect of Root Locations on the Transient Response of Sampled-data Systems, *Trans. AIEE*, vol. 75, pt. II, March, 1955.
22. Jury, E. I.: Discrete Compensation of Sampled-data and Continuous Systems, *Trans. AIEE*, paper 56-644, 1956.
23. Jury, E. I.: Correlation between Root Locus and Transient Response of Sampled-data Control Systems, *Trans. AIEE*, January, 1956.
24. Jury, E. I.: Hidden Oscillations in Sampled-data Control Systems, *Univ. Calif. Inst. Eng. Research, ser.* 60, *issue* 155, December 14, 1955.
25. Jury, E. I.: The Effect of Pole and Zero Locations on the Transient Response of Sampled-data Systems, *Trans. AIEE*, pt. II, paper 55-186, 1955.
26. Kalman, R. E.: Investigations of Non-linear Control Systems Operating on Sampled-data, *Tech. Note* TN-4/127, Department of Electrical Engineering, Columbia University, New York, July 31, 1956.
27. Kalman, R. E., and J. E. Bertram: General Synthesis Procedure for Computer Control of Single and Multiple-loop Systems, *Trans. AIEE*, vol. 56, pt. II, 1957.
28. Kranc, G. M.: The Analysis of Multiple-rate Sampled Systems, *Tech. Rept.* T-11/B, Department of Electrical Engineering, Columbia University, New York, Sept. 15, 1955.
29. Kranc, G. M.: Additional Techniques for Sampled-data Problems, *Convention Record, Wescon, IRE*, 1957. Also, *Rept.* No. T-21/B, Department of Electrical Engineering, Columbia University, New York, 1957.
30. Kranc, G. M.: Multi-rate Sampled Systems, *Tech. Rept.* T-14/B, Department of Electrical Engineering, Columbia University, New York, May 7, 1956.
31. Kranc, G. M.: Compensation of an Error Sampled System by a Multi-rate Controller, *Tech. Note* TN-2/127, Department of Electrical Engineering, Columbia University, New York, June 30, 1956. Also, *Trans. AIEE*, vol. 56, pt. II, July, 1957.
32. Lago, G. V., and J. G. Truxal: The Design of Sampled-data Feedback Systems, *Trans. AIEE*, vol. 74, pt. II, pp. 247–252, November, 1954.
33. Lago, G. V.: Additions to Z-transformation Theory for Sampled-data Systems, *Trans. AIEE*, vol. 75, pt. II, pp. 403–408, January, 1955.
34. Laning, J. H., Jr., and R. H. Battin: "Random Processes in Automatic Control," McGraw-Hill Book Company, Inc., New York, 1956.
35. Laplace, P. S.: "Théorie analytique des probabilités, Pt. I: Du Calcul des fonctions génératrices," Paris, 1812.
36. Lawden, D. F.: A General Theory of Sampling Servo Systems, *Proc. IEE*, London, vol. 98, pt. IV, October, 1951.
37. Lees, A. B.: Interpolation and Extrapolation of Sampled-data, *Trans. IRE, Professional Group on Information Theory*, vol. IT-2, no. 1, March, 1956.

38. Linvill, W. K.: Sampled-data Control Systems Studies through Comparison with Amplitude Modulation, *Trans. AIEE*, vol. 70, pt. II, pp. 1779–1788, 1951.

39. Linvill, W. K., and J. M. Salzer: Analysis of Control Systems Involving a Digital Computer, *Proc. IRE*, vol. 41, no. 7, pp. 901–906, 1953.

40. Linvill, W. K., and R. W. Sittler: Extension of Conventional Techniques to the Design of Sampled-data Systems, *Convention Record, IRE*, pt. I, pp. 99–104, 1953.

41. Lloyd, S. P., and B. McMillan: Linear Least Squares Filtering and Prediction of Sampled Signals, *Proc. Symposium on Modern Network Synthesis*, Polytechnic Institute of Brooklyn, April, 1955.

42. MacColl, L. A.: "Fundamental Theory of Servomechanisms," chap. 10, D. Van Nostrand Company, Inc., Princeton, N.J., 1945.

43. Maitra, K. K., and P. E. Sarachik: Digital Compensation of Continuous-data Feedback Control Systems, *Trans. AIEE*, vol. 76, pt. II, no. 24, May, 1956.

44. Miller, K. S., and R. J. Schwarz: Analysis of Sampled-data Servomechanisms, *J. Appl. Phys.*, vol. 21, no. 4, pp. 290–294, April, 1950.

45. Mori, M.: Statistical Treatment of Sampled-data Control Systems for Actual Random Inputs, *ASME paper* 57-IRD-10.

46. Oldenbourg, R. C., and R. Sartorius: "The Dynamics of Automatic Controls," chap. 5, American Society of Mechanical Engineers, New York, N.Y.

47. Oliver, B. M., J. R. Pierce, and C. E. Shannon: The Philosophy of Pulse Code Modulation, *Proc. IRE*, vol. 36, no. 11, pp. 1324–1331, November, 1948.

48. Porter, A., and F. Stoneman: A New Approach to the Design of Pulse-monitored Servo Systems, *Proc. IEE*, vol. 97, pt. II, p. 597, 1950.

49. Ragazzini, J. R., and L. A. Zadeh: The Analysis of Sampled-data Systems, *Trans. AIEE*, vol. 71, pt. II, pp. 225–234, November, 1952.

50. Ragazzini, J. R., and A. R. Bergen: A Mathematical Technique for the Analysis of Linear Systems, *Proc. IRE*, vol. 42, no. 11, pp. 1645–1651, November, 1954.

51. Ragazzini, J. R.: Digital Computers in Feedback Systems, *IRE, Convention Record*, pt. IV, pp. 33–42, March, 1957. (Also, Columbia University, Electronics Research Laboratories, *Rept.* T-16/B, March, 1957.)

52. Raymond, F. H.: Analysis of Discontinuous Servomechanism, *Ann. Tele-Communications*, vol. 4, pp. 250–256, July, 1949, pp. 307–314; August–September, 1949; pp. 347–357, October, 1949.

53. Russell, F. A.: "Design Criterion for Stability of Sampled-data On-off Servomechanisms," doctoral thesis, Department of Electrical Engineering, Columbia University, New York, June, 1953.

54. Salvadori, M., and M. Baron: "Numerical Methods in Engineering," Prentice-Hall, Inc., Englewood Cliffs, N.J., 1952.

55. Salzer, J. M.: "Treatment of Digital Control Systems and Numerical Processes in the Frequency Domain," Sc.D. thesis, Department of Electrical Engineering, Massachusetts Institute of Technology, Cambridge, Mass., 1947.

56. Salzer, J. M.: Frequency Analysis of Digital Computers Operating in Real Time, *Proc. IRE*, vol. 42, no. 2, pp. 457–466, February, 1954.

57. Samuelson, P. A.: "Foundations of Economic Analysis," Harvard University Press, Cambridge, Mass., 1947.

58. Seal, H. L.: The Historical Development of the Use of Generating Functions in Probability Theory, *Mitt. Ver. Schweiz. Versich. Math.*, vol. 49, pp. 209–228, 1949.

59. Sklansky, J.: Pulsed RC Networks for Sampled-data Systems, *IRE Convention Record*, pt. 2, pp. 81–99, March, 1956.
60. Sklansky, J., and J. R. Ragazzini: Analysis of Errors in Sampled-data Feedback Systems, *Trans. AIEE*, vol. 75, pt. II, May, 1955.
61. Steward, R. M.: Statistical Design and Evaluation of Filters for the Restoration of Sampled-data, *Proc. IRE*, vol. 44, no. 2, pp. 253–257, February, 1956.
62. Stone, W. M.: A List of Generalized Laplace Transforms, *Iowa State Coll. J. Sci.*, vol. 22, no. 3, pp. 215–225, April, 1948.
63. Teichmann, T.: Closed-loop Control System Containing a Digital Computer, *Trans. IRE. Group on Electronic Computers*, vol. EC-4, no. 3, pp. 106–117, September, 1955.
64. Truxal, J. G.: "Automatic Feedback Control System Synthesis," chap. 9, McGraw-Hill Book Co., Inc., New York, 1955.
65. Tsipkin, Y. Z.: Theory of Intermittent Regulation, *Avtomatica i Telemekhanica*, vol. 10, no. 3, pp. 189–224, 1949.
66. Tsipkin, Y. Z.: Frequency Method of Analyzing Intermittent Regulating Systems, *Avtomatika i Telemekhanica*, vol. 14, no. 1, pp. 11–33, 1953.
67. Zadeh, L. A., and J. R. Ragazzini: Optimum Filters for the Detection of Signals in Noise, *Proc. IRE*, vol. 40, pp. 1223–1231, October, 1952.
68. Zadeh, L. A., and J. R. Ragazzini: An Extension of Weiner's Theory of Prediction, *J. Appl. Phys.*, vol. 21, no. 7, July, 1950.

ADDITIONAL REFERENCES

B1. Gardner, M. F., and J. L. Barnes: "Transients in Linear Systems," chap. 9, pp. 286–332, John Wiley & Sons, Inc., New York, 1942.
B2. Crawford, P. O.: "Automatic Control by Arithmetic Operation," thesis, Massachusetts Institute of Technology, Cambridge, Mass., 1942.
B3. Shannon, C. E., J. R. Pierce, and B. M. Oliver: The Philosophy of Pulse Code Modulation, *Proc. IRE*, vol. 36, no. 11, pp. 1324–1331, November, 1948.
B4. Shannon, C. E., and W. Weaver: "The Mathematical Theory of Communication," University of Illinois Press, Urbana, Ill., 1949.
B5. Tukey, J. W.: The Sampling Theory of Power Spectrum Estimates, *Symposium on Applications of Autocorrelation Analysis to Physical Problems*, ONR Publ. NAVEXOS-P-735, 1950.
B6. Lawden, D. F.: The Functions in z^n and Associated Polynomials, *Proc. Cambridge Phil. Soc.*, vol. 47, p. 309, 1951.
B7. Tootell, G. C.: Note on Digital Computing for the Extrapolation of Discontinuous Information, *Proc. D.S.I.R. Conf. on Automatic Control*, Butterworth's Scientific Publications, London, 1951.
B8. Stafford, B. H.: Frequency Analysis of Some Closed-cycle Sampled-data Control Systems, *Naval Research Lab. Rept.* 3910, January, 1952.
B9. Salzer, J. M.: Fundamental Characteristics of Digital and Analog Units, *Proc. Nat. Electronics Conf.*, vol. 8, pp. 621–628, 1952.
B10. Sartorius, H.: Deviation Dependent Step-by-step Control Systems and Their Stability, "Automatic and Manual Control," (A. Tustin, ed.), Butterworth's Scientific Publications, London, 1952, pp. 421–434.
B11. Tsien, H. S.: "Engineering Cybernetics," chap. 7, pp. 83–93, McGraw-Hill Book Co., Inc., New York, 1954.

B12. Thomasson, L. T.: Digital Servomechanisms, *Electronics*, vol. 27, no. 8 pp. 134–139, August, 1954.

B13. Jury, E. I., and G. Farmanfarma: Table of Z-transforms and Modified Z-transforms of Various Sampled-data Systems Configurations, *Univ. Calif., Berkeley, Electronics Research Lab. Rept.* 136A, *Ser.* 60, 1955.

B14. McDonnell, D., and W. R. Perkins: The Stability and Time Response of Fast-operating Closed-loop Pulsed Radar Circuits, *Proc. IEE*, vol. 102, pt. III, pp. 191–202, September, 1955.

B15. Johnson, C. W., and D. P. Nordling, and D. P. Lindorff: Extension of Continuous-data System Design Techniques to Sampled-data Control Systems, *Trans. AIEE*, vol. 74, pt. II, pp. 252–263, September, 1955.

B16. Barker, R. H.: A Servo System for Digital Data Transmission, *Proc. IEE.*, vol. 103, pt. III, pp. 52–64, January, 1956.

B17. Boxer, R., and S. Thaler: A Simplified Method of Solving Linear and Nonlinear Systems, *Proc. IRE*, vol. 44, no. 1, pp. 89–101, January, 1956.

B18. Kalman, R. E.: Nonlinear Aspects of Sampled-data Control Systems, *Proc. Symposium on Nonlinear Circuit Analysis*, MRI Symposia Series, vol. 6, Polytechnic Institute of Brooklyn, 1956.

B19. Siegel, A.: Automatic Programming of Numerically-controlled Machine Tools, *Control Eng.*, pp. 65–70, October, 1956.

B20. Jury, E. I., and W. Schroeder: Discrete Compensation of Sampled-data and Continuous Control Systems, *Trans. AIEE*, vol. 75, pt. II, pp. 317–325, January, 1957.

B21. Farmanfarma, G.: Analysis of Linear Sampled-data Systems with Finite Pulse Width, Open Loop, *Trans. AIEE*, vol. 75, pt. I, pp. 808–819, January, 1957.

B22. Gimpel, D. J.: Sampled-data Systems, *Control Eng.*, pp. 99–105, February, 1957.

INDEX

Advanced z transform (*see* z transform)
Approximation of continuous systems
 by sampled models, 283–301, 304–308
 estimation of errors, 293–295
 insertion of initial conditions, 304–308
 use of z forms, 295–301
Auxiliary variable z, 53–54

Boxcar data hold (*see* Zero-order data hold)
Bypass digital controllers, 186–192
 design of, rules for, 189

Cancellation of poles and zeros outside of unit circle, 156–157
Cardinal data hold, 30–31
Carrier modulation systems, 26–27
Cascaded continuous elements, 87–90
Chopper-bar galvanometer, 7
Clamp circuit, 5, 34
 (*See also* Zero-order data hold)
Closed-loop sampled-data systems, compensation of, 155–163
 rules and restrictions for, 158
Compensation of sampled systems, feedback configuration, 155–163
 rules and restrictions, 158
 by use, of bypass digital controllers, 186–192
 of digital controllers, 147–148
 of pulsed networks, 136–143
 open-loop configuration, 153–155

Complex convolution, use of, to derive z transform, 54–55
Continuous systems, approximation by sampled model, closed-loop, 290–295
 estimation of errors in, 292–295
 open-loop, 283–290
 with initial conditions, 304–308
 method of approximation by z forms, 295–301
 with time-varying coefficients, 301–304
Controller, digital (*see* Digital controller)
Convolution summation, 66–67

Data hold, 4, 23, 29–51, 287–288
 cardinal, 30–31
 first-order (*see* First-order data hold)
 higher-order, 42–43
 implementation of, 43–49
 polygonal, 287–288
 transfer function of, 288
 zero-order (*see* Zero-order data hold)
Data links, 3
Data reconstruction, 3, 29–51
 (*See also* Data hold; Extrapolation)
Delayed z transform, 64–66
Desampling filter (*see* Data hold)
Digital controller, 6, 92, 145–197, 244–248
 bypass type, 186–192
 equivalent, 173–178
 implementation of, laboratory, 195–197

Digital controller, multirate (*see* Multirate digital controller)
sampled-data, 3
speed-up with multirate techniques, 244–248
Digitally controlled systems, effect of disturbances on, 192–195
Dominant poles in sampled-data systems, 109–110
Double-rate sampling, 203–206

Early feedback sampled-data systems, equivalent digital controller, 173–178
state variable, 173
Error-sampled feedback systems, 5–7, 90–105
Extrapolation, exponential, 49–50
Gregory-Newton formula, 32
polynomial, 31–34
(*See also* Data hold)
Extrapolator, data (*see* Data hold)
polynomial, 43–49
Porter-Stoneman, 44–49

Fail-safe systems (*see* Bypass digital controllers)
Feedback sampled-data systems, 5–7, 90–105
with digital element, 92–93
error-sampled, 90–91
stability of, 93–105
(*See also* Sampled-data-system design; Sampled-data systems)
Final-value theorem, 61–63
Finite pulse-width sampling, 14, 21–23, 255–256
Finite settling-time systems, 178–181
(*See also* Minimal prototype response functions; Minimum prototype response functions; Ripple-free sampled-data systems)
First-order data hold, 37–44, 127–129
approximation by continuous element, 127–129

First-order data hold, frequency response of, 38–39
open-cycle implementation of, 43–44
partial-velocity (*see* Partial-velocity first-order data hold)
partial-velocity correction, 40–42
transfer function of, 38
Frequency response of sampled-data systems, 110–115
periodicity of, 111–112
relation to pulse transfer locus, 114–115

Generating function (*see* z transform)
Generating triangle for polygonal approximation, 287–288
Gregory-Newton extrapolation formula, 32

Hidden oscillations in sampled-data systems, 93–94, 136, 199, 217–218
Higher-order data hold (*see* Data hold)

Implementation of pulse transfer functions, 75–77, 139–143, 195–197
of digital controllers, 195–197
using pulsed networks, 139–143
Impulse modulation, 19
Impulse sampling, 19–23
Impulse sequence, frequency spectrum of, 20
Laplace transform of, 23–26
Infinite series, evaluation by sampling techniques, 308–311
Initial-value theorem, 61–62
Integrated-square error, minimization of, in sampled-data systems, 179–181
Inverse Laplace transform, approximation by sampling techniques, 295–301
table of z forms, 298
Inversion of z transforms (*see* z transform)

Laplace transform, approximation
using *z* forms, 295–301
of impulse sequence, 23–26
inverse (*see* Inverse Laplace transform)

Minimal prototype response functions,
148–153
requirements for, 148
table of, 151
Minimum prototype response functions, 162
Miscellaneous applications of sampled-data theory, 10–11, 282–312
Modified *z* transforms (*see* *z* transform, advanced)
Multirate digital controller, design of,
basic requirements for, 235–238
using single-rate techniques, 244–248
properties of, 232
pulse transfer function of, 234
synthesis of, 232–234
Multirate sampled-data systems, 9,
220–249
analysis by phantom output sampling, 227–229
closed-loop systems, 229–232
fast input, slow output sampling,
222–229
open-loop, 221–229
pulse transfer function of, 222
slow input, fast output sampling,
221–222
switch decomposition technique,
223–226
Multirate sampling, applied to computation of ripple, 202–206
of feedback systems, 205–206
of open-loop systems, 202–205

Numerical integration process, pulse
transfer function of, 73–75, 305

Open-loop sampled-data systems (*see*
Sampled-data systems)

Partial-fraction technique for determination of ripple, 206–212
Partial-velocity first-order data hold,
40–42
frequency response of, 41–42
transfer function of, 40–41
Phase shift, of first-order data hold, 38–39
of zero-order data hold, 36
Poisson summation rule, 25
applied to evaluation of infinite
series, 308–311
Polygonal data hold (*see* Data hold)
Polynomial extrapolation, 31–34
Polynomial extrapolators, 43–49
Porter-Stoneman extrapolator, 44–49
Pulse transfer function, 8–9, 66–77,
139–143
of digital system, 70–75
implementation of, 75–77
by pulsed networks, 139–143
of pulsed continuous system, 68–69
Pulse transfer locus, use of, to determine stability, 100–105
Pulsed networks, for compensation of
sampled-data systems, 136–143
phase lag, 137
phase lead, 137
synthesis of pulse transfer function,
139–143
Pulsed transfer function (*see* Pulse
transfer function)

Radar, scanning search, 3
Random signals, autocorrelation function, 251–254
cross-correlation function, 252–253
expected value, 251
first-order probability density function, 250–251
mean-square value, 251
power spectrum of, 259–267
sampled (*see* Sampled random signals)
in sampled-data systems, 261–267

Random signals, second-order probability density function, 251
    spectral density function, 254–255
Regulator systems, 192
Ripple, 6, 18, 199–219
    approximation of, in feedback systems, 202
    using infinite summation, 199–202
    determination of, by use, of advanced z transforms, 212–217
        of multirate sampling technique, 202–206
        of partial fraction summation, 206–212
Ripple-free sampled-data systems, 169–173
    design of, rules for, 170
        using state variable feedback, 173–178
Root locus for sampled-data systems, 105–110
Routh-Hurwitz stability criterion for sampled-data systems, 98–100

Sample sequence, sum of squares of, 78–79
Sampled-data processing unit, 92
    (*See also* Digital controller)
Sampled-data system design, equivalent digital controller, 173–178
    minimal prototype, 148–153
    minimizing integrated square error, 178–181
    with plant saturation, 181–186
    ripple-free, 169–173
    by use, of continuous networks, 117–136
        of digital controllers, 145–173, 186–192
        (*See also* Digital controller)
        of pulsed networks, 136–143
        of root locus, 138–139
Sampled-data systems, 4–5, 86–116, 130–133, 153–155, 181–186, 192–195, 320

Sampled-data systems, approximation by use of most important sidebands, 130–133
    behavior between sampling instants (*see* Ripple)
    closed-loop, 155–163
    compensation of (*see* Compensation of sampled systems)
    digital controllers for (*see* Digital controller)
    dominant poles of, 109–110
    effect of disturbances on, 192–195
    feedback, 5–7, 90–105
    frequency response of (*see* Frequency response of sampled-data systems)
    hidden oscillations in, 93–94, 136, 199, 217–218
    minimization of integrated square error in, 179–181
    multirate (*see* Multirate sampled-data systems)
    open-loop, 4–5
        compensation of, 153–155
    random signals in, 261–267
    (*See also* Random signals)
    root locus, 105–110
    saturation in, 181–186
    stability of (*see* Stability of sampled-data systems)
    table of basic relationships, 320
Sampled-data theory, miscellaneous applications of, 10–11, 282–312
Sampled elements in cascade, 86–90
Sampled random signals, 255–258
    optimum linear filtering of, 267–280
        comparison to zero-order data hold, 278–280
        feedback implementation, 277–278
        mean-square error, 272
        transfer function of optimum filter, 272
    (*See also* Random signals)
Sampling, approximation by most important sidebands, 130–133
    double-rate, 203–206

Sampling, finite pulse width, 14, 21–23, 255–256
impulse approximation, 19–23
Sampling instant, 1, 13
Sampling interval, 12
Sampling operation, 1
Sampling process, 12–28
mathematical description of, 13–16
Sampling theorem, 16–19
Saturation, design of sampled-data systems with, 181–186
Sidebands, most important, design of systems using, 130–133
Spectra of sampled signals, 20
Spectrum, power, of random signal, 259–267
of sampled signal, 15
Stability of sampled-data systems, 93–105
definition of, 94
modified Routh-Hurwitz criterion, 98–100
necessary and sufficient conditions for, 95
use of transfer locus to determine, 100–105
Staircase data hold (*see* Zero-order data hold)
Staleness factor, implementation of systems using, 163–169
value minimizing integrated-square error, 167–169
State variable, 173
Sum of squares of sample sequence, 78–79
Systems, analogue, 1
continuous, 1
sampled-data (*see* Sampled-data systems)

Tables, of advanced z transforms, 318–319

Tables, of integrated-square error sequences, 180
of minimal prototype response functions, 151
of output transforms of basic sampled-data systems, 320
of z forms, 298
of z transforms, 314–317
Time-varying continuous systems, approximation using sampling techniques, 301–304
Transfer locus, pulse, 100–105
Two-sided z transform, 79–83

z, auxiliary variable, 53–54
definition of, 53
z plane, definition of, 53
relation to s plane, 53–54
z transform, 52–83
advanced, 64–66
table of, 318–319
use of, to determine ripple, 212–217
closed form, 57
delayed, 64
inversion of, 57–61
by contour integration, 58
by long division, 60–61
mathematical derivation, 54–57
modified (*see* advanced, *above*)
table of, 314–317
two-sided, 79–83
Z transformation, 7–10
Zero-order data hold, 34–37, 49–50, 123–124
approximation by continuous element, 123–124
frequency response of, 36
network representation of, 49–50
transfer function of, 35